BOOK 1

Summit MATHS

Ray Allan • Martin Williams

Nelson

Thomas Nelson and Sons Ltd
Nelson House
Mayfield Road
Walton-on-Thames
Surrey KT12 5PL
United Kingdom

First published by Thomas Nelson and Sons Ltd 1998
ISBN 0-17-431490-6
9 8 7 6 5 4 3 2
02 01 00 99

Acknowledgements

The authors and publishers would like to thank the following for all their help and assistance in the preparation of this book:

Fran Ashworth, Consultant

Ashburton High School, Croydon; Bensham Manor School, Croydon; Bradon Forest School, Swindon; Breeze Hill School, Oldham; Edenham High School, Croydon; Farleigh College, Bath; Harold Hill Community School, Romford; Hollins High School, Accrington; Park View School, Birmingham; Parklands Middle School, Northampton; Pinner Wood Middle School, Harrow; Sacred Heart of Mary Girls' School, Upminster; South Halifax High School, Halifax; St. Angela's Ursuline Convent, Forest Gate, London; St. Anne's Catholic School, Palmers Green, London; St. Chad's School, Tilbury, Essex; The Minster School, Southwell, Nottingham; The Park School, Barnstable; William Brookes School, Salop.

Editor: Marie Lister
Design: Moondisks Ltd, Cambridge
Printed in Croatia by Zrinski, Cakovec

Contents

Chapter 1 Direction and Position

Step-up

1 Look at the picture. Use the word **left** or **right** to complete the statements.

(a) Kim will turn ? for the lift.
(b) Kim will turn ? for the stairs.
(c) Her bag is in her ? hand.
(d) Kim is looking to the ? .

2 You are standing by the entrance to the park.

(a) Where does the **second** path on the **left** lead you?
(b) The pool is on your **left**. True or false?
(c) Take the **first** path on the **left**. What do you find?
(d) To find the café you take the ? turning on the ? .
(e) The bench is down the **second** turning on the right. True or false?

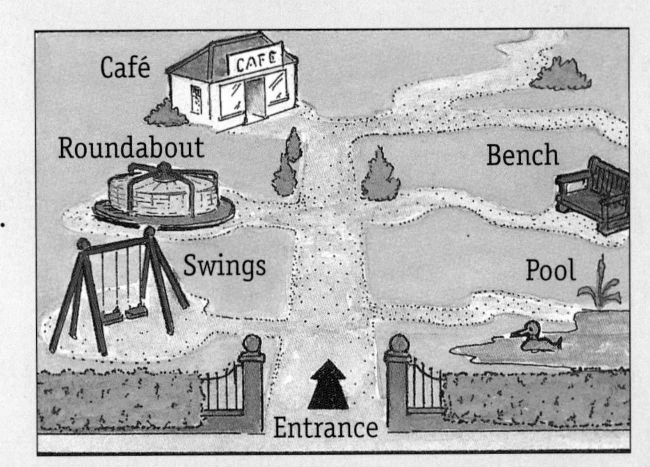

3 Use the map to answer the questions below.

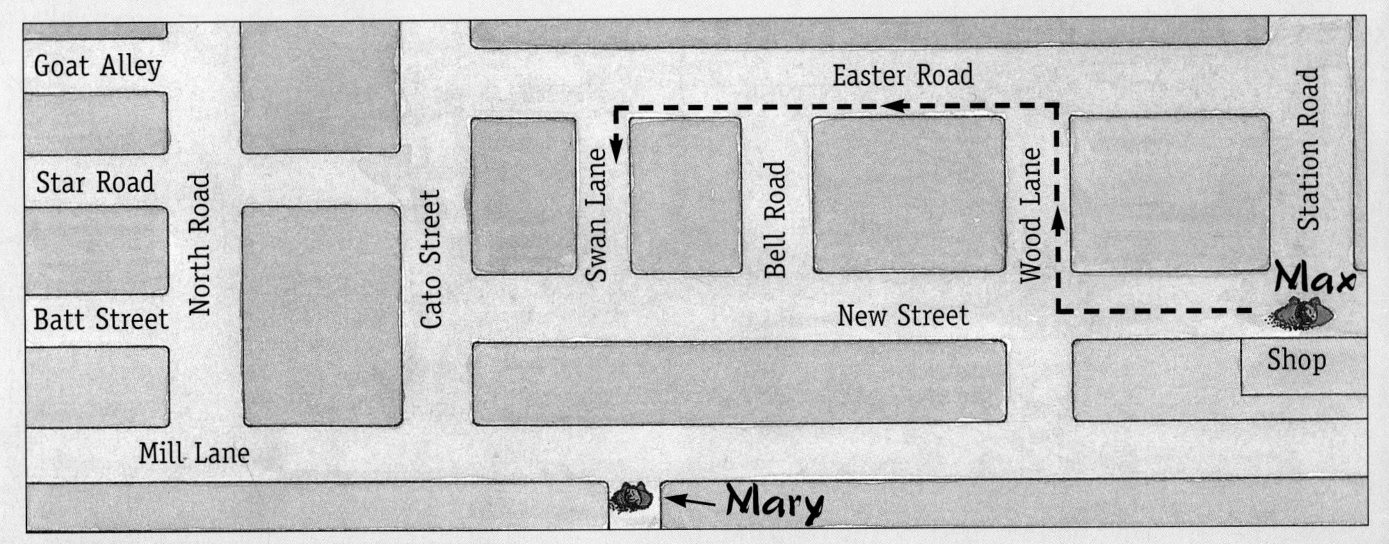

(a) Where does Mary get to?
(Use the map to follow Mary's journey.)
Mary walks **forward**. She turns **left** into Mill Lane. She takes the **second** turning on the **right**. Then she takes the **second** turning on the **left**. Where is she now?

(b) Max's journey
(Use the map of Max's journey to complete these.)
Max leaves the shop and turns ? . He then turns ? into Wood Lane. He then turns left into Easter Road and takes the ? turning on the ? into Swan Lane.

Exercise 1

Copy and complete the sentences below using one of these directions.

left **straight ahead** **right**

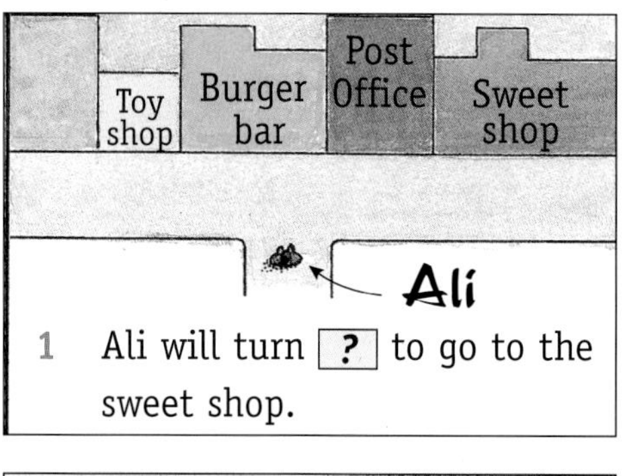

1 Ali will turn [?] to go to the sweet shop.

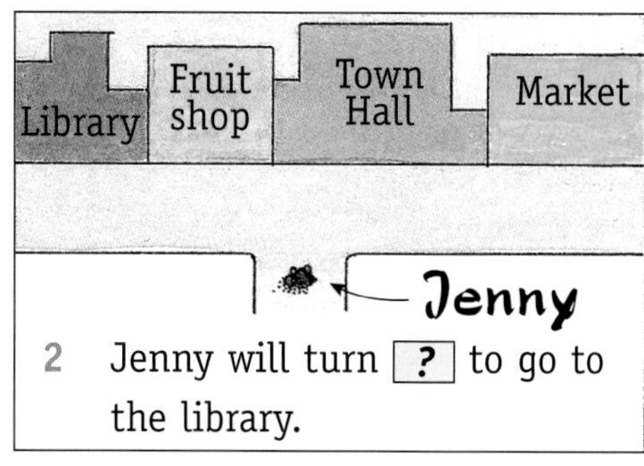

2 Jenny will turn [?] to go to the library.

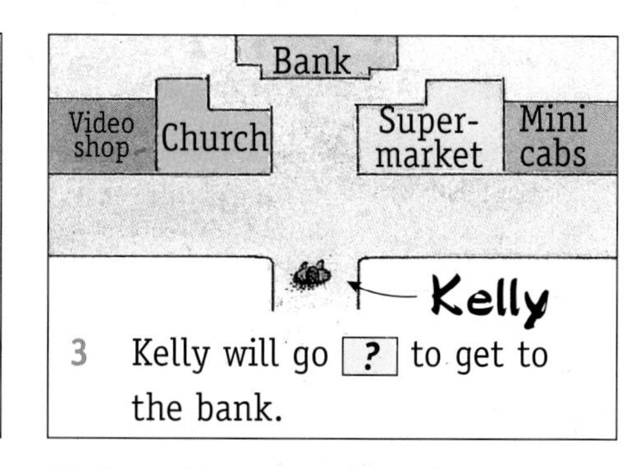

3 Kelly will go [?] to get to the bank.

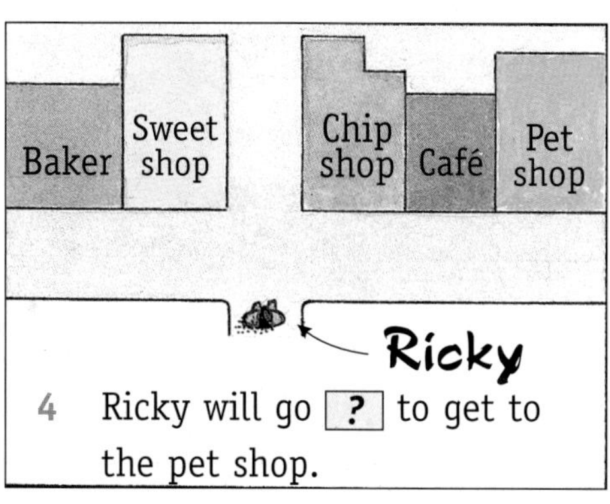

4 Ricky will go [?] to get to the pet shop.

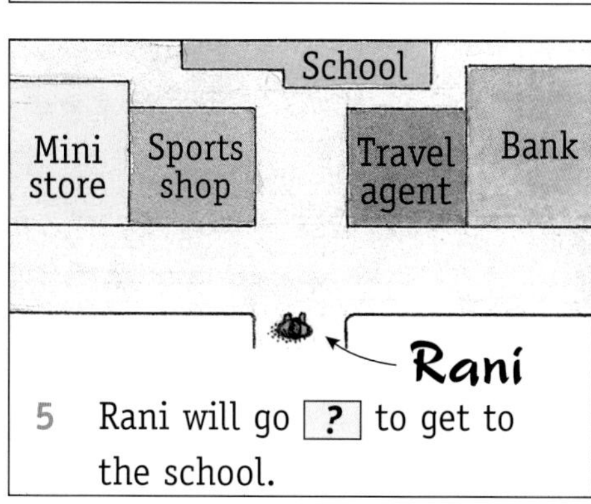

5 Rani will go [?] to get to the school.

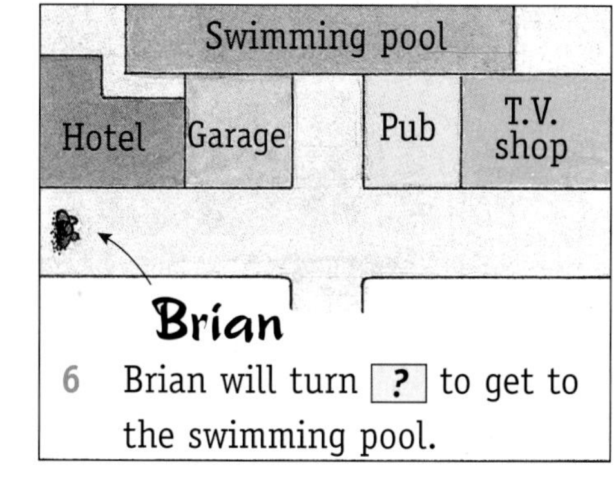

6 Brian will turn [?] to get to the swimming pool.

Exercise 2

1 Kim is walking along the High Street.

(a) Which road is **second** on the **left**?

(b) Which street is **first** on the **right**?

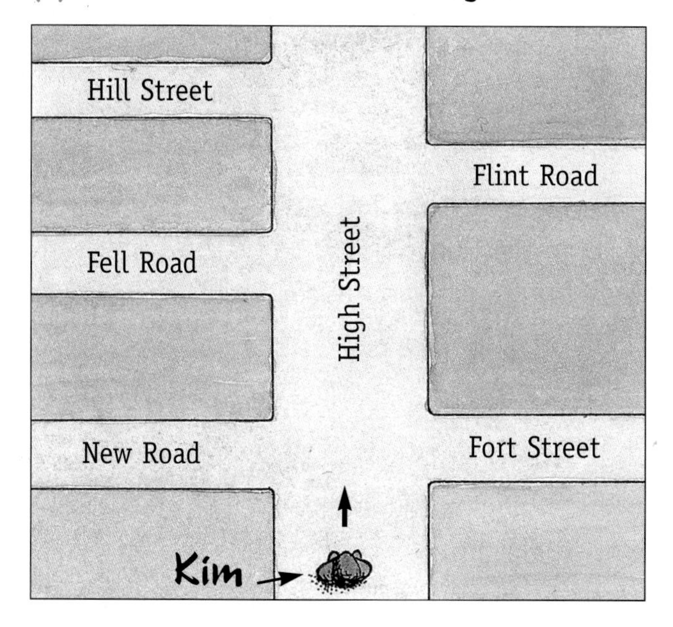

2 Farzad is walking along Carr Road.

(a) Which road is **second** on the **right**?

(b) Which lane is **third** on the **left**?

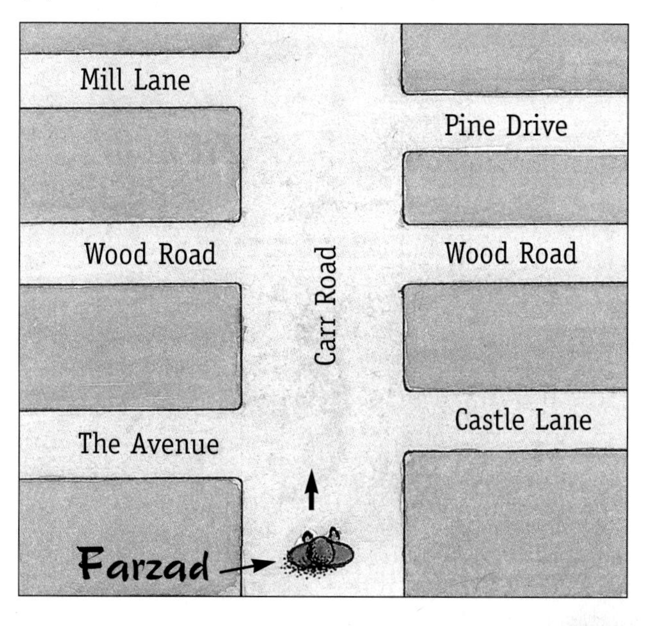

Exercise 3

Answer these questions about the map below.

1 In which road is the Post Office?

2 Which road leads to Rose Park?

3 The bank is on the corner of which two roads?

4 On which road is the school?

5 On which street is the market?

6 Which lane leads to the pond?

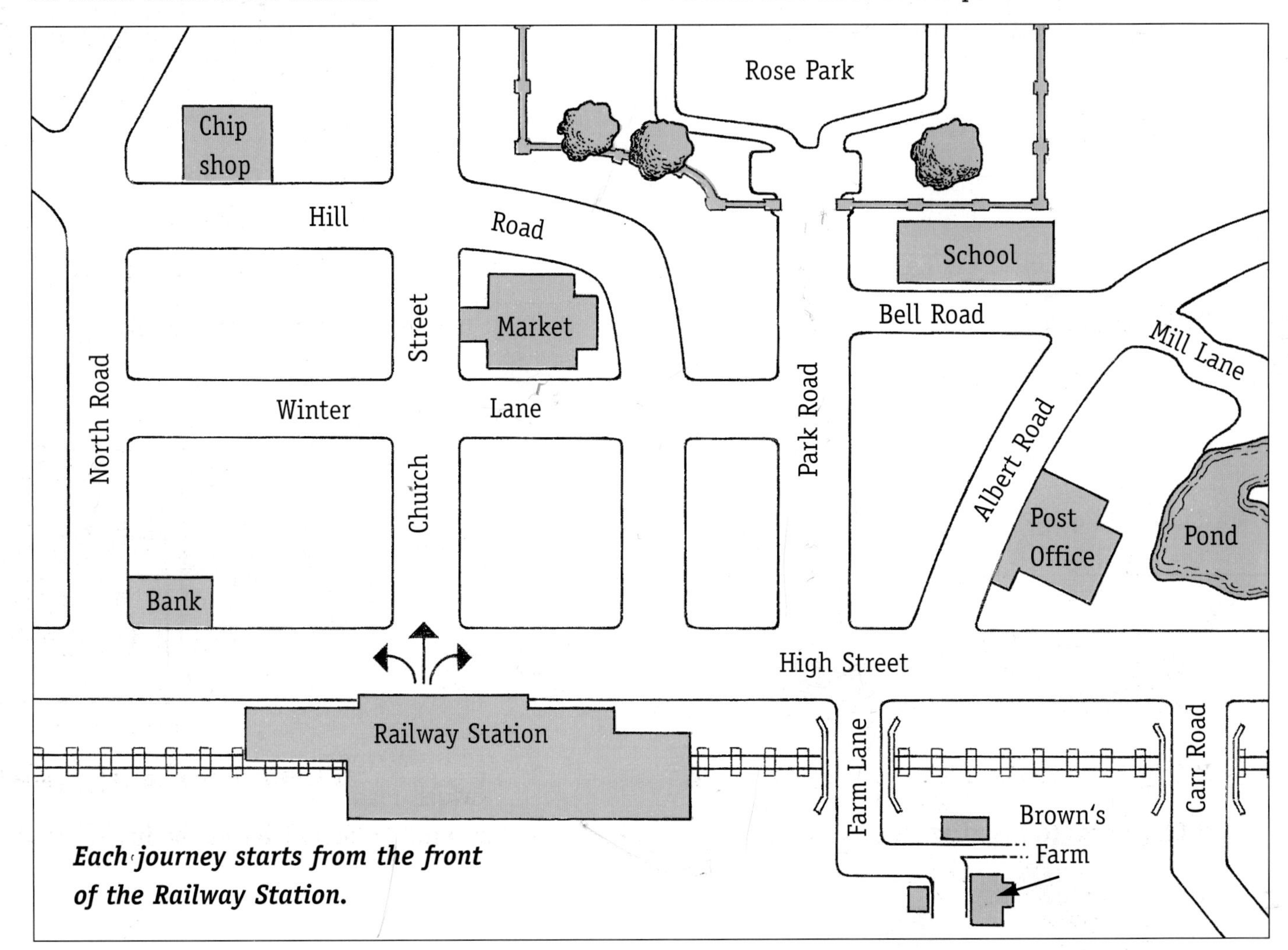

7 Turn **right** out of the station. Then take the next **right** turn.

(a) Which lane are you in?

(b) What is at the end of the lane?

8 Turn **right** out of the station. Take the **first** turning on the **left**. Then take the **first** turning on the **right**.

(a) Which lane are you in?

(b) Which road is at the end of this lane?

9 Turn **left** out of the station. Take the **first** turning on the **right**. Now take the **second** turning on the **right**.

(a) Which road are you in?

(b) What shop will you find there?

10 Walk **straight ahead** from the station. Take the **first** turning on the **right**. Then take the **second** turning on the **left**.

(a) Which road are you in?

(b) List the roads you have travelled along.

Exercise 4

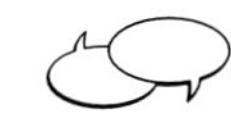

Copy and complete each sentence using **left** or **right**.

1 To see the bears, Liz must turn to her **?**.

2 To see the lions, Liz must turn to her **?**.

3 To go to Bradford, Tom must turn to his **?**.

4 To go to Leeds, Tom must turn to his **?**.

5 If Chip turns to her **left** she will find her **?**.

6 If Chip turns to her **right** she will find her **?**.

7 If Jim turns to his **right** he will be in **?** Road.

8 If Jim turns to his **left** he will be in **?** Road.

9 To go up the steps Kelvin will turn to his **?**.

10 To go down the steps Kelvin will turn to his **?**.

The ringed code on the ticket tells you the position of your seat.

The Jazz Band
+ support
Sat 29th May 7.30pm
Seat M 17

Caxton Rangers
V
Hinton United
Kick Off 2.30pm
Seat G 163

ODEAN
Cinema
Raiders return
8.00 to 10.00pm
Seat B7

The first part of the code shows you which **column** you are in. The second part of the code shows you which **row** you are in.

So, if your ticket has B4 printed on it, it means that your seat is in **column B**, and in **row 4**.

5	□	□	□	□	□	□
4	□	□	□	□	□	□
3	□	□	□	□	□	□
2	□	□	□	□	□	□
1	□	□	□	□	□	□
	A	B	C	D	E	F

Exercise 5

Here is the seating plan for a cabin of an aeroplane. To find which seat people are sitting in, you must know the **column** and the **row**.

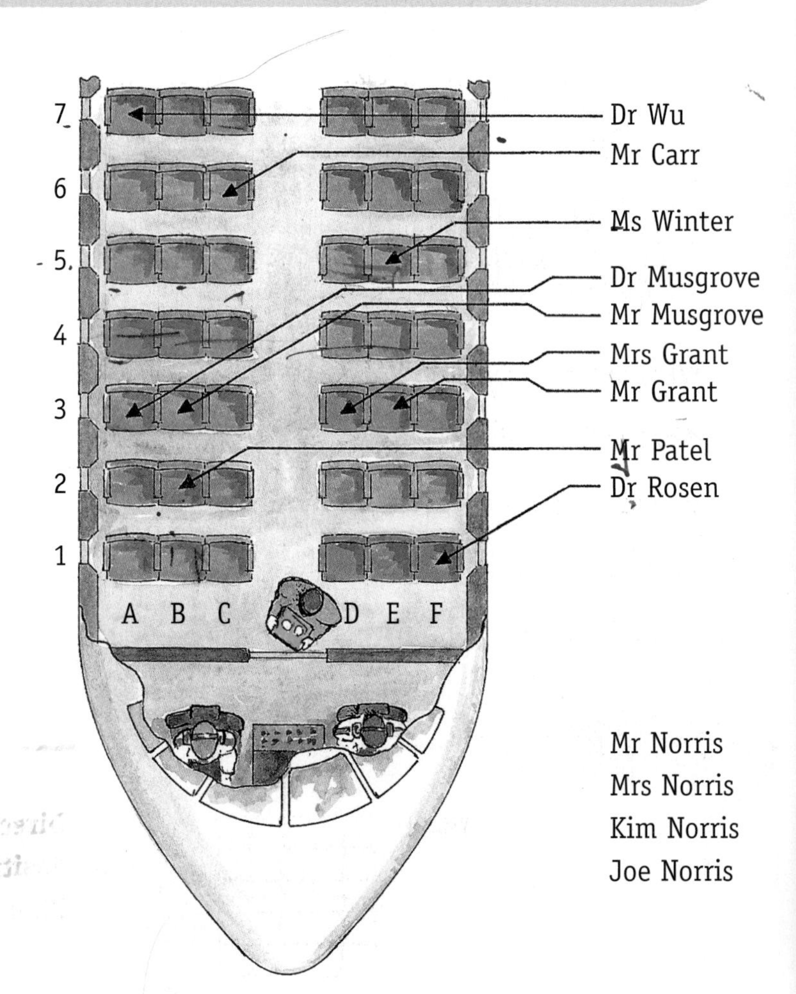

1 Who is in seat D3?

2 Who is sitting beside her?

3 Who is in seat A7?

4 Is seat C5 empty?

5 In which seat is Mr Patel?

6 Who is sitting behind seat C5?

7 Where is Ms Winter sitting?

8 Who is sitting next to the person in B3?

9 What is the seat number behind Dr Rosen?

10 There are four people in the Norris family. Seat them together and give the seat numbers.

Exercise 6

Use the grid on the map to answer the questions below. First read the letters across the bottom, and then the numbers up the side to find each position.

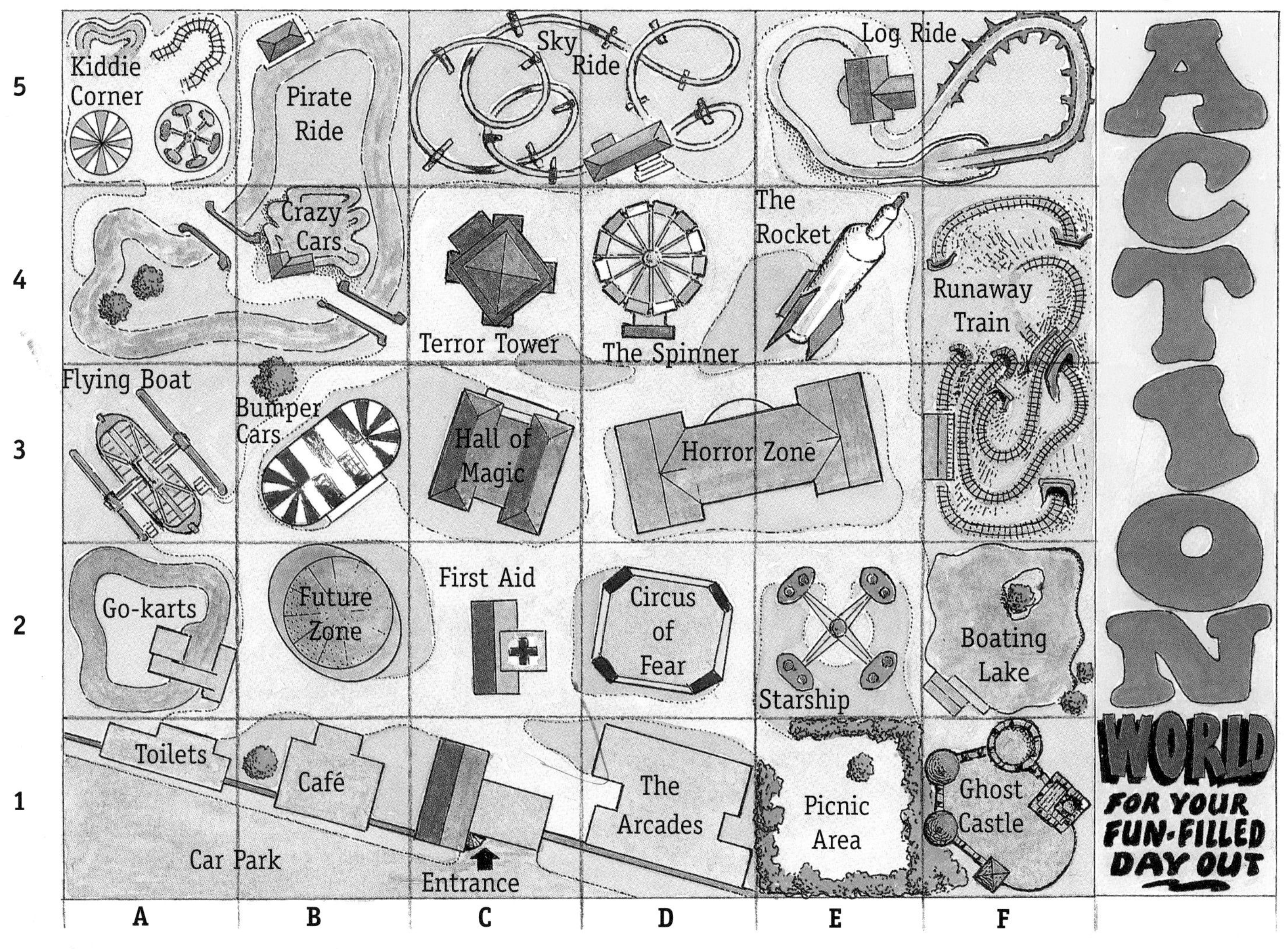

1 What will you find in square E1?

2 What will you find in square E4?

3 What will you find in square A2?

4 What will you find at F3 and F4?

5 In which square is the Ghost Castle?

6 In which square is Kiddie Corner?

7 In which square is the Circus of Fear?

8 In which two squares will you find the Log Ride?

9 Is the First Aid room in square C2?

10 Which squares does the Pirate Ride pass through?

Key ideas

Grid –

Direction – the way something is facing.
Position – where something is placed.
Plan – map

Chapter 2 Addition

Step-up 1

Addition Card One

1 How many bottles are there?

2 How many sweets are there?

3 How many pencils are there?

4 How many boxes are there?

Addition Card Two

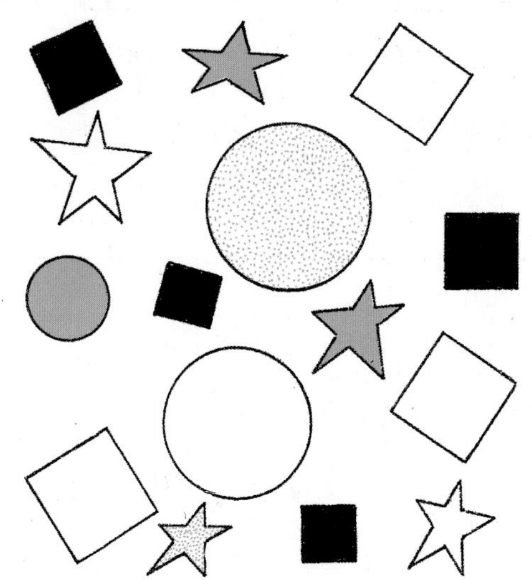

Count the following items.

1 How many stars are there?
2 How many circles are there?
3 How many black squares are there?
4 How many white squares are there?
5 How many squares are there in all?

1 Write down the score each person gets.

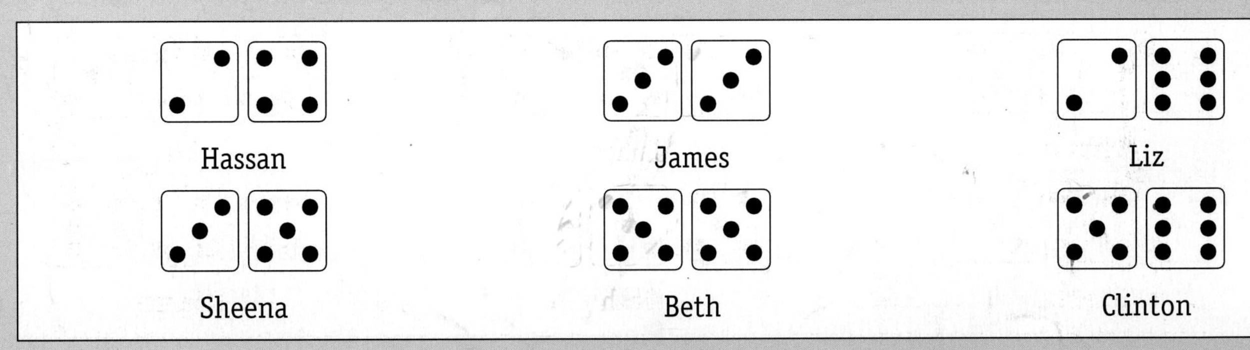

2 Using two dice, write down:

(a) ways of scoring 5

(b) ways of scoring 7

(c) the **biggest** score you can get with two dice.

Addition Card Three

1 $4 + 2 =$? 2 $4 + 4 =$?
3 $3 + 3 =$? 4 $2 + 6 =$?
5 $5 + 3 =$? 6 $0 + 8 =$?
7 $1 + 7 =$? 8 $5 + 4 =$?

Addition Card Four

1 $7 + 2 =$? 2 $3 + 6 =$?
3 $1 + 9 =$? 4 $8 + 2 =$?
5 $5 + 6 =$? 6 $6 + 6 =$?
7 $8 + 3 =$? 8 $7 + 6 =$?

Addition Card Five

Written problems. The first has been done for you.

1 Six add three equals nine.
2 Five add four makes ? .
3 Three add four equals ? .
4 Three plus seven equals ? .
5 Six add five equals ? .
6 Six plus nine is ? .
7 Five plus eight equals ? .
8 Nine add ten equals ? .
9 Seven plus twelve equals ? .
10 Nine plus eight is ? .

Addition Card Six

1 $3 + 2 + 2 =$? 2 $4 + 1 + 3 =$? 3 $3 + 3 + 2 =$? 4 $2 + 5 + 3 =$?
5 $1 + 6 + 5 =$? 6 $3 + 4 + 5 =$? 7 $7 + 0 + 8 =$? 8 $5 + 2 + 7 =$?
9 $3 + 6 + 8 =$? 10 $4 + 7 + 5 =$? 11 $6 + 5 + 6 =$? 12 $7 + 4 + 8 =$?

3 Write down the score each person gets.

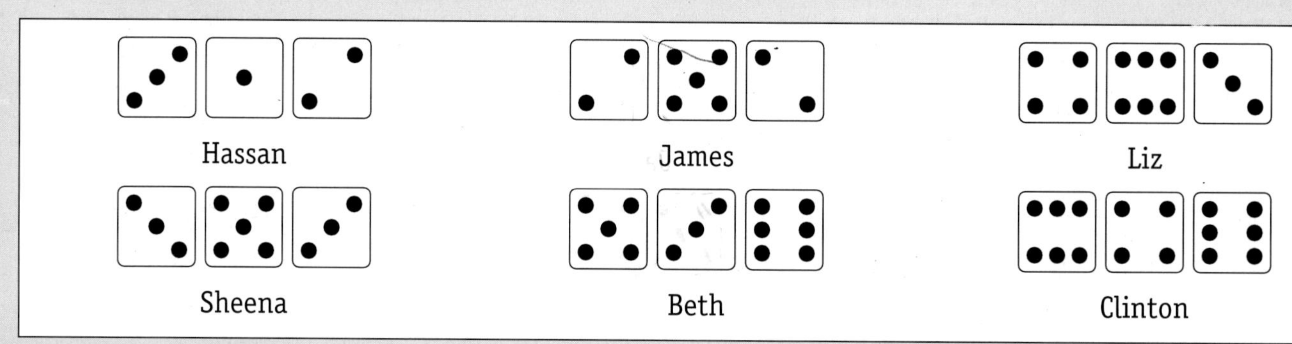

4 Using three dice, write down:

(a) three ways of scoring 10

(b) three ways of scoring 15

(c) the **biggest** score you can get with three dice.

Exercise 1

Complete these sentences.

1 There are [?] flowers.

2 There are [?] bottles.

3 There are [?] books.

4 There are [?] keys.

Exercise 2

Here are four groups of sweets. Answer the questions about them.

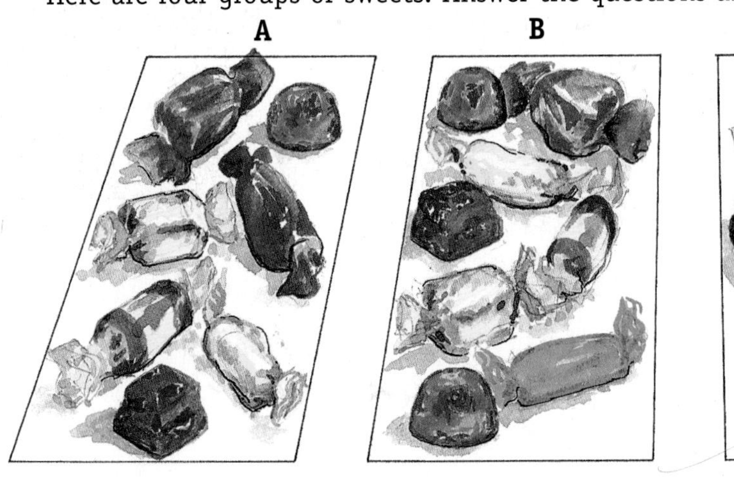

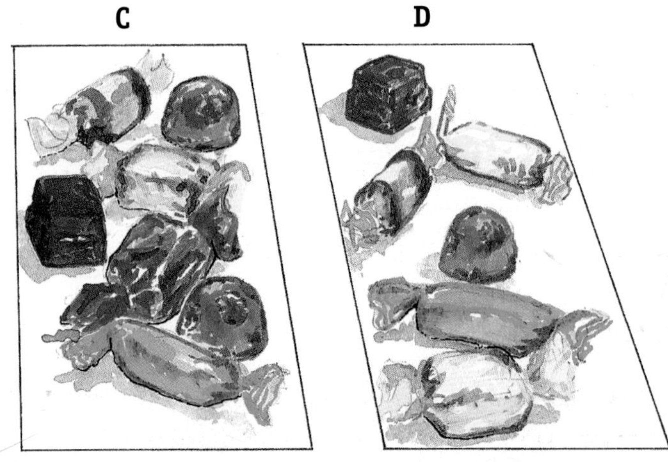

1 Group [?] has the most sweets.

2 Group [?] has the smallest number of sweets.

3 Group [?] and [?] have the same number of sweets.

Exercise 3

Write out the **smallest** and the **biggest** numbers from each group.

1 8, 7, 5, 3, 9.

2 7, 6, 5, 9, 8.

3 4, 22, 15, 2, 18.

4 11, 10, 9, 12, 6.

5 25, 10, 9, 16, 15.

6 20, 8, 22, 9, 21.

7 30, 10, 40, 50, 20.

8 16, 19, 14, 17, 15, 18.

Exercise 4

Write out these numbers in order. Write the **smallest** number first.

1 5, 8, 1, 3, 9.

2 8, 3, 10, 2, 5.

3 8, 6, 12, 15, 7.

4 4, 29, 6, 3, 15.

5 20, 12, 5, 21, 8.

6 19, 6, 2, 38, 15.

7 9, 17, 33, 1, 27.

8 20, 7, 40, 30, 50.

Exercise 5

This machine puts toffees and chocolates into boxes. There should be **10** sweets in each box. The number of toffees and chocolates are shown on the red displays. Find the displays which show that there are 10 sweets in a box. Write down the question numbers.

1 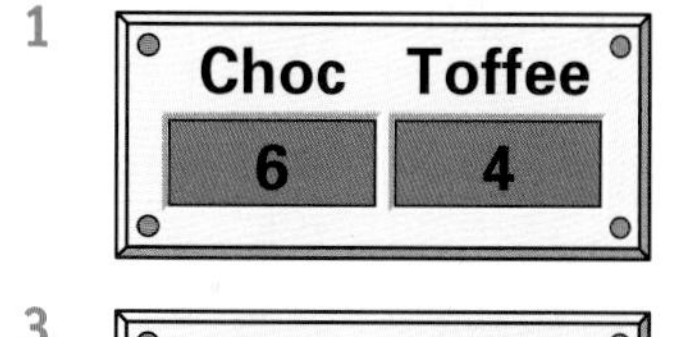

2 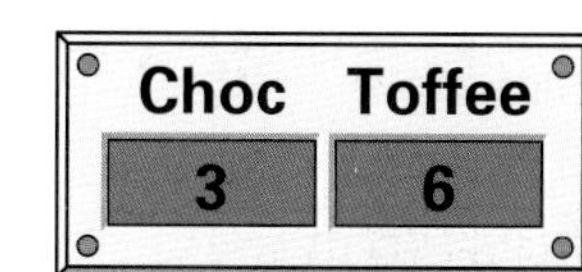

3 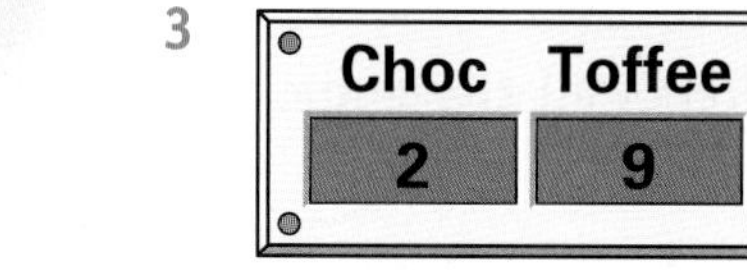

4 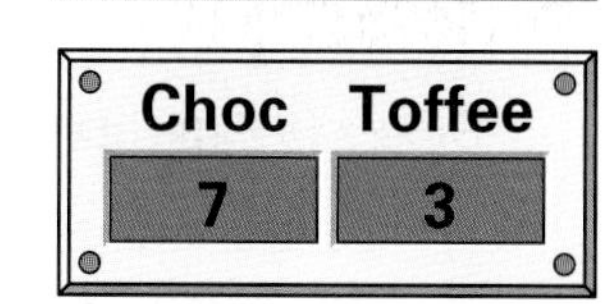

5 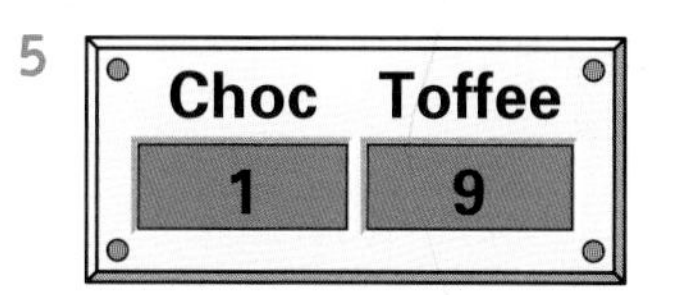

6 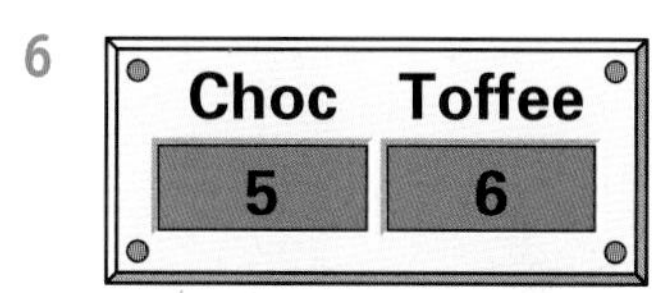

7 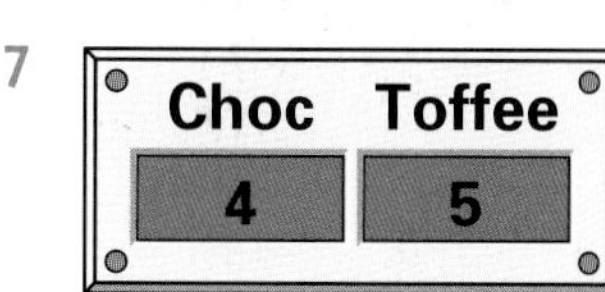

8 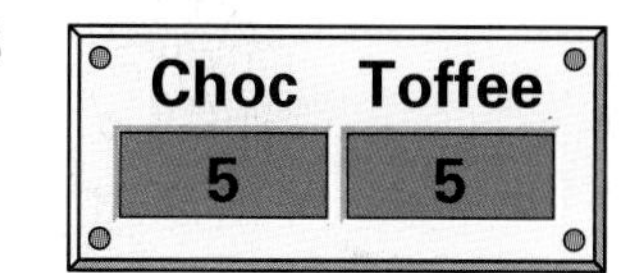

9 Write down other groups of chocolates and toffees that add up to 10.

Exercise 6

There should be **20** sweets in each box. Find the displays which show that there are 20 sweets in a box. Write down the question numbers.

1 Choc Toffee 10 8

2 Choc Toffee 12 8

3 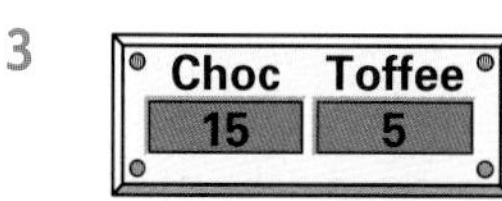

4 Choc Toffee 6 12

5 Choc Toffee 9 11

6 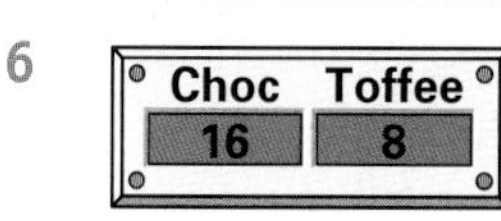

7 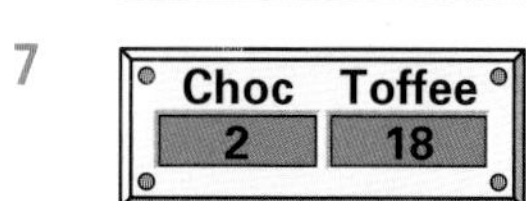

8 Choc Toffee 10 14

9 Choc Toffee 10 10

10 Write down other groups of chocolates and toffees that add up to 20.

Exercise 7

Use numbers from the circle to complete these problems.

1 ? + ? = 4

2 ? + ? = 7

3 ? + ? = 6

4 ? + ? = 5

5 ? + ? = 9

6 ? + ? = 10

7 ? + ? = 12

8 ? + ? = 11

9 ? + ? + ? = 10

10 ? + ? + ? = 15

Fred has a farm. On his farm he has a hen house, where his hens lay eggs.

Each day Fred collects all the eggs.

He puts 10 eggs into each box.

Exercise 8

Look at each group of eggs.

1 Copy and complete the table below to record how many eggs are in each group. The first is done for you.

A

B

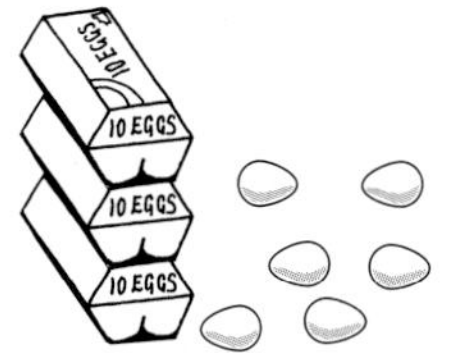

C

D

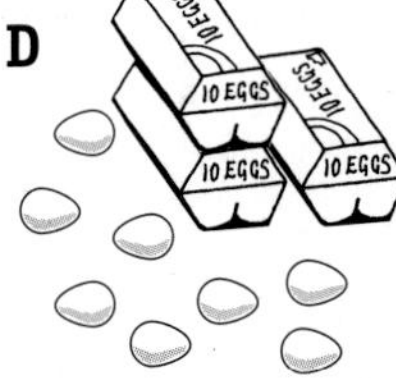

E

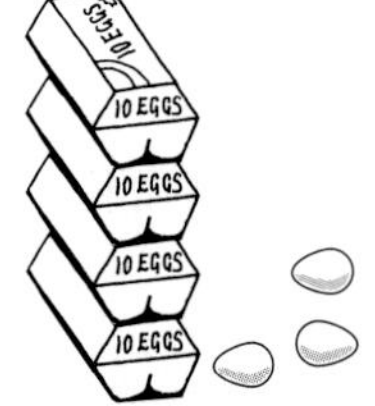

F

G

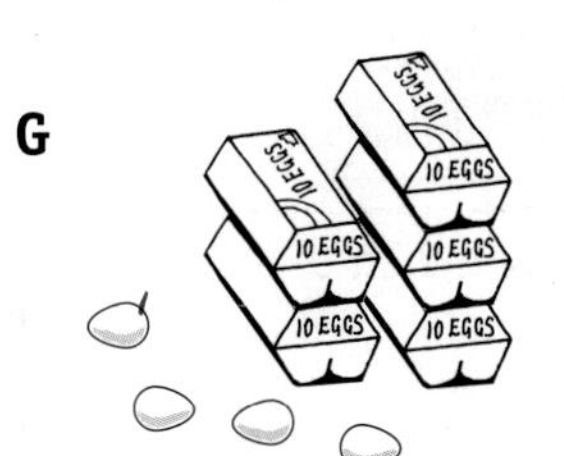

H

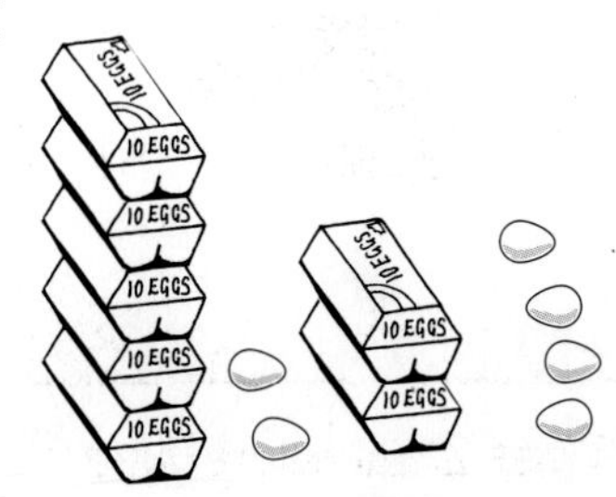

Group of eggs	Number of 10s boxes	Number of single eggs	Total number of eggs
A	1	4	14
B	?	?	?
C	?	?	?
D	?	?	?
E	?	?	?
F	?	?	?
G	?	?	?
H	?	?	?

2 How many boxes and single eggs would you see for:

(a) 23 eggs (b) 72 eggs (c) 45 eggs (d) 7 eggs

Exercise 9

Choose the correct answer for each question.

1 53 Does the 5 in this number stand for **5 tens** or **5 units**?

2 29 Does the 9 in this number stand for **9 tens** or **9 units**?

3 47 Does the 7 in this number stand for **7 tens** or **7 units**?

4 38 Does the 3 in this number stand for **3 tens** or **3 units**?

5 16 Does the 6 in this number stand for **6 tens** or **6 units**?

Exercise 10

Write how many **tens** and **units** there are in each number.
The first is done for you.

1 **27** There are **2** tens and **7** units in this number.

2 42 There are ? tens and ? units in this number.

3 65 There are ? tens and ? units in this number.

4 30 There are ? tens and ? units in this number.

5 87 There are ? tens and ? units in this number.

Addition Card Seven

1 32 + 24	2 13 + 55	3 24 + 35
4 71 + 17	5 53 + 24	6 22 + 56
7 28 + 31	8 50 + 38	9 63 + 30
10 40 + 49	11 72 + 17	12 37 + 51

Exercise 11

1

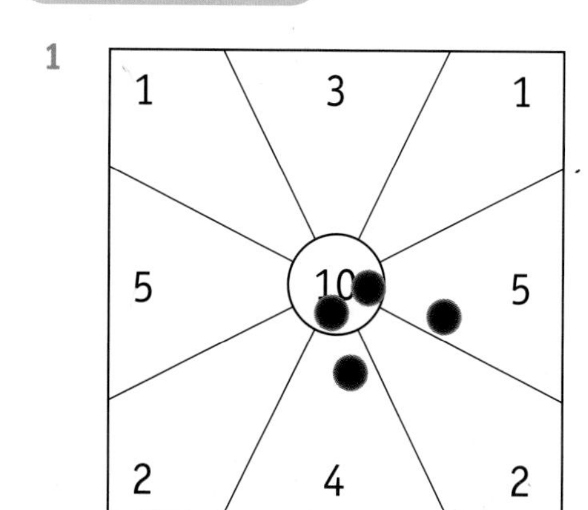

(a) What is the score here?
(b) How could 27 be scored with 4 hits?

2

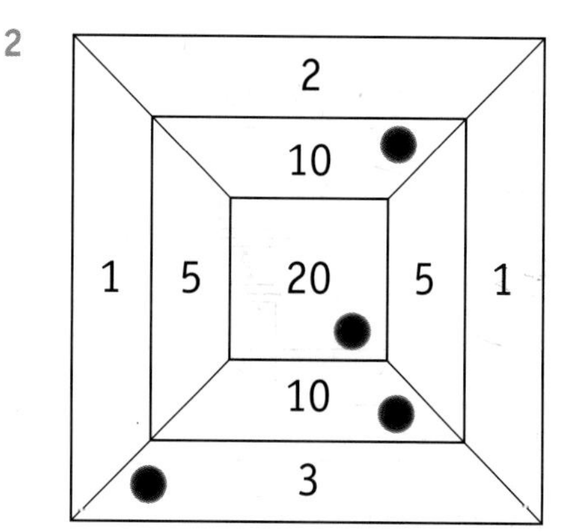

(a) What is the score here?
(b) How could 33 be scored with 4 hits?

3

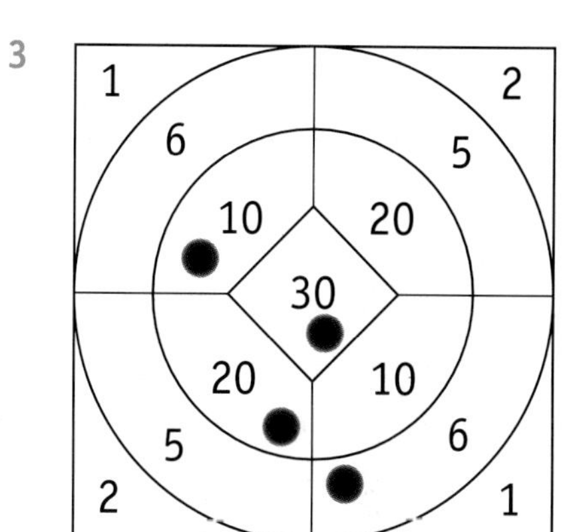

(a) What is the score here?
(b) How could 41 be scored with 4 hits?

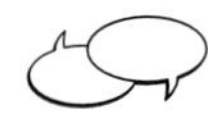

Fred the farmer packs the egg boxes into cases.

He puts 10 egg boxes into each case.

There will be 100 eggs in each case.

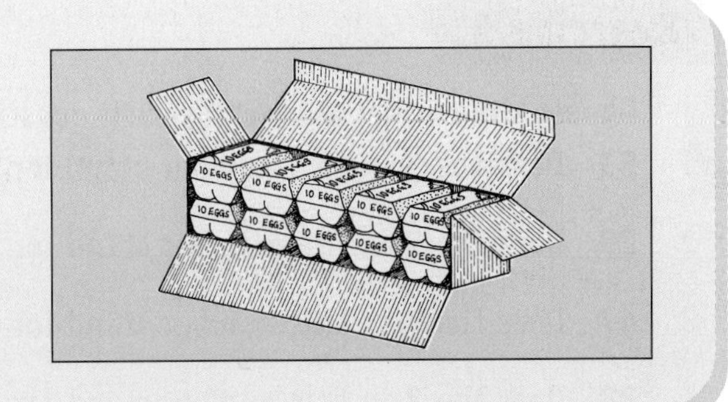

Exercise 12

Look at each group of eggs.

1 Copy and complete the table below and record how many eggs there are. The first one has been done for you.

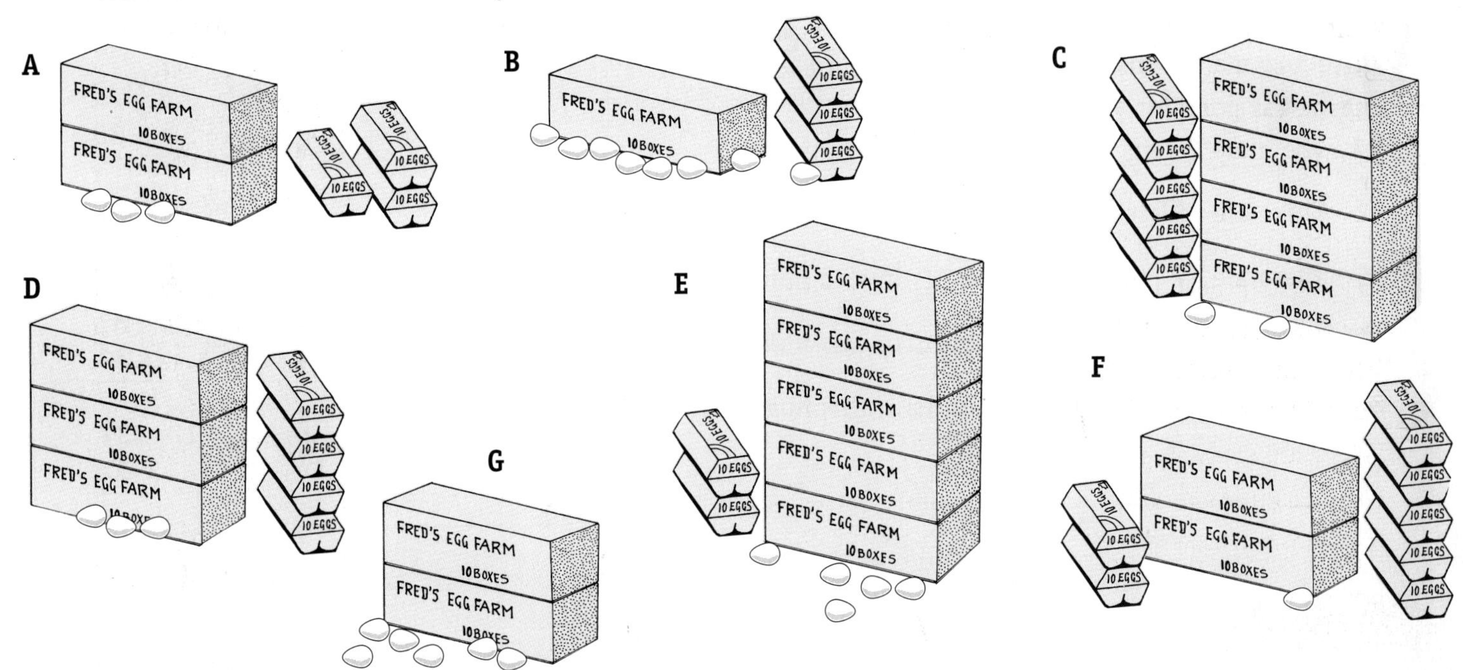

Group of eggs	Number of 100s cases	Number of 10s boxes	Number of single eggs	Total number of eggs
A	2	3	3	233
B	?	?	?	?
C	?	?	?	?
D	?	?	?	?
E	?	?	?	?
F	?	?	?	?
G	?	?	?	?
H	?	?	?	?

H

2 How many cases, boxes and single eggs would you see for:

(a) 354 eggs (b) 280 eggs (c) 406 eggs (d) 83 eggs

Exercise 13

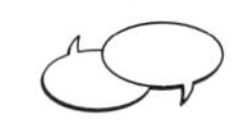

Write these numbers as words.
You can use the list of numbers to help you.
The first one is done for you.

1	54 – fifty-four	2	24	3	59	4	63
5	37	6	45	7	66	8	136
9	324	10	461	11	273	12	579
13	210	14	550	15	203	16	909

1 – one
2 – two
3 – three
4 – four
5 – five
6 – six
7 – seven
8 – eight
9 – nine
10 – ten
11 – eleven
12 – twelve
13 – thirteen
14 – fourteen
15 – fifteen
16 – sixteen
17 – seventeen
18 – eighteen
19 – nineteen
20 – twenty
30 – thirty
40 – forty
50 – fifty
60 – sixty
70 – seventy
80 – eighty
90 – ninety
100 – hundred

Exercise 14

Write these numbers as figures. The first is done for you.

1 Sixty-four – 64
2 Thirty-seven
3 Seventy-three
4 Forty
5 One hundred and twenty
6 Two hundred and fifteen
7 Five hundred and fifty
8 Three hundred and twenty-five
9 Four hundred and eighty-two
10 Six hundred and seventy-nine
11 Two hundred and sixty-six
12 Three hundred and nine

Exercise 15

Choose the correct answer to each question.

1 261 Does the figure 6 in this number stand for:
(a) 6 hundreds (b) 6 tens (c) 6 units

2 584 Does the figure 4 in this number stand for:
(a) 4 hundreds (b) 4 tens (c) 4 units

3 397 Does the figure 3 in this number stand for:
(a) 3 hundreds (b) 3 tens (c) 3 units

4 147 Does the figure 7 in this number stand for:
(a) 7 hundreds (b) 7 tens (c) 7 units

5 459 Does the figure 4 in this number stand for:
(a) 4 hundreds (b) 4 tens (c) 4 units

Addition Card Eight

These problems involve 'carrying'.

1. 16 + 15
2. 17 + 25
3. 27 + 27
4. 17 + 36
5. 38 + 15
6. 19 + 24
7. 15 + 8
8. 26 + 6
9. 8 + 14
10. 5 + 25
11. 7 + 33
12. 27 + 9

Addition Card Nine

These problems involve 'carrying'.

1. 18 + 16
2. 18 + 18
3. 28 + 67
4. 23 + 29
5. 15 + 27
6. 34 + 58
7. 36 + 27
8. 48 + 26
9. 26 + 39
10. 35 + 18
11. 24 + 57
12. 47 + 46

Exercise 16

Copy and complete the answers. Try to work out the answers in your head.

1. Jenny has £9. She is given £3 more. How much does she have in total?
   Jenny has [?] in total.
2. Ahmed has 6 comics. Thomas has 8 comics. How many comics have they got altogether?
   They have [?] comics altogether.
3. Kate counted 4 red cars, 3 blue cars and 5 black cars. How many cars altogether?
   Kate counted [?] cars altogether.
4. Danny has 9 pence in one hand and 11 pence in the other. How much money in total?
   Danny has [?] pence in total.
5. Ruth carried 14 boxes and Jade carried 8 boxes. How many boxes in all?
   Ruth and Jade carried [?] boxes in all.
6. Tom has 6 pens, Samina has 5 pens and Carl has 3. How many pens in total?
   They have [?] pens in total.
7. Mary has 4 hamsters, 5 cats and 6 rabbits. How many animals altogether?
   Mary has [?] animals altogether.
8. Choi got 7 birthday cards from his family and 16 from his friends. How many cards altogether?
   Choi got [?] birthday cards altogether.
9. Carol has 3 brothers, Fatima has 4 brothers, Sarah has 5 brothers and Jean has 2. How many brothers in total?
   They have [?] brothers in total.
10. Kay got 6 marks, Beth got 5 marks, Troy got 5 marks and Toby got 4 marks. How many marks altogether?
    The group have [?] marks altogether.

Addition Card Ten

1. 10 + 23 + 15
2. 37 + 11 + 11
3. 22 + 14 + 23
4. 26 + 10 + 31
5. 12 + 23 + 12
6. 20 + 21 + 16
7. 22 + 12 + 25
8. 53 + 12 + 24
9. 34 + 20 + 13

Addition Card Eleven

These problems involve 'carrying.'

1. 125 + 126
2. 238 + 113
3. 426 + 167
4. 425 + 229
5. 519 + 168
6. 247 + 147
7. 388 + 206
8. 209 + 136
9. 567 + 107
10. 160 + 150
11. 270 + 350
12. 266 + 181

Key ideas

One **unit** is a **single** (1) counting object; for example, **one** egg.

One **ten** is a group of **10** objects. 10 units equals **1 ten**.

One **hundred** is **10** groups of 10 objects. **10 tens** equals **100**.

When we **add** a number of objects to another group of objects, we find out how many objects there are altogether.

We use a 'short-cut' sign for add: **+**
It is used like this: **4 + 3 = 7**

4 + 3 = 7

Other words that mean the same as **add** are: **'and'** and **'plus'**.

Chapter 3 Reflection Symmetry

Step-up

1 Follow these steps to complete Worksheet 8. 8

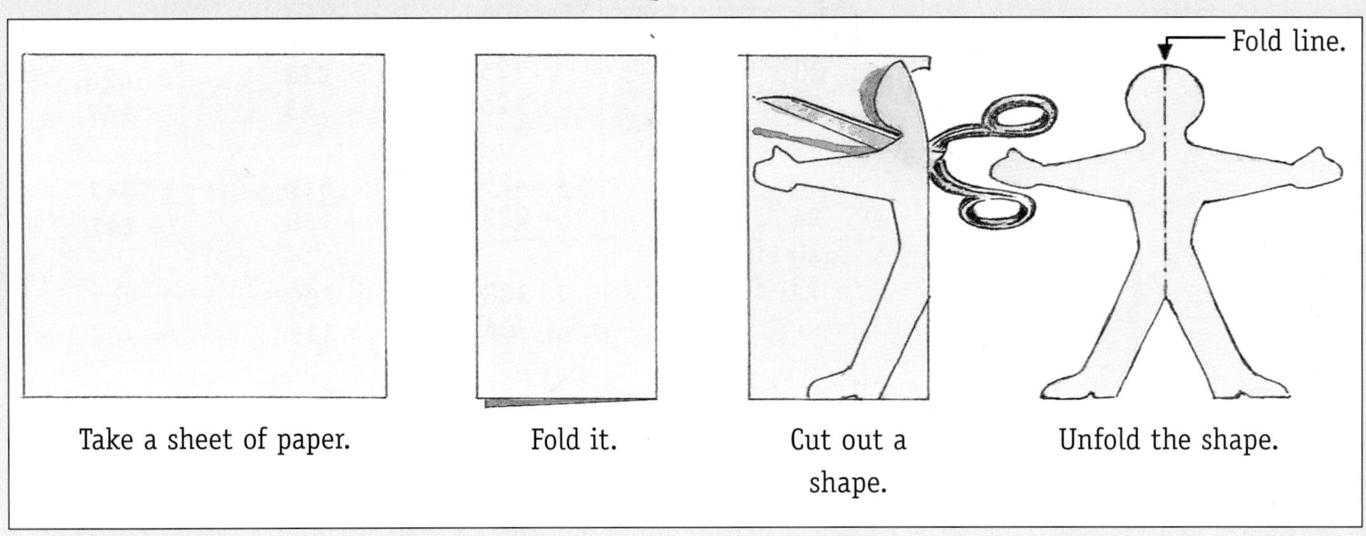

2 If you make this cut, which shape will you get: **A**, **B** or **C**?

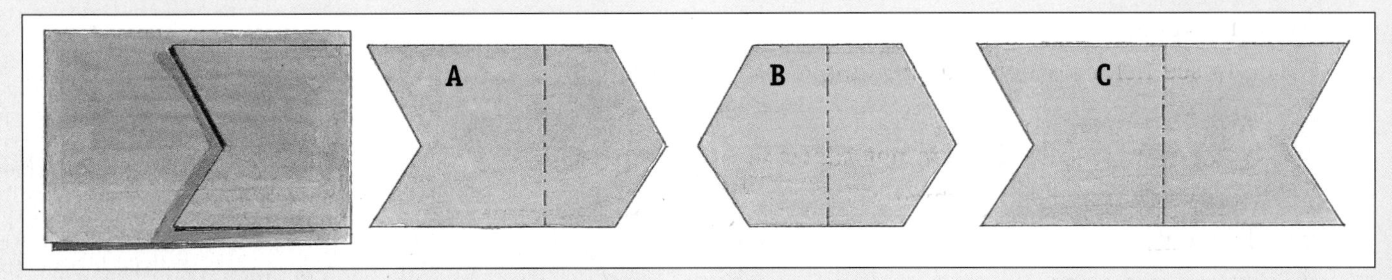

3 If you make this cut, which shape will you get: **A**, **B** or **C**?

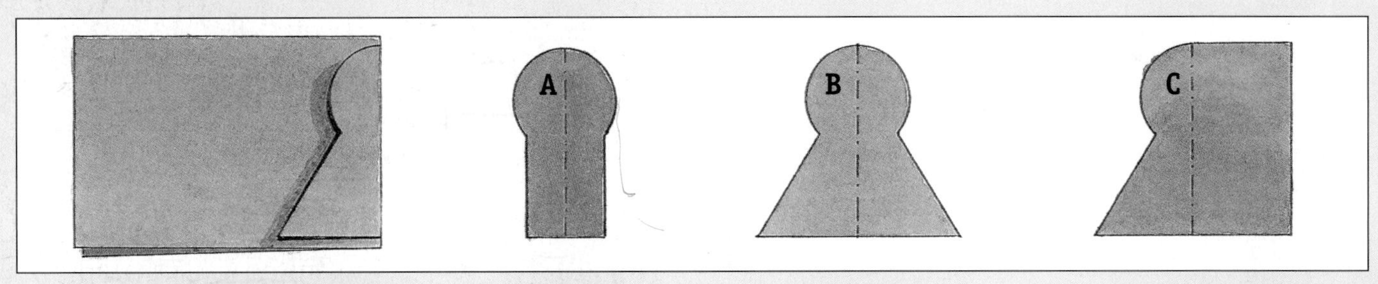

4 If you make this cut, which shape will you get: **A**, **B** or **C**?

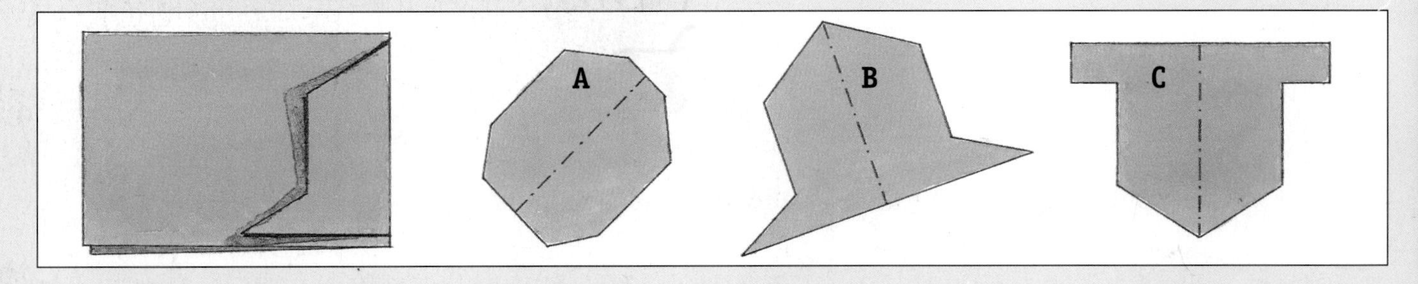

This is a photograph of a lakeland scene. The lake **reflects** the land around it. 

Exercise 1

Meena is taking a picture.
You can see her **reflection** in the shop window.
There are some objects that are not shown in the reflection and some which are different.
How many errors can you spot?

Exercise 2

One drawing in each pair below is needed to make sure that the picture above is a true reflection.

Choose the correct drawing: **A** or **B**.

1 Tree

A 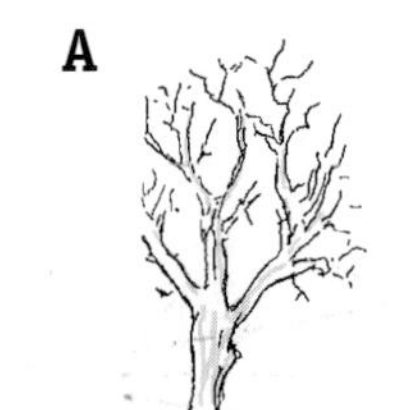 **B** 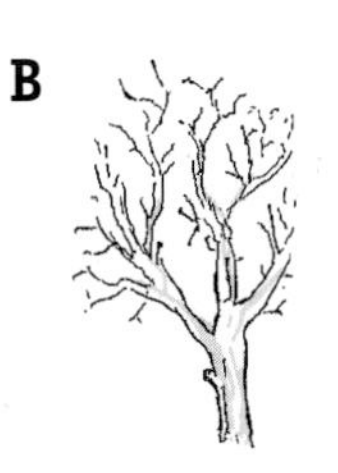

2 Man-hole cover

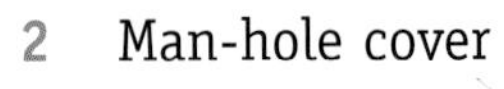

A **B**

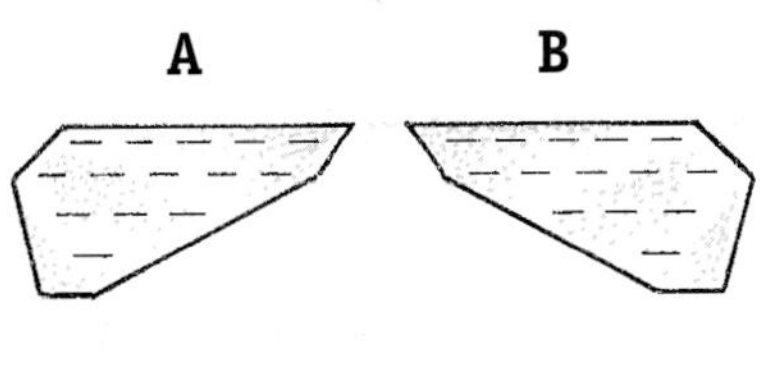

3 4-pane window

A 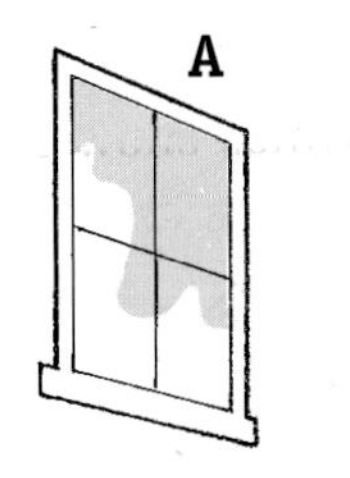 **B** 

4 Chimney

A **B**

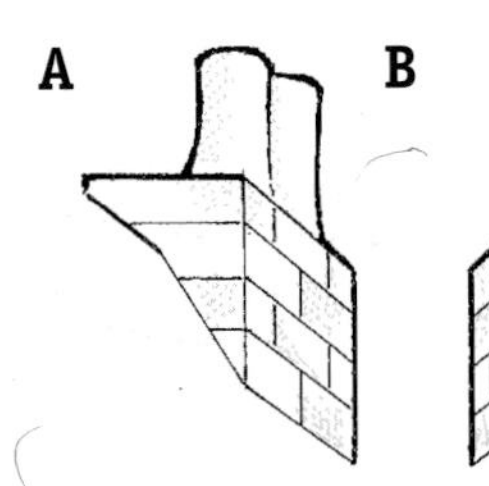

5 Lamppost

A **B**

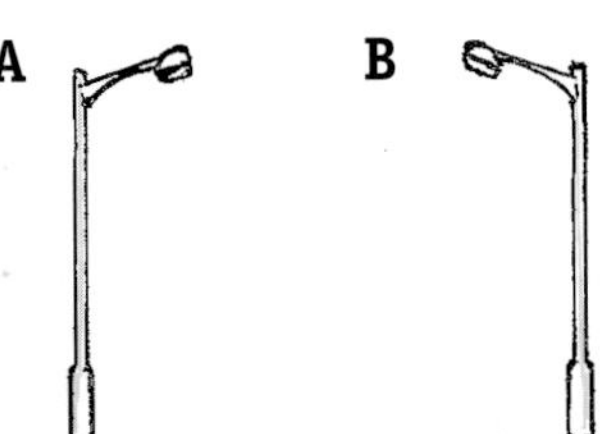

6 Traffic lights

A 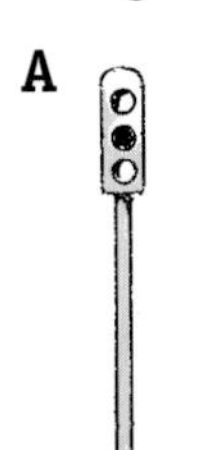 **B** 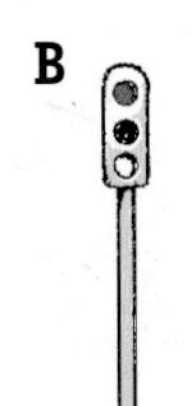

7 Door and step

A 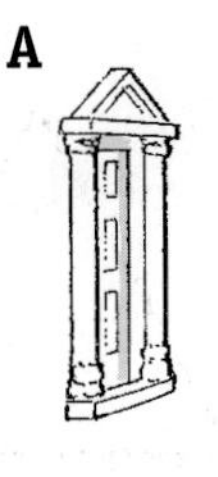 **B**

8 Grate

A 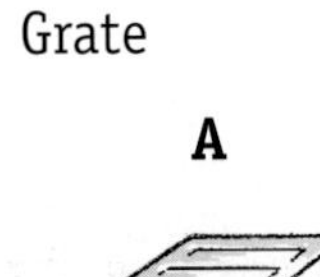 **B** 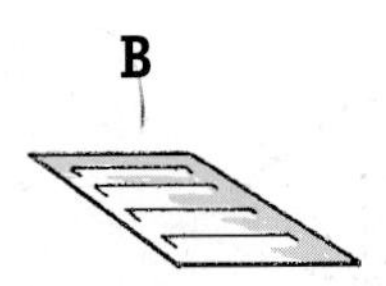

9 9-pane window

A 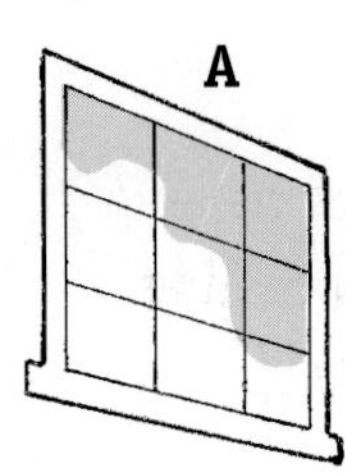 **B** 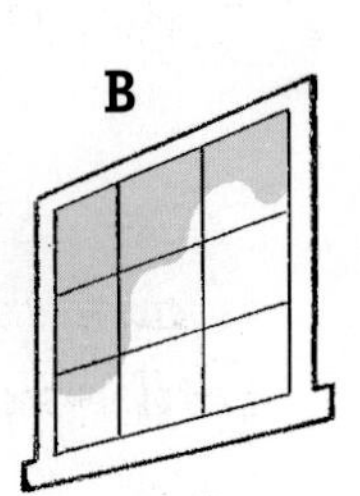

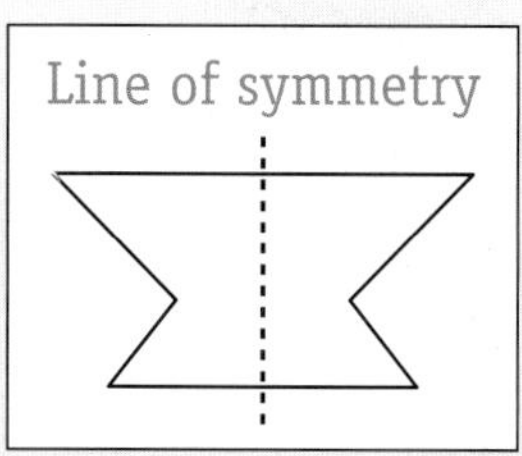

This is a **line of symmetry**. It divides the shape into two **identical** parts.

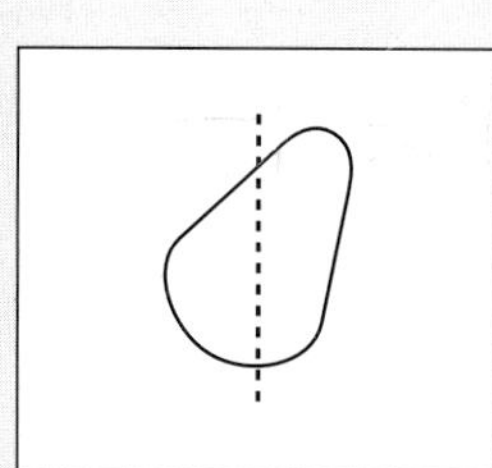

This line is in the wrong position. It does **not** divide the shape into identical parts.

Exercise 3

Which shapes have a correct **line of symmetry**?

1 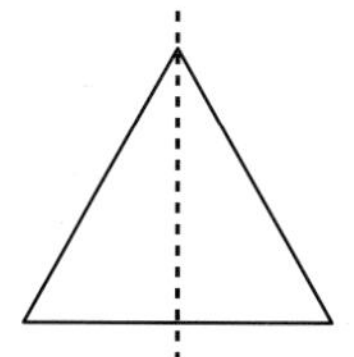

2 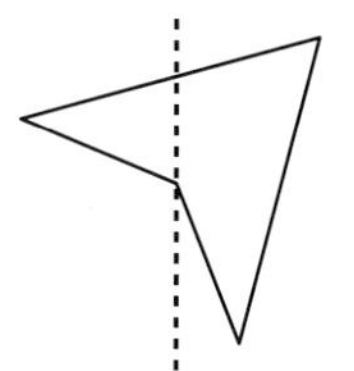

3 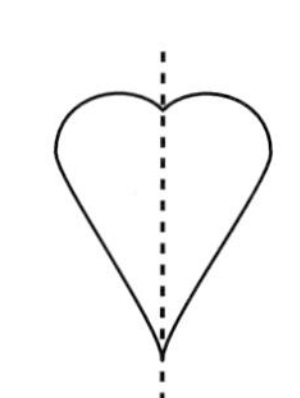

4 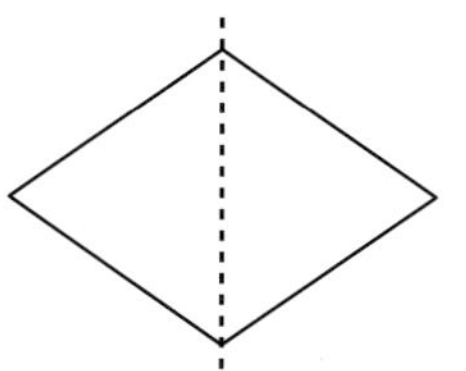

5 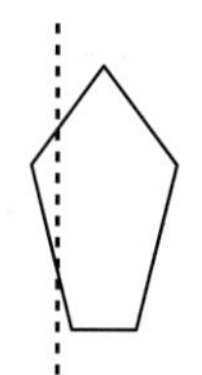

6 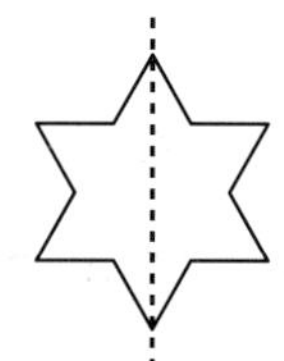

7 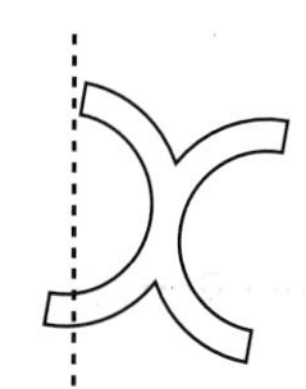

8 

Exercise 4

Which drawings show the correct **symmetrical reflection** of the coloured shape?

1 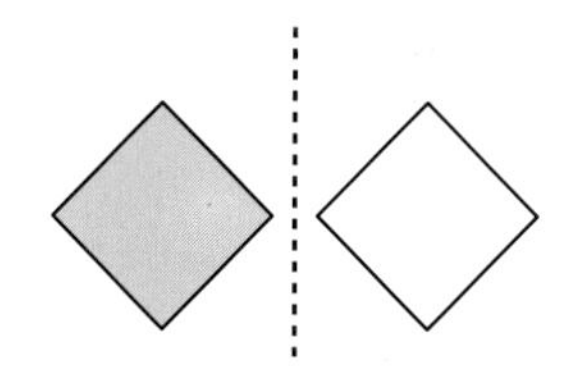

2 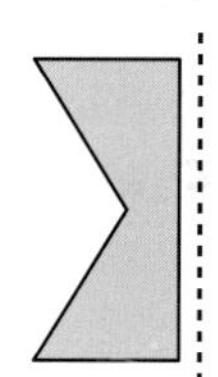

3 

4 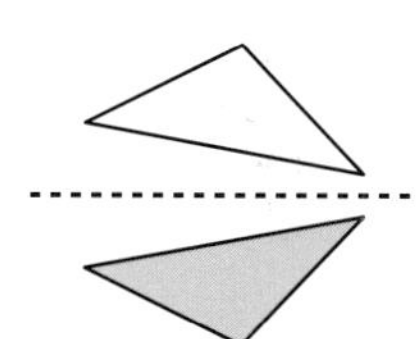

5 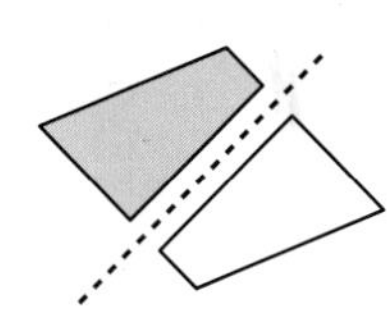

6 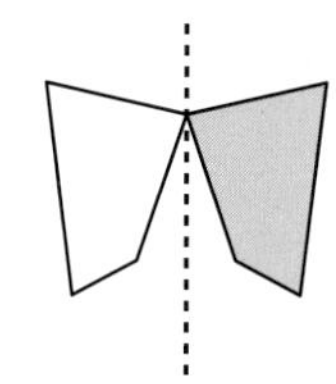

7 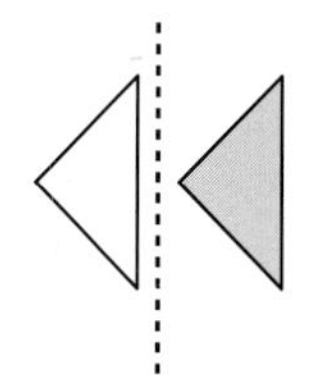

8 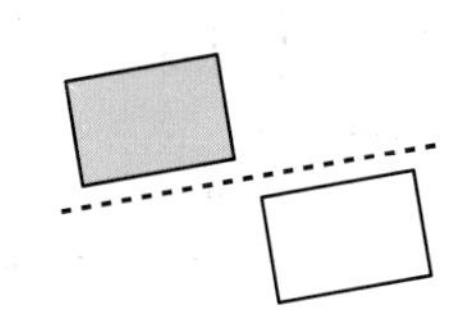

Exercise 5

Some shapes have more than one line of symmetry.

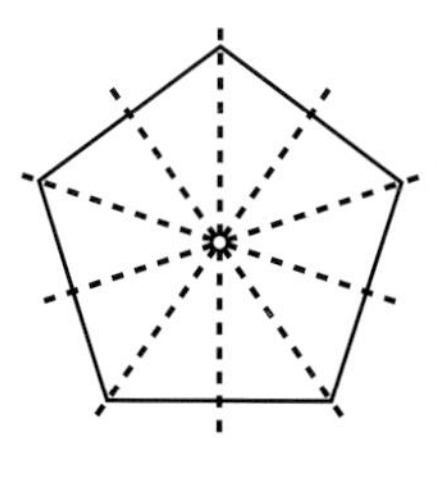

Copy these shapes and draw as many lines of symmetry as you can.

1 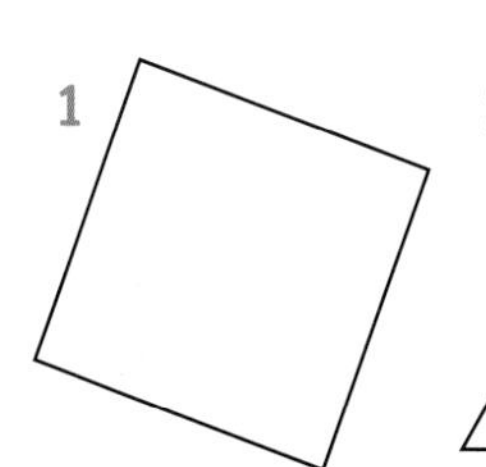

2

Here are the letters of the alphabet written in capitals.

A B C D E F G H I J K L M N O P Q R S T U V W X Y Z

Exercise 6

Copy the symmetrical letters and show the line or lines of symmetry, like this:

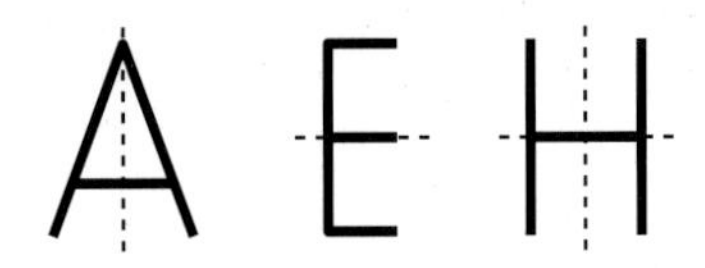

Exercise 7

The letters in these words have (horizontal) symmetry.
Complete the symmetry to find the words, like this:

DID DICK KICK BOB?

1 DECK 2 BOX 3 KID 4 CHICK

5 COOK BOOK 6 HE HID

Exercise 8 

Using tracing paper or grid paper, copy and complete the **symmetrical** shapes below.

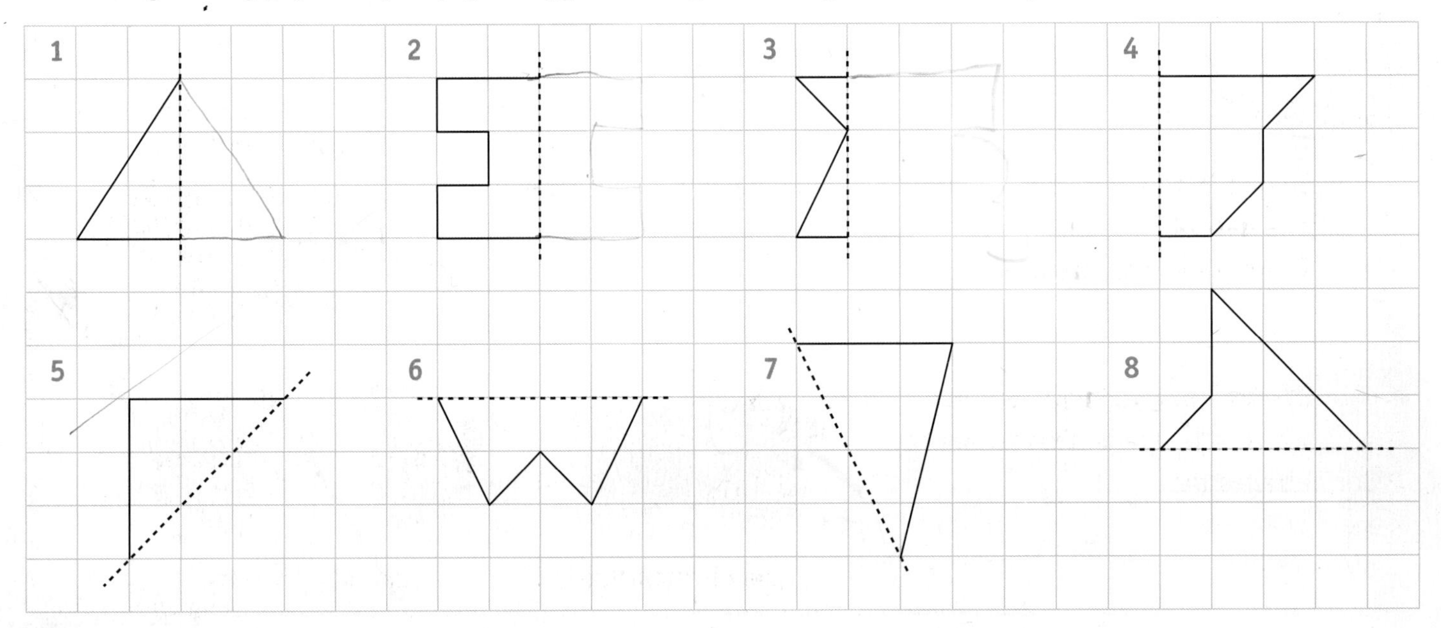

Exercise 9

On the left-hand side of the grid below are six shapes.
The **symmetrical reflection** of shape **a** is shown as **a**¹ on the right.
Shape **a**¹ is on **co-ordinates** squares (F, 2) and (G, 2).
Give the co-ordinates for the **reflections** of shapes **b**, **c**, **d**, **e**, and **f**.

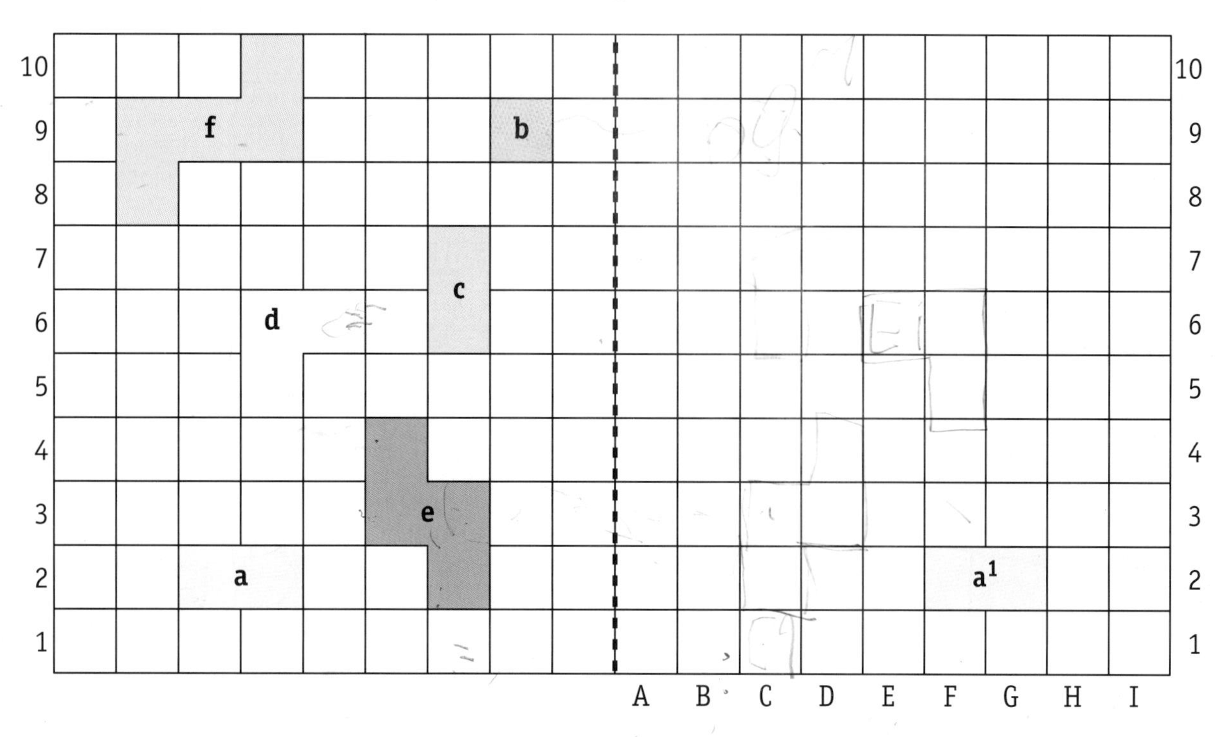

Exercise 10

1 Is your left hand symmetrical?

2 Do you think that your face is symmetrical?

3 Name things in your classroom that are symmetrical.

Key ideas

Shapes have symmetry when a line can be drawn through them so that one **half** of the shape is a true reflection of the other half.
These are **symmetrical** shapes.

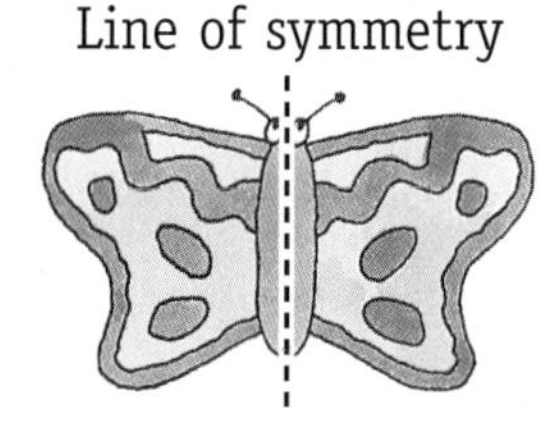
Line of symmetry

The **line of symmetry** is a line which acts like a mirror to make a reflection.

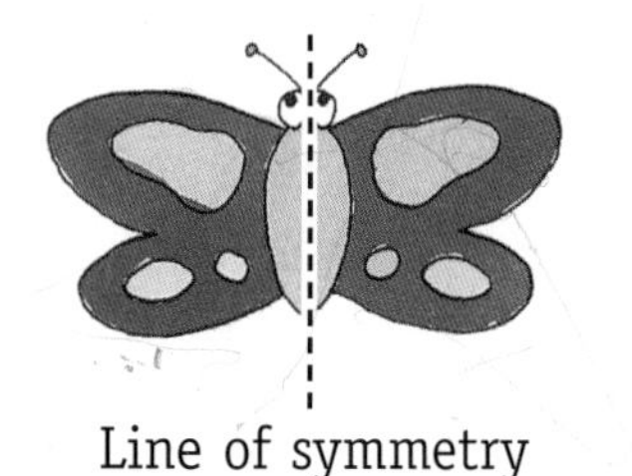
Line of symmetry

Line of symmetry

Chapter 4 Subtraction

Step-up

1 Look at the problems that are written on the picture below. Work out the answers in your head.

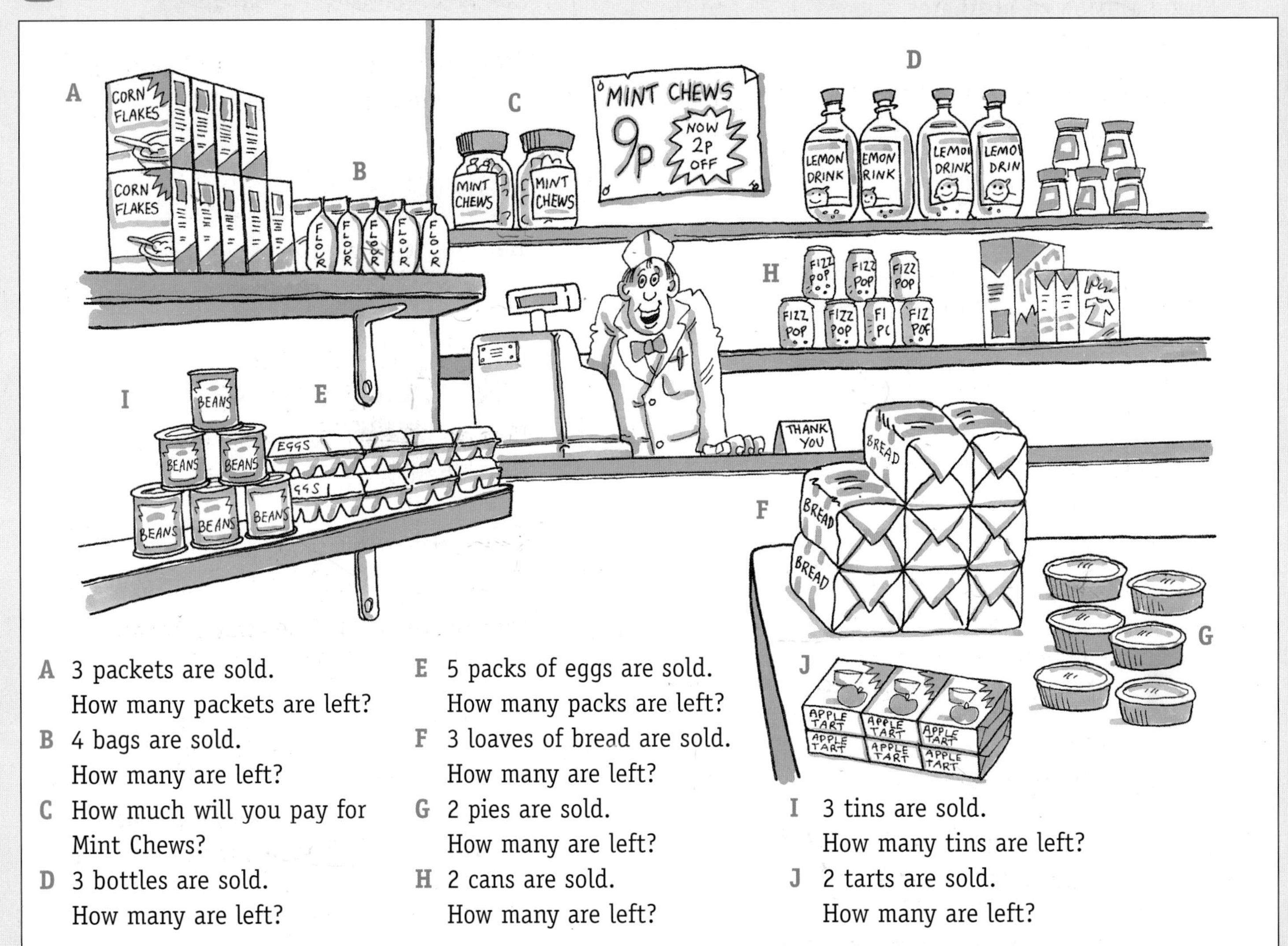

A 3 packets are sold.
How many packets are left?

B 4 bags are sold.
How many are left?

C How much will you pay for Mint Chews?

D 3 bottles are sold.
How many are left?

E 5 packs of eggs are sold.
How many packs are left?

F 3 loaves of bread are sold.
How many are left?

G 2 pies are sold.
How many are left?

H 2 cans are sold.
How many are left?

I 3 tins are sold.
How many tins are left?

J 2 tarts are sold.
How many are left?

2 Rewrite the problems below using only the '–' sign, the '+', the '=' sign, and **figures**.
Follow the two examples. Answer your problems.

Examples

Jack had 10p but he lost 4p. How much did he have left? 10p – 4p = 6p

Mary had £6, Ian had £7. How much altogether? £7 + £6 = £13

(a) The lift went from floor 15, down to floor 9. How many floors did it go down?

(b) The temperature starts at 4 °C. It rises by 11 °C. What is the new temperature?

(c) Yesterday Shola could remember how to play 18 notes on his flute. Today he can only remember how to play 9 notes. How many notes has he forgotten?

(d) James saves £19. He gives Elizabeth some money for her birthday. He is left with £9. How much did he give away?

Subtraction Card One

1 Here are 6 eggs. Take away 4 eggs.
There are ? eggs left.

2 Here are 7 eggs. Take away 3 eggs.
There are ? eggs left.

3 Here are 8 eggs. Take away 7 eggs.
There are ? eggs left.

4 Here are 9 eggs. Take away 4 eggs.
There are ? eggs left.

5 Here are 7 eggs. Take away 7 eggs.
There are ? eggs left.

Subtraction Card Two

1 Here are 9 pencils. Take away 2 pencils.
There are ? pencils left.

2 

Here are 10 coins. Take away 6 coins.
There are ? coins left.

3 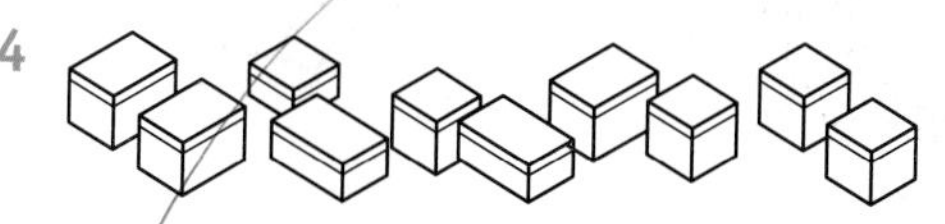

Here are 10 stars. Take away 8 stars.
There are ? stars left.

4 

Here are 10 boxes. Take away 3 boxes.
There are ? boxes left.

5 Here are 11 people. Take away 4 people.
There are ? people left.

Subtraction Card Three

The words **minus** and **subtract** mean the same as **take away**.
Do these in your head.

1 5 take away 4 is ?.

2 8 minus 6 is ?.

3 9 minus 4 is ?.

4 7 take away 7 is ?.

5 8 take away 5 is ?.

6 Take 4 away from 6.

7 Subtract 5 from 8.

8 Subtract 7 from 9.

9 Take 3 away from 8.

10 Subtract 5 from 7.

Burglar Bob and Light-fingered Lil are robbers. They 'take away' from jewellery shops ... without paying!

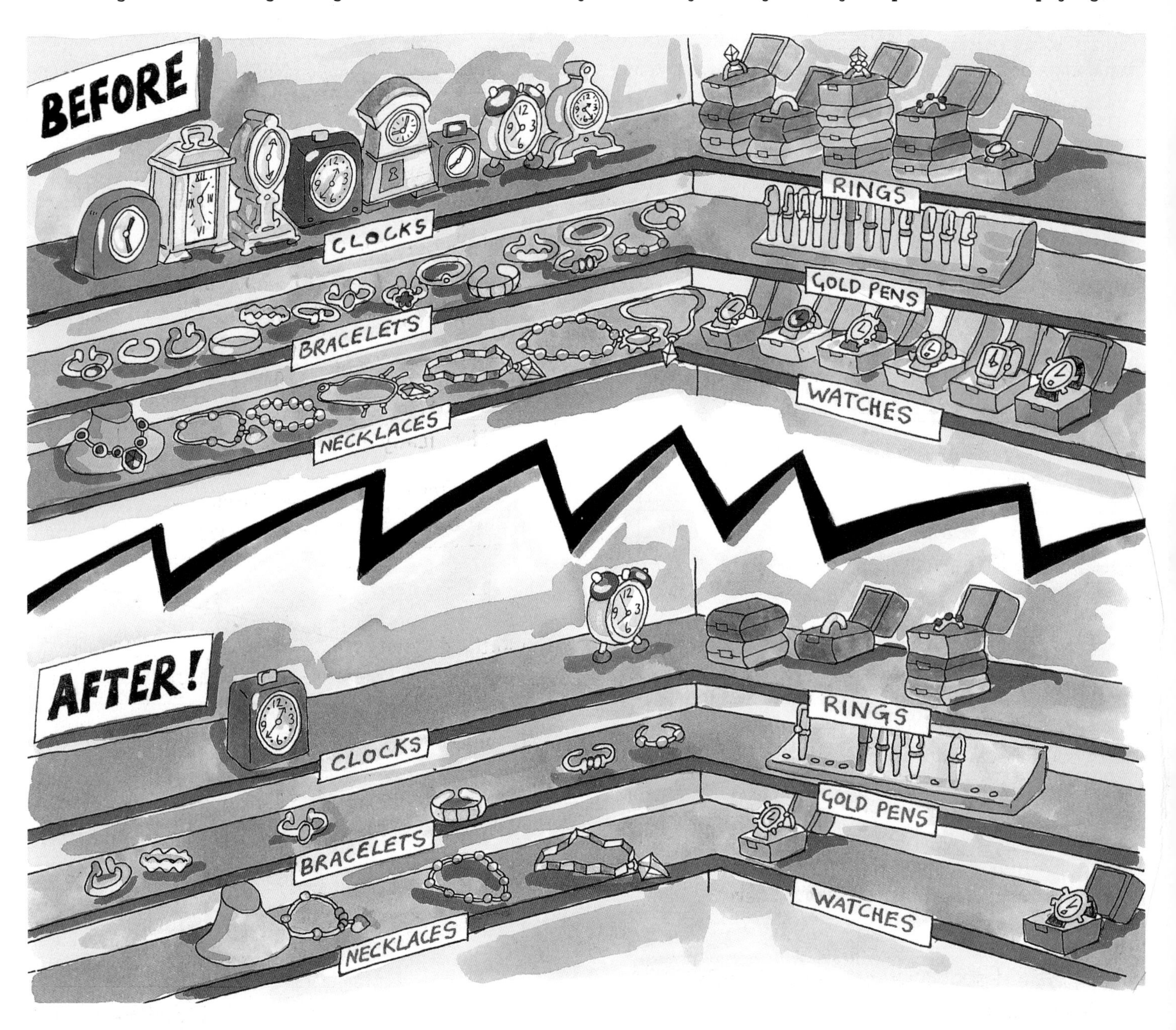

Exercise 1

Here are pictures of the jewellery shop before and after the robbery.
Use the two pictures to answer these questions.

1 How many watches have been taken?
2 How many clocks have been taken?
3 How many rings have been taken?
4 How many bracelets have been taken?
5 How many necklaces have been taken?
6 How many gold pens have been taken?

Subtraction Card Four

Do this workcard in your head.

1 18 − 5 = ?

2 13 − 3 = ?

3 12 − 7 = ?

4 17 − 7 = ?

5 14 − 8 = ?

6 20 − 15 = ?

7 18 − 9 = ?

8 20 − 9 = ?

Subtraction Card Five

You can do these in your head or write them into your book.

1 Jack had 12p. He lost 5p.
How much has he got left?

2 16 people are on a bus. 9 get off.
How many are left on the bus?

3 17 crows on a tree. 8 fly away.
How many are left on the tree?

4 20 cakes in a tin. 9 are eaten.
How many cakes are left?

Exercise 2

A glass lift travels up and down on the outside wall of the Rutland Tower. Write out each question as a subtraction problem and give the answer.

1 I start at level 17 and go **down** 5 levels.
Where am I now?

2 I start at level 13 and go **down** 9 levels.
Where am I now?

3 I start at level 20 and go **down** 7 levels.
Where am I now?

4 I start at level 18 and go **down** 16 levels.
Where am I now?

5 I start at level 13 and go **down** 13 levels.
Where am I now?

6 If I get on the lift at level 16 and get off at level 3, how many levels have I gone down?

7 If I get on the lift at level 20 and get off at level 8, how many levels have I gone down?

8 I get on the lift at level 14. I go **up** 5 levels.
I then go **down** 17 levels.
At what level do I finish?

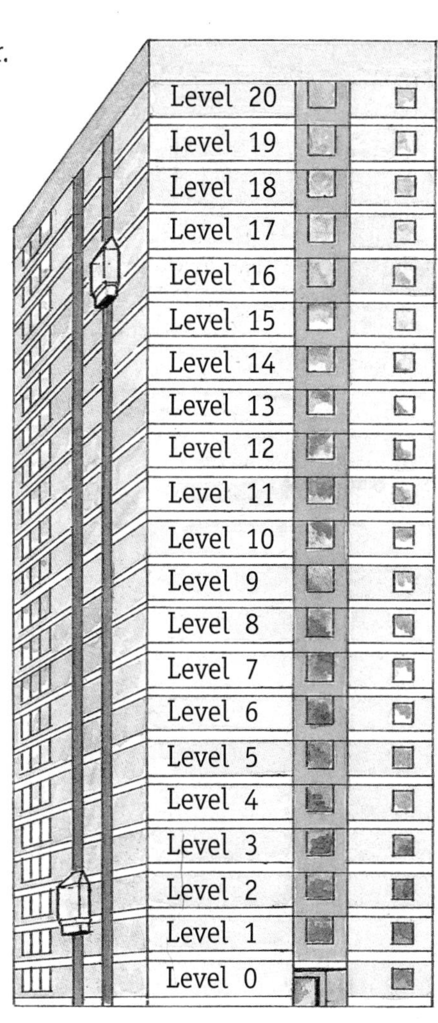

Ali has 32 cans of Polar Cola in his shop. Sam wants to buy 7 cans.
How many cans will be left?

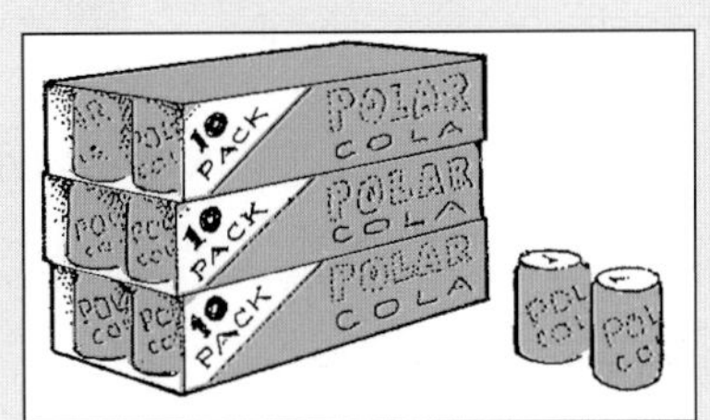

Ali has 32 cans …
three '10 packs' and 2 single cans.

He will take 7 cans from this group.

$$\begin{array}{r} 32 \\ -\ \ 7 \\ \hline \\ \hline \end{array}$$

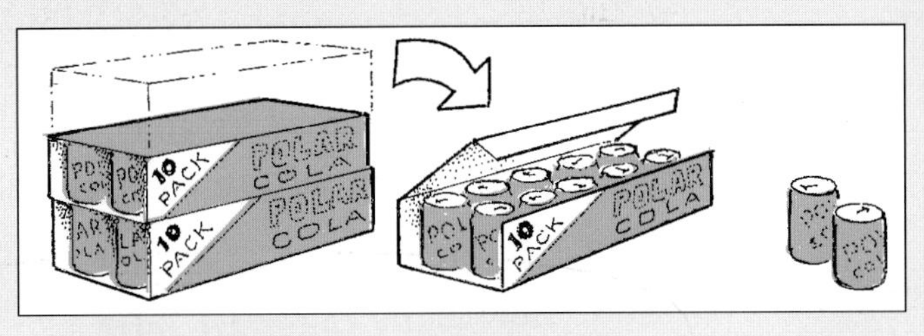

He moves one '10 pack' across and opens it.

$$\begin{array}{r} {}^{2}\not{3}{}^{1}2 \\ -\ \ 7 \\ \hline \\ \hline \end{array}$$

He then removes 7 cans.

He has 25 cans left.

$$\begin{array}{r} {}^{2}\not{3}{}^{1}2 \\ -\ \ 7 \\ \hline 25 \\ \hline \end{array}$$

Subtraction Card Six

You will need to 'carry across' a ten.

1. 32 − 6
2. 41 − 8
3. 23 − 5
4. 25 − 7
5. 34 − 8
6. 22 − 9
7. 30 − 5
8. 50 − 7
9. 40 − 8
10. 20 − 15
11. 40 − 35
12. 60 − 35

Subtraction Card Seven

You will need to 'carry across' a ten.

1. 50 − 24
2. 40 − 28
3. 32 − 16
4. 34 − 27
5. 43 − 26
6. 62 − 35
7. 80 − 38
8. 70 − 49
9. 66 − 28
10. 91 − 37
11. 53 − 48
12. 74 − 67

The **difference** between 8 and 3 is 5. $8 - 3 = 5$

The **difference** between 15 and 9 is 6. $15 - 9 = 6$

Exercise 3

Find the differences between these numbers. Some of these can be done in your head.
Write: 'The difference between 5 and 7 is **2**.'

1 6 and 8
2 2 and 11
3 5 and 15
4 21 and 27
5 17 and 9
6 17 and 25
7 47 and 17
8 91 and 58

Exercise 4

Work out these differences in your head.

1 Write pairs of numbers that have a difference of 3.

2 Write pairs of numbers that have a difference of 6.

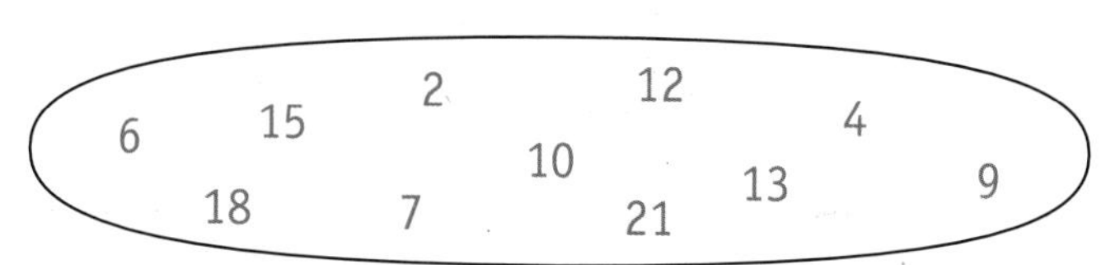

3 Which pair of numbers have a difference of 10?
22 and **31** **17** and **27** **15** and **22**

4 Which pair has a difference of 8?
17 and **24** **23** and **31** **8** and **18**

5 Write 5 pairs of numbers that have a difference of 11.

Exercise 5

Use these amazing records to answer the questions.

In 1984 Peter Dowdeswell swallowed 13 raw eggs in one second.
Dr Ronald Alkana ate 17 bananas in 2 minutes in 1973.
In June 1986, Peter Dowdeswell ate 144 prunes in 31 seconds.
Pat Donahue scoffed 91 pickled onions in 68 seconds.

1 Robert guzzled 9 bananas in 2 minutes. How many bananas was he short of the record?

2 Ray ate 144 prunes in 68 seconds. How many seconds slower was Ray than Peter Dowdeswell?

3 Liz's record is only 5 pickled onions in 68 seconds. What is the difference between the two records?

4 Jean can eat 9 raw eggs in one second. How many more eggs would she have to eat to break the record?

Subtraction Card Eight

Copy and complete the answers.

1 19 sheep are in a field. 11 are taken away. How many are left?

There are ? sheep left in the field.

2 23 eggs are in a bowl. 9 eggs are taken. How many are left?

There are ? eggs left.

3 33 ducks on a lake. 17 fly away. How many are left?

There are ? ducks left.

4 Ahmed has 60 pence. He spends 28 pence. How much does he have left?

Ahmed has ? pence left.

5 There are 43 people on a train. The train stops and 25 get off. How many are left on the train?

There are ? people left on the train.

6 Angus had 54 comics. He gave 38 comics to his friend. How many has he left?

Angus has ? comics left.

7 There are 21 sweets in a box. Joy takes 3, Paul takes 5 and Kim takes 4. How many sweets are left?

There are ? sweets left.

8 Jill has 97 pence. She spends 55 pence on a magazine and 24 pence on sweets. How much money has she got left?

Jill has ? pence left.

Exercise 6

Use the target to solve these problems.

The winner of this darts game is the first to reach a total score of 99 points.

1 Grant has scored 71 points so far. How far short of the total is he?

2 He has three darts and he must finish exactly on the target score (99). Using the three darts, write different ways that he can reach the target score exactly. (20, 10, 10 does not count … it would take him past 99.)

3 Sheena has scored 63 points. How far short of the total is she?

4 She uses three darts to finish exactly on 99. Show three ways that she can reach this total.

Subtraction Card Nine

You will need to 'carry across' a 'ten' for some of these problems.

1	2	3
30 − 10	50 − 20	26 − 16
4 25 − 15	**5** 34 − 14	**6** 29 − 19
7 36 − 19	**8** 51 − 38	**9** 97 − 39
10 43 − 19	**11** 45 − 25	**12** 35 − 35

Subtraction Card Ten

You will need to 'carry across' a 'ten' to answer these problems.

1	2	3
52 − 44	78 − 29	82 − 29
4 64 − 37	**5** 72 − 23	**6** 62 − 34
7 85 − 38	**8** 77 − 39	**9** 56 − 18
10 91 − 69	**11** 73 − 49	**12** 96 − 67

Key ideas

When we **subtract** from a number of objects, we **take away** some of the objects and find out how many are **left over**.

The short-cut sign for **subtraction** is this: **–**
It is used like this: **8 – 6 = 2**

8 – 6 = 2

Other terms that mean the same as **subtract** are: **'take away'** and **'minus'**.

Chapter 5 To the Nearest...

Step-up

Roberto's class are looking at this picture. Tracey says that there are about 10 people, Aaron thinks that there are about 30 people, and Roberto says that there are 18 people. Who do you think gave the nearest answer?

Without counting, how many windows do you think you can see in the picture? These are all approximate answers. They are called **estimates**.

1 Without counting, estimate how many objects are shown in each group. You can work with a partner. Write the answer in your book.

A

B

C

D

This machine measures your strength as you hit the target with a hammer.

Here we see Diane's score. It says that she is between 'Powerful' and 'Amazing'.

Look at the position of the arrow carefully.
Is the arrow nearer to 'Powerful' or to 'Amazing'?

Exercise 1

Look at these scores.
To which score is the arrow nearer?

1 Roger's attempt.

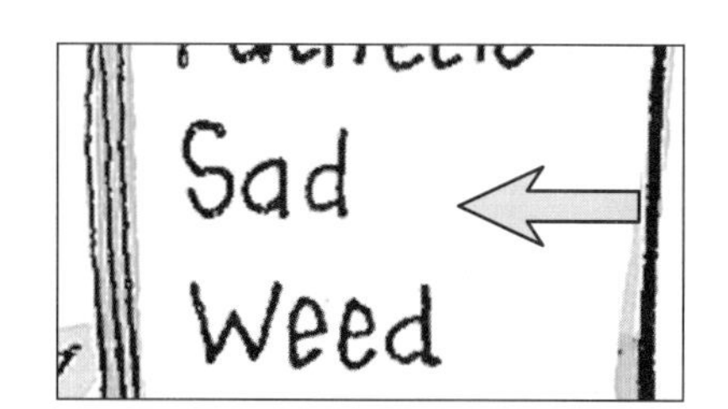

2 Tim's attempt.

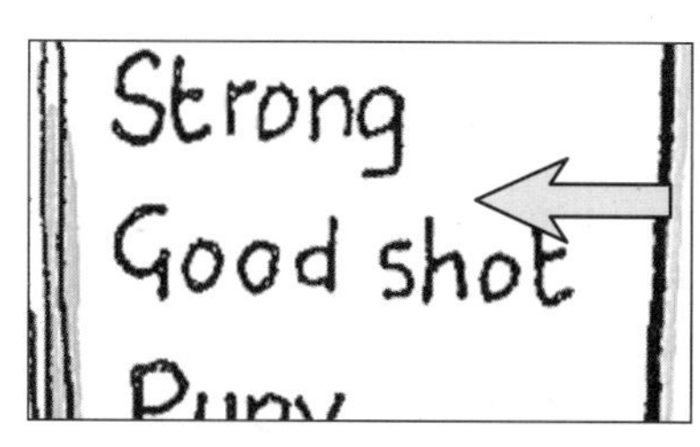

3 Pat's attempt.

This machine caused many arguments.
The owner decides to replace the words with a scale.
The scale goes up in 10s.

Exercise 2

Not many of the scores will land exactly on a number.
To the nearest 10, what are these scores?

1

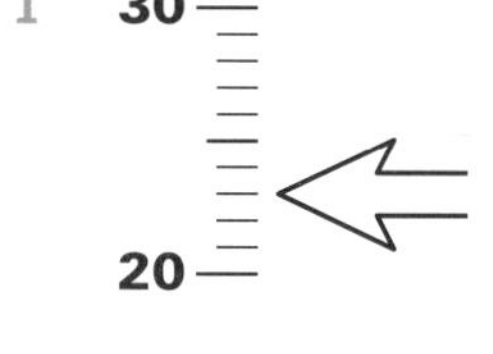

2

50

40

3

20

10

4

60

50

5

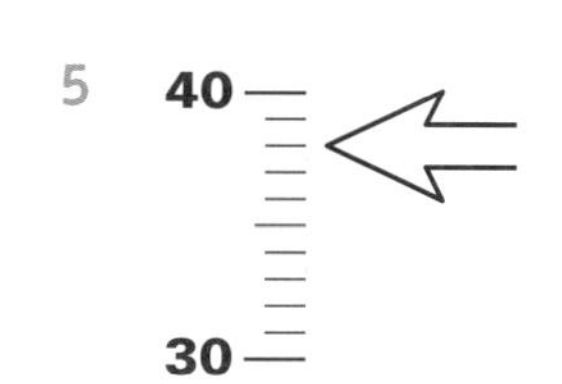

6

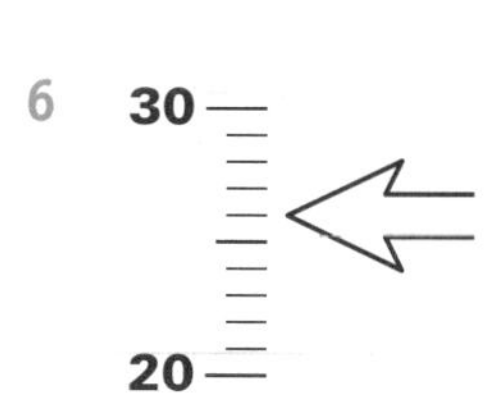

Exercise 3

1 Here is a number line written out in 10s.
What number, **to the nearest 10**, is each of these arrows pointing to?

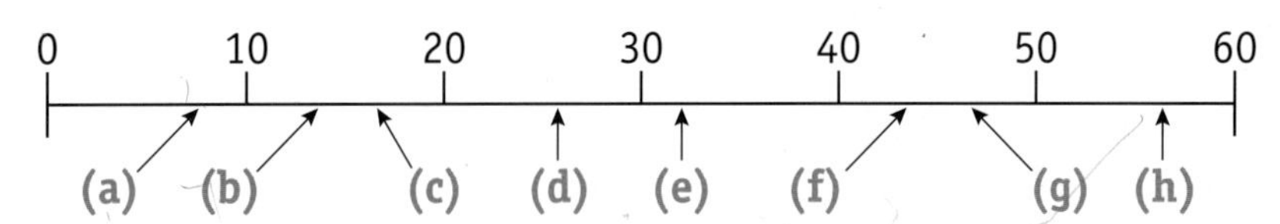

On the next number line we can see single **units** between the 10s.
The arrow is pointing at 25, which is exactly half-way between 20 and 30.
When this happens we always 'round up' to the next 10.

So 25 rounded to the nearest ten, is 30.

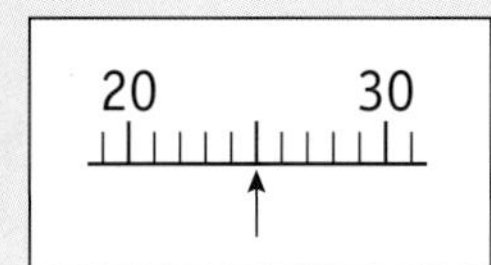

Exercise 4

Using the scale, give these numbers to the nearest 10. Take care.

1 10 20

2 0 10

3 40 50

4 60 70

5 30 40

6 10 20

7 30

8 20

9 60 70

Exercise 5

Say what these scales read, to the nearest 10.

1

2

3

4 13 cm

5

6 35 POINTS

Exercise 6

Give each person's height to the **nearest** 10 centimetres.

Exercise 7

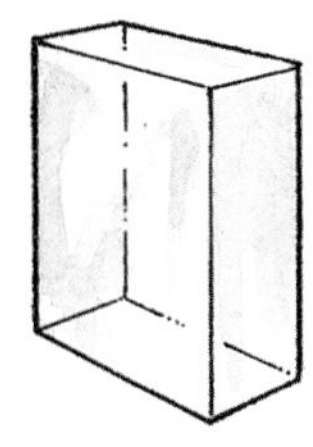

1 Estimate how many boxes would fit into this glass tank.

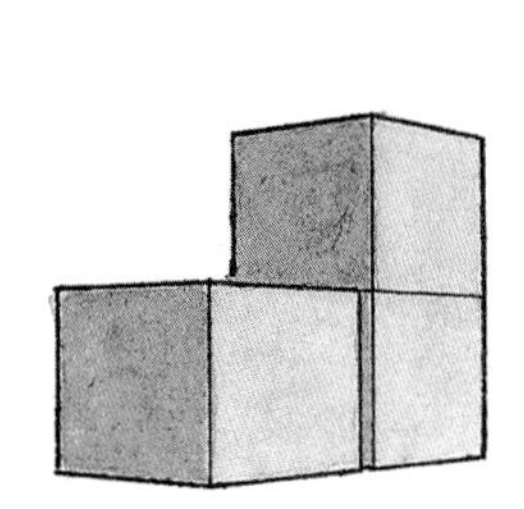

2 Estimate how many boxes might be loaded onto the lorry.

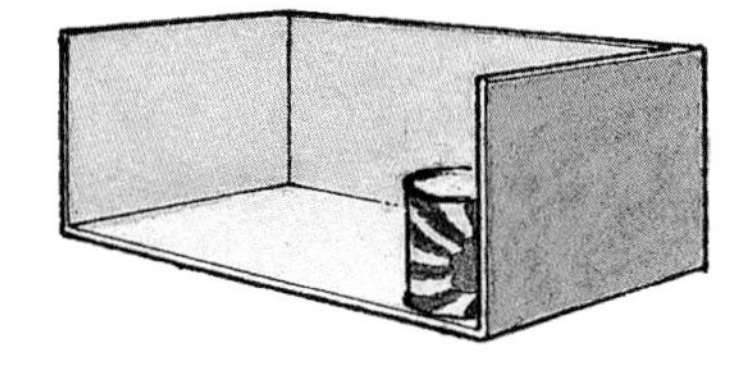

3 Estimate how many paint tins would fit into this box.

Key ideas

We do not always have to be totally accurate, but a close answer can be just as useful.
When you give a close answer, this is called an **estimate**.
To make an **estimate** you 'round off' to the nearest **useful amount**.

Examples

17 is nearer to 20 than it is to 10, so we say that 17 rounded up to the nearest ten is 20.
13 is nearer to 10 than it is to 20, so we say that 13 rounded down to the nearest ten is 10.

Even though 15 is half-way between 10 and 20 we round up to 20.
We do this for every number which is half-way between two tens.

Chapter 6 Measurement (1)

Step-up

1 Without using instruments, what **units** could you use to measure:

(a) the length of the school playground?

(b) the height of your friend?

(c) the width of a postage stamp?

2 John uses paces to measure the length of the playground and Sam uses hand-spans.
Will they get the same result?
Give a reason for your answer.

Your little finger is about **1 centimetre** wide.

You can use your little finger to **estimate** the length of a line.

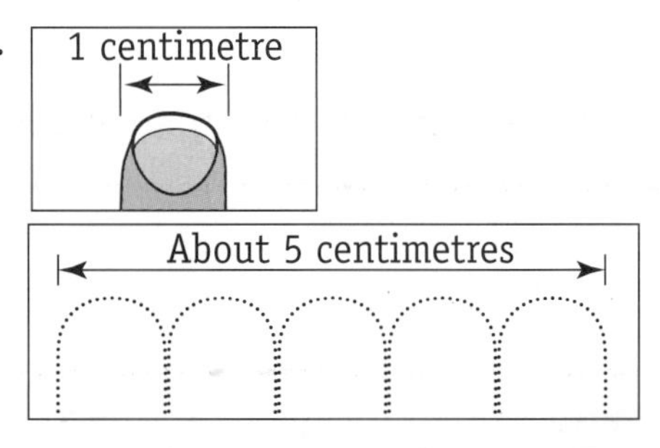

3 Use your little finger as a **unit** to estimate the length of each line.

(a) ________

(b) ________

(c) ________

(d) ________

When measuring with a ruler, always place the zero mark at one end of the line, and then measure off the length.

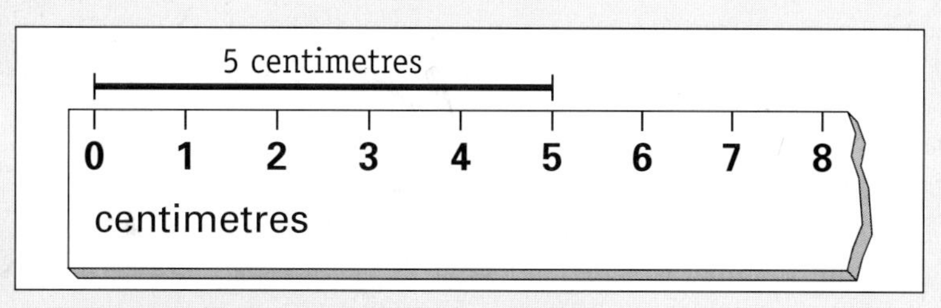

Exercise 1

How long is each line? Give your answers in **centimetres**. You can write the word **centimetre** as **cm**.

1

0 1 2 3 4 5 6
centimetres

2

0 1 2 3 4 5 6 7
centimetres

3

0 1 2 3 4 5 6 7
centimetres

4

0 1 2 3 4 5 6
centimetres

5

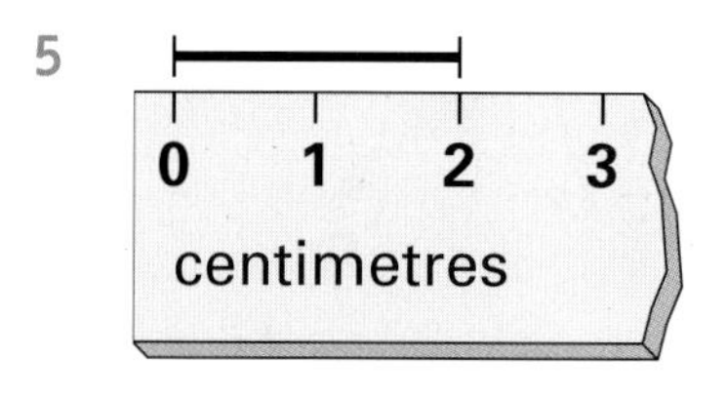

6

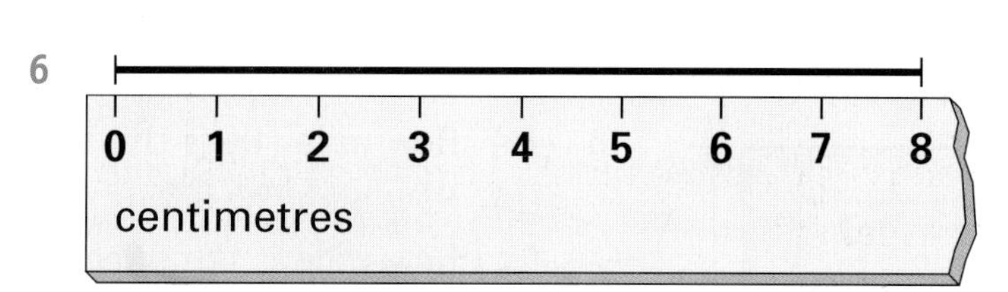

Exercise 2

Use a ruler to measure each line. Give your answers in **centimetres**.

1

2

3

4

5

6

Exercise 3 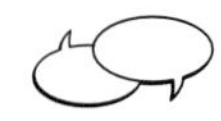

Measure these objects and give your answers in **centimetres**.

1 How long is this pencil?

2 How wide is this badge? MONITOR

3 (a) How wide (w) is this mini camera?
(b) How high (h) is this mini camera?

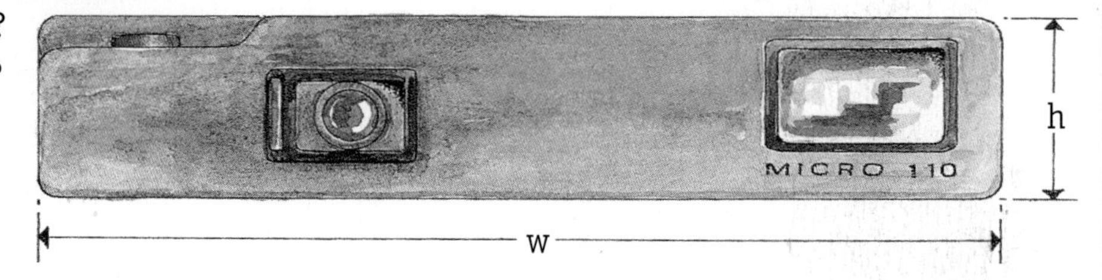

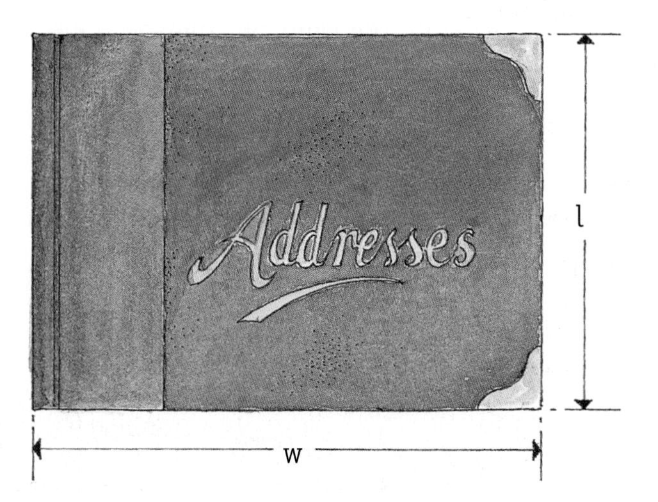

4 (a) How wide (w) is this address book?
(b) How long (l) is this address book?

5 How tall (t) is each jug?

6 (a) How wide (w) is this game?
(b) How high (h) is this game?
(c) How wide is the screen?
(d) How high is the screen?
(e) How long is the on/off switch?

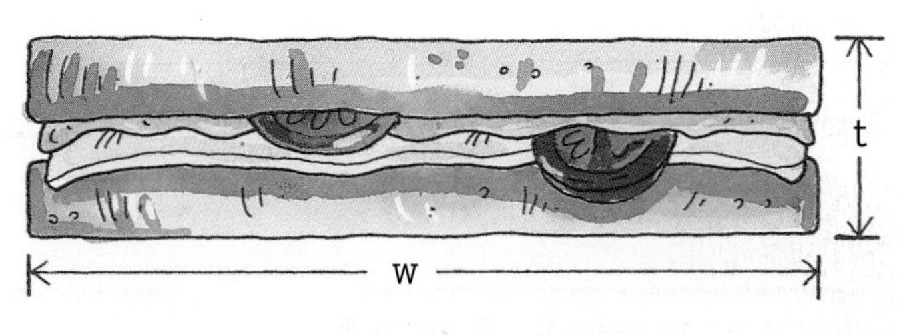

7 (a) How thick (t) is this sandwich?
(b) How wide (w) is this sandwich?

This line is between 4 cm and 5 cm long. It is **nearer** to the 5 cm mark.

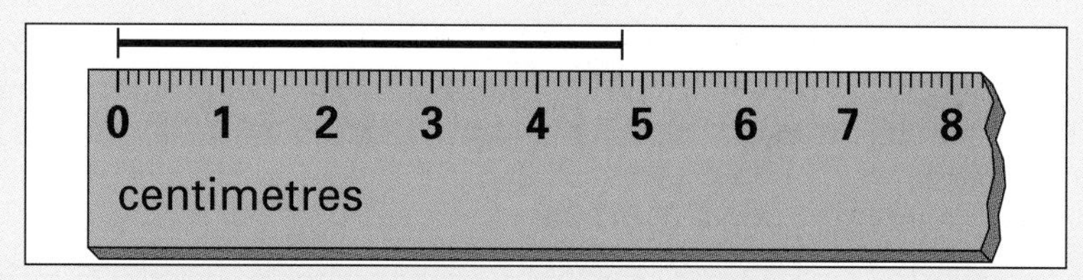

So we say: '**To the nearest centimetre, this line is 5 centimetres long.**'

Exercise 4

How long is each line? Give your answers to the nearest centimetre.

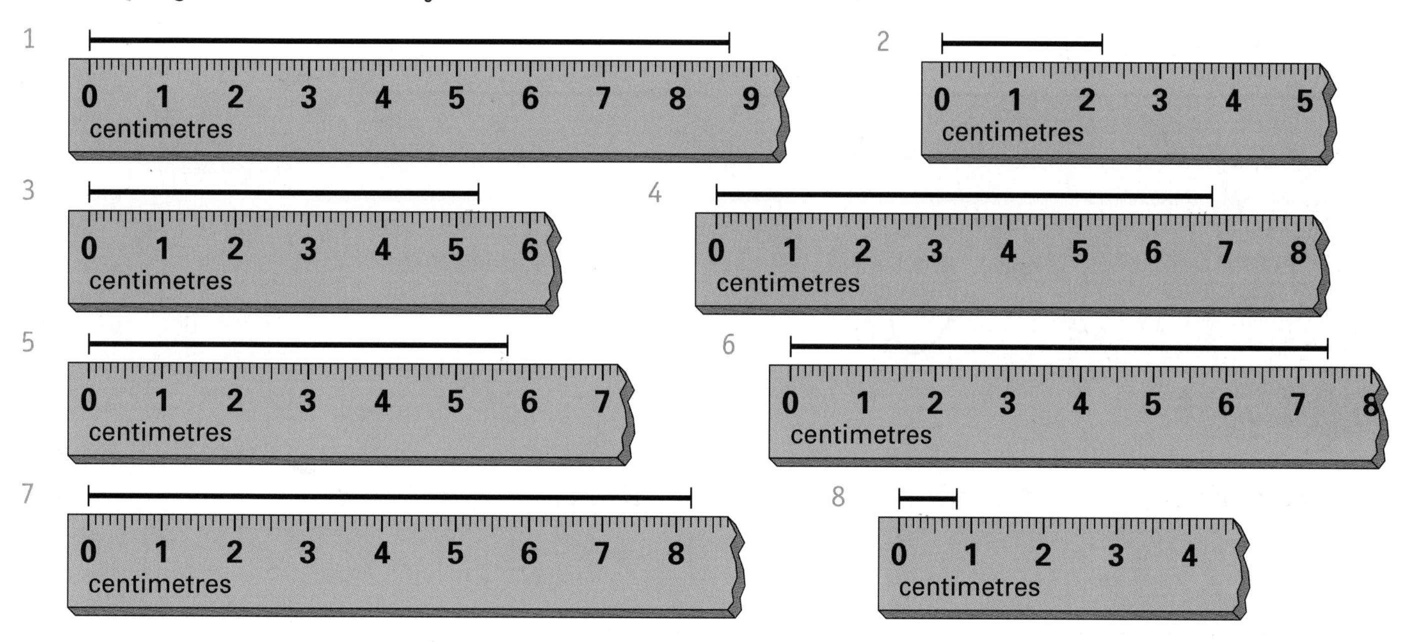

Exercise 5

Estimate the length of each line.

Exercise 6

Check your answers for Exercise 5.

Use a ruler to measure the lines **to the nearest centimetre**.

How accurate were your **estimates**?

The length of the line is exactly **half way** between 3 cm and 4 cm. 

This line is $3\frac{1}{2}$ cm long.

0 1 2 3 4 5 6 7 8
centimetres

Exercise 7

How long is each line? You will need to use $\frac{1}{2}$ **cm** in your answers.

1

2

3

4

5

6

7

8

Exercise 8

Measure the **length** (l) and the **width** (w) of each rectangle.

1

w

l

2

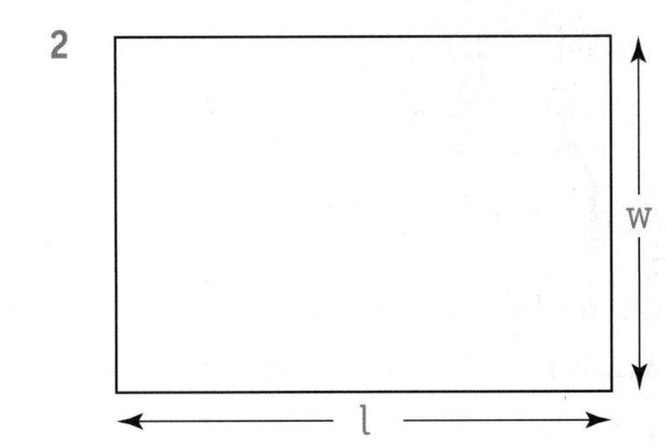

3

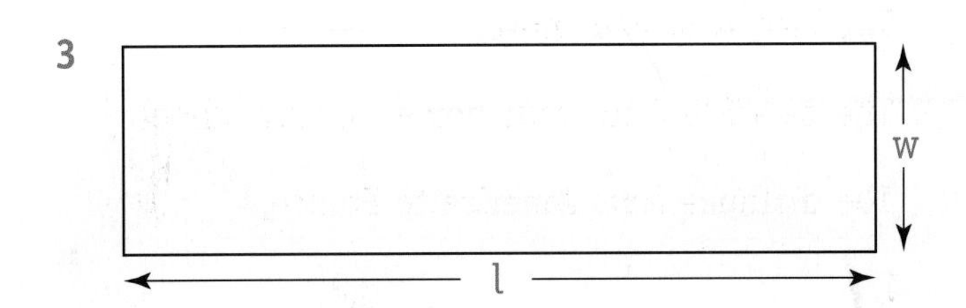

4

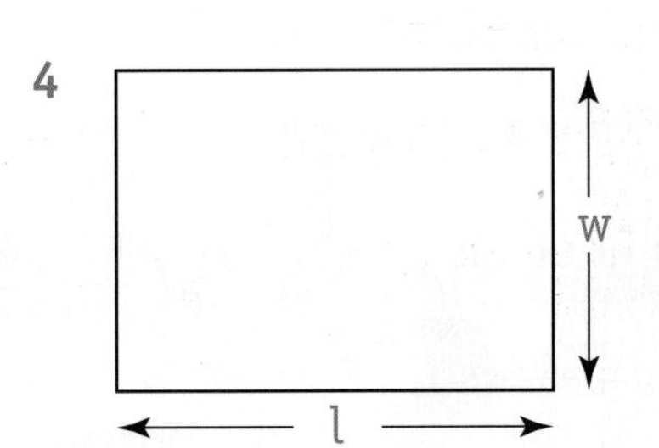

Choosing which unit to use

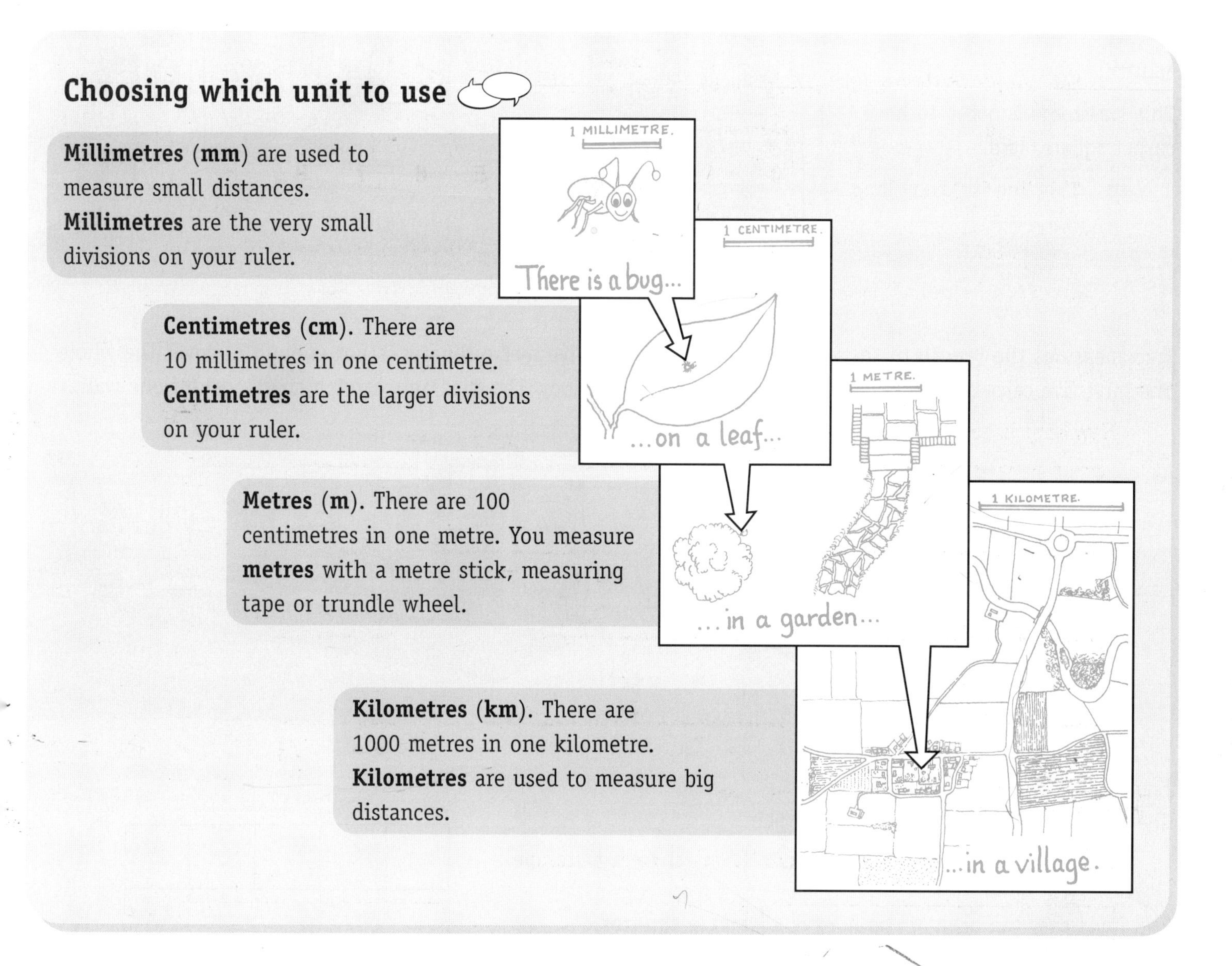

Millimetres (**mm**) are used to measure small distances. **Millimetres** are the very small divisions on your ruler.

Centimetres (**cm**). There are 10 millimetres in one centimetre. **Centimetres** are the larger divisions on your ruler.

Metres (**m**). There are 100 centimetres in one metre. You measure **metres** with a metre stick, measuring tape or trundle wheel.

Kilometres (**km**). There are 1000 metres in one kilometre. **Kilometres** are used to measure big distances.

Exercise 9

Which unit would you use to make each measurement? Choose from **millimetres**, **centimetres**, **metres** or **kilometres**.

1 The length of your middle finger.

2 The distance from the Earth to the Moon.

3 The length of your classroom.

4 The thickness of a shoe-lace.

5 The width of this maths book.

6 The length of your nose.

7 The length of a drawing pin.

8 The distance from your home to your school.

9 The length of an ant.

10 The distance from America to France.

This classroom is going to have carpet squares laid.

Fran measures the **length** of the room – it is **5 m** long. She buys five carpet squares, each **1 metre square**.

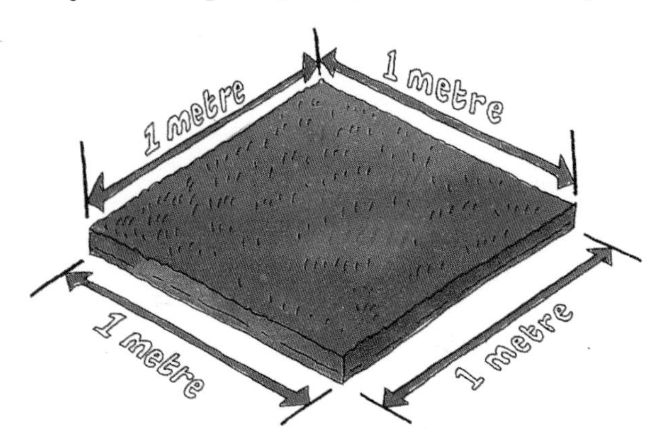

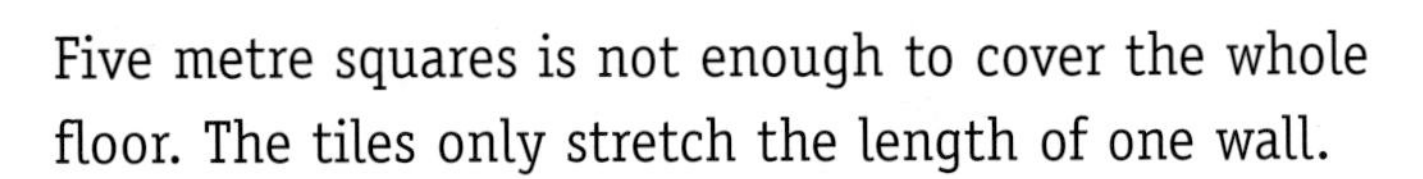

Five metre squares is not enough to cover the whole floor. The tiles only stretch the length of one wall.

Fran makes a plan of the floor.
She draws the metre squares onto the plan.

She finds that the **area** of the floor is **15 metre squares**, so she needs 15 carpet tiles.

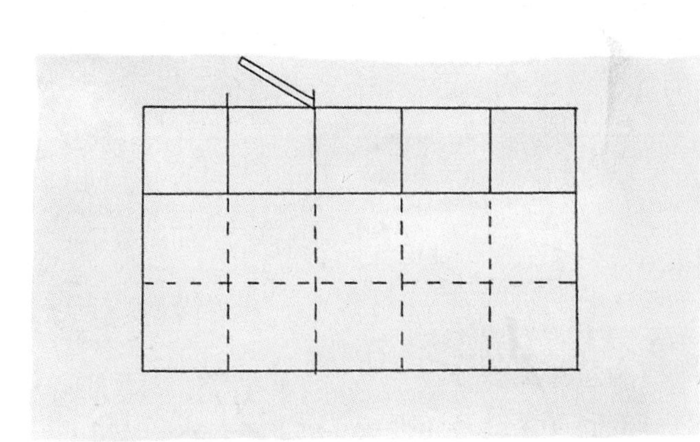

Exercise 10

Count the squares on each floor plan. Say how many tiles are needed for each floor.

1

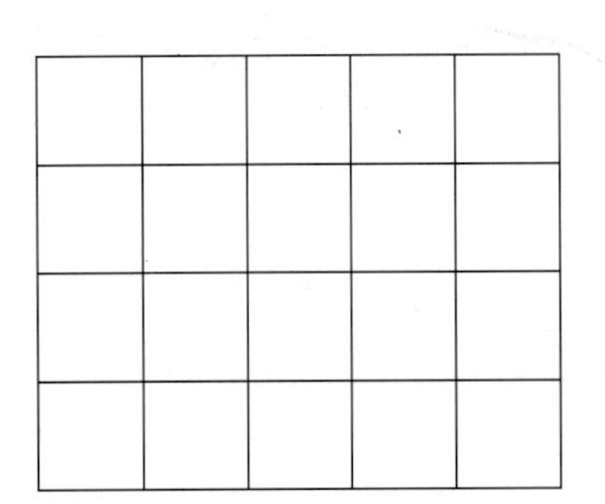

2

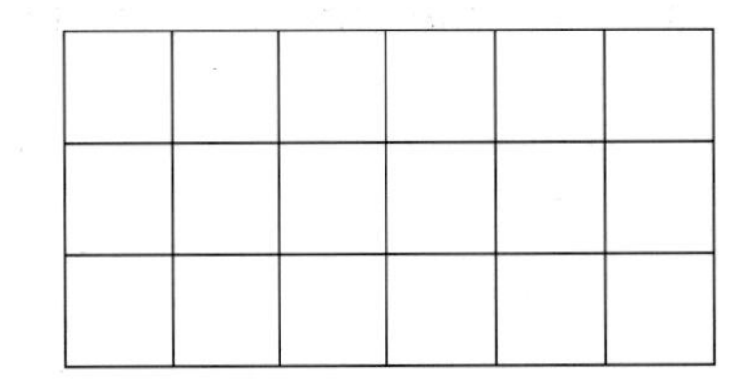

3

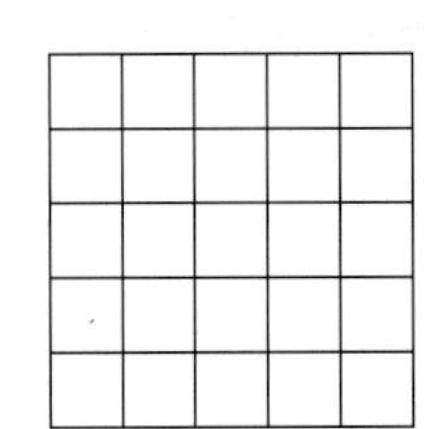

4

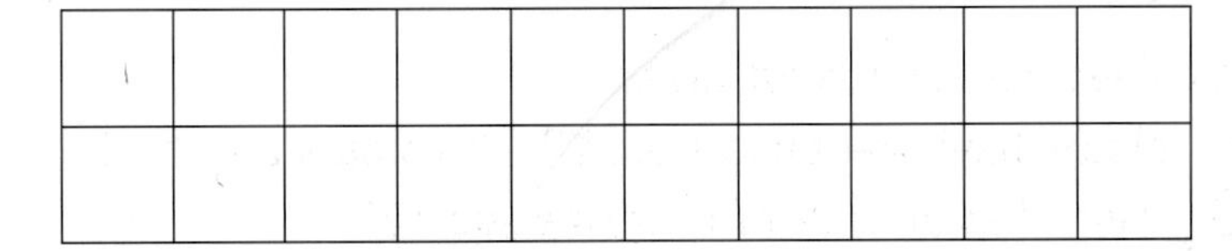

Exercise 11

Look at the pictures and then answer the questions.

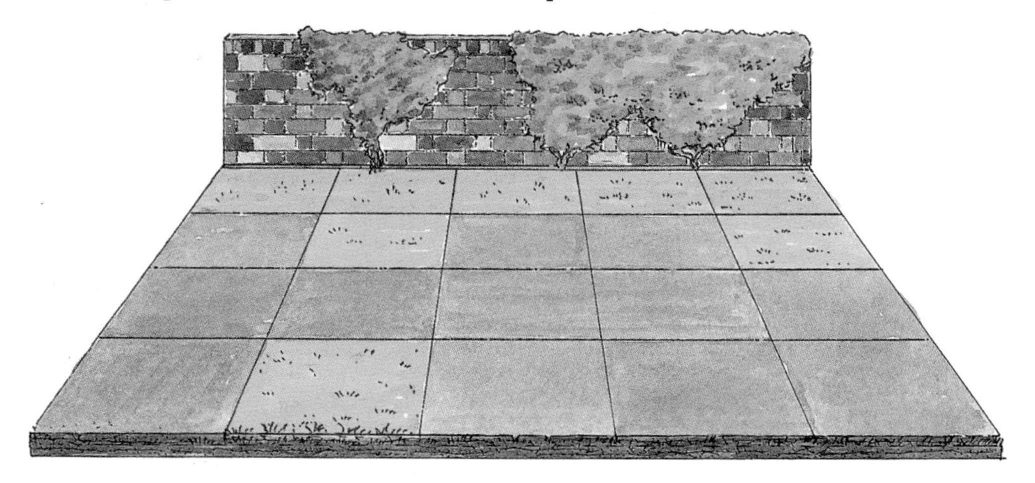

1 Fran has divided the garden into squares so that she can sow the lawn evenly.
The green squares are seeded.

(a) What area is seeded?

(b) What area is not seeded?

2 This is a patch-work quilt. Use the squares on the quilt to find the area of the quilt that is:

(a) green

(b) yellow

(c) blue

(d) orange

(e) brown

(f) What colour has the largest area?

(g) Three colours have the same area. Which colours are they?

(h) Which colour has an area of only one square?

Monsieur Decart has painted four pictures. He has used grids to help him.

The grids are made from **centimetre squares**.

Exercise 12

Use **estimation** or **counting** to answer these questions.

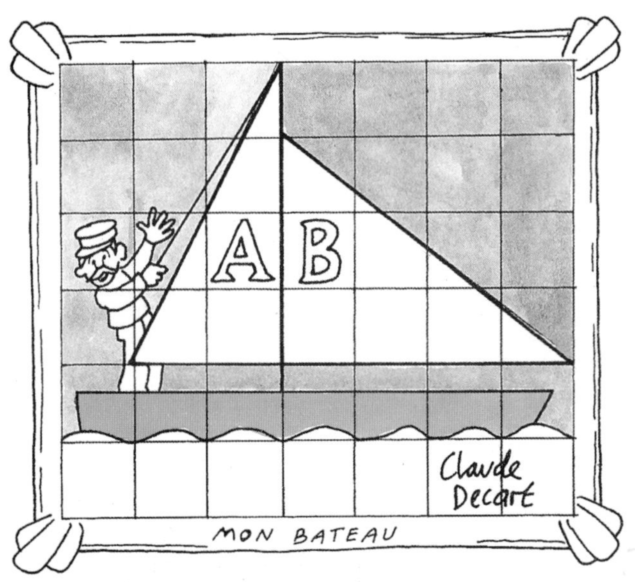

1 (a) Which is the larger sail – **A** or **B**?
  (b) Which is the larger area, sail B or the blue hull?

2 (a) Which colour has Monsieur Decart used the most?
  (b) How many centimetre squares does the pot cover?

3 (a) How long is the moustache?
  (b) Which colour has the largest area?

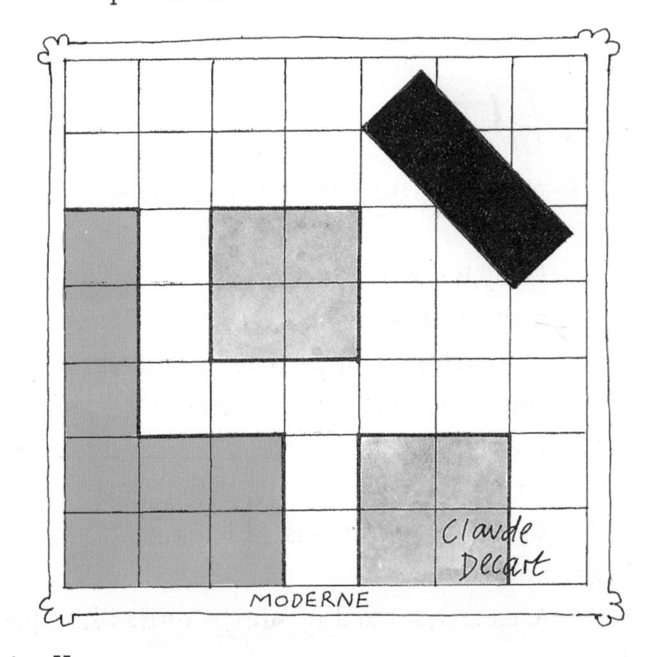

4 How many squares are:
(a) black? (b) grey? (c) blue?

Exercise 13

Choose at least two of these tasks.

Use squared paper to help.

Task 1

Draw three **different** shapes, each with an area of 20 squares.

Task 2

This rectangle has an area of 8 squares.
Draw two **different** shapes.
The area of each shape must be
twice as big as the area of this rectangle.

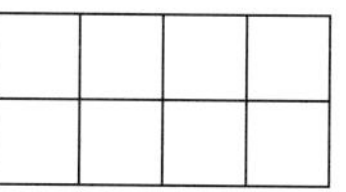

Task 3

Find the area of your hand. You can use a pencil and squared paper.

Task 4

Draw a square with an area of:

(a) 4 centimetre squares;

(b) 9 centimetre squares;

(c) 16 centimetre squares.

Task 5

Use squared paper to draw two capital letters: **L** and **F**.
The letters must be the same height and must be the same area.

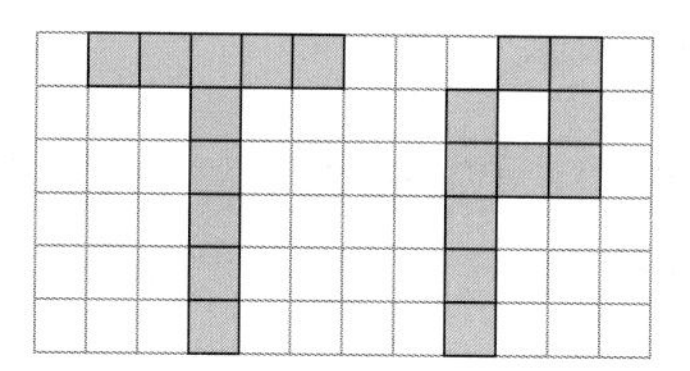

Key ideas

When you **measure** you find the size of a line or object. We use different **units** to measure.

Length can be measured in:
millimetres (**mm**) for very small distances like the thickness of a match;
centimetres (**cm**) for small distances like the length of a book or a desk;
metres (**m**) for longer distances like the length of the classroom;
kilometres (**km**) for much greater distances like the distance between towns.

To **estimate** you must think about the problem and then try to guess the answer.

Area is measured in **square units** like **square centimetres**.

Chapter 7 Angles

Step-up

Tom is playing on a roundabout. When the roundabout turns a little, Tom faces a different direction. We say that the roundabout has turned through an **angle**.

This is the angle Tom turned on the roundabout.

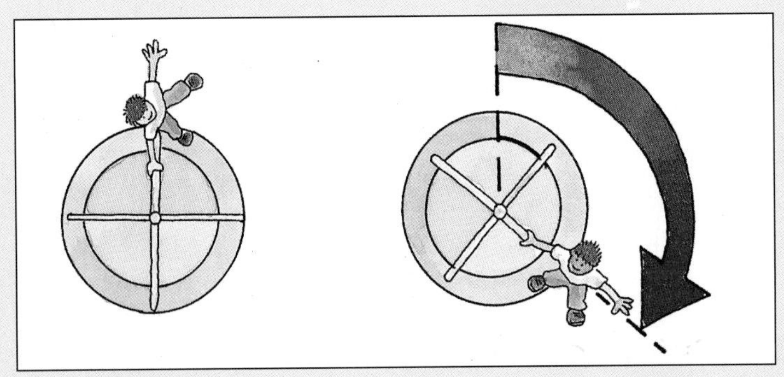

Notice that the turn is **clockwise** – the same direction that the hands of a clock turn.

Here are drawings of Tom turning on the roundabout. The drawings are out of order.

1. Which drawing shows the biggest angle of turn?
2. Which drawing shows the smallest angle of turn?
3. Put the drawings in order to show Tom turning on the roundabout.

The handrail divides the roundabout into four angles.
This type of angle is called a **right angle**.

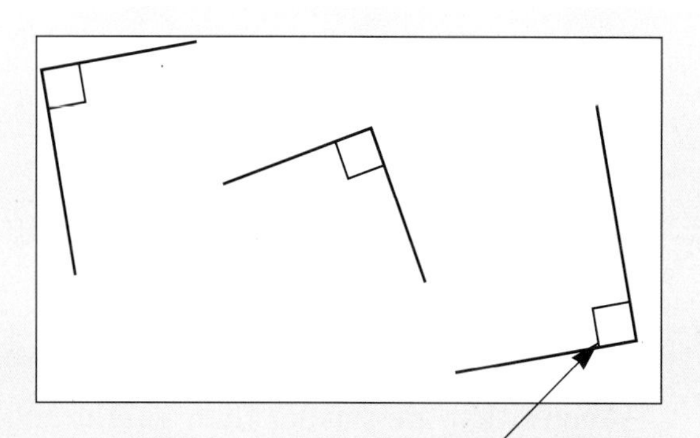

To show that an angle is a **right angle**, we draw a square in the corner of the angle.

Exercise 1

Which of these are **right angles**?

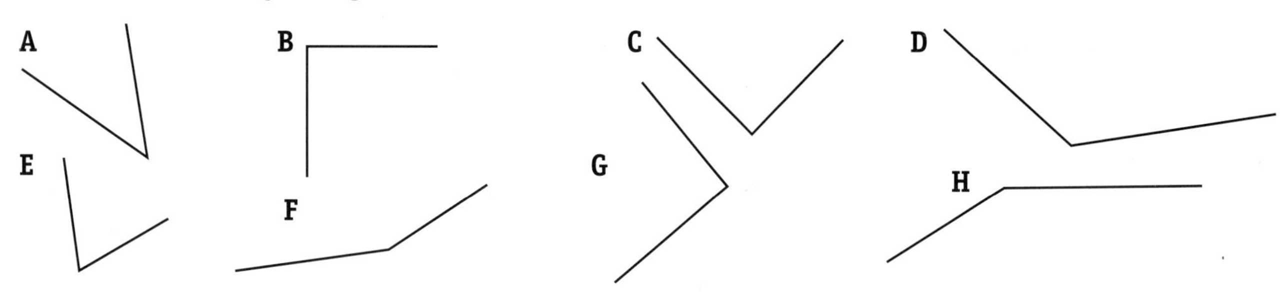

Exercise 2

There are lots of angles in this picture. Which ones are **right angles**?

These are **right angles.**

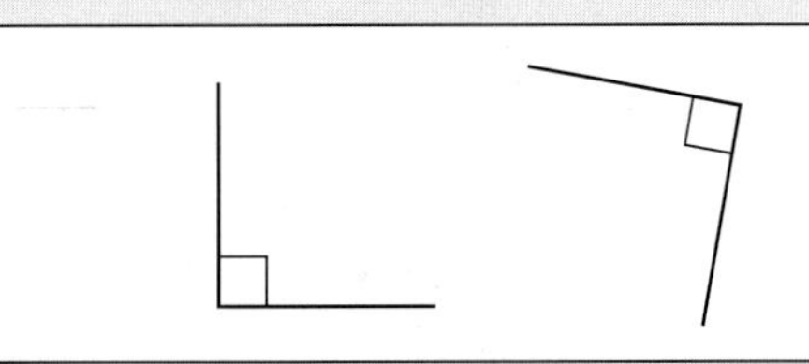

The square in the corner of the angle shows that it is a **right angle.**

Angles that are smaller than a right angle are called **acute angles.**

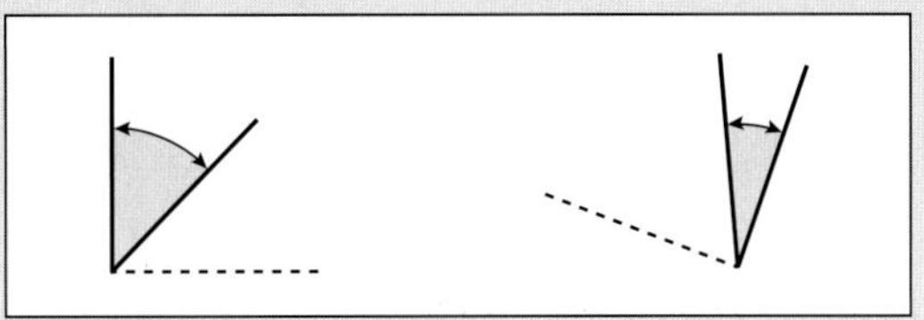

Angles that are bigger than a right angle, but less than half a turn, are called **obtuse angles.**

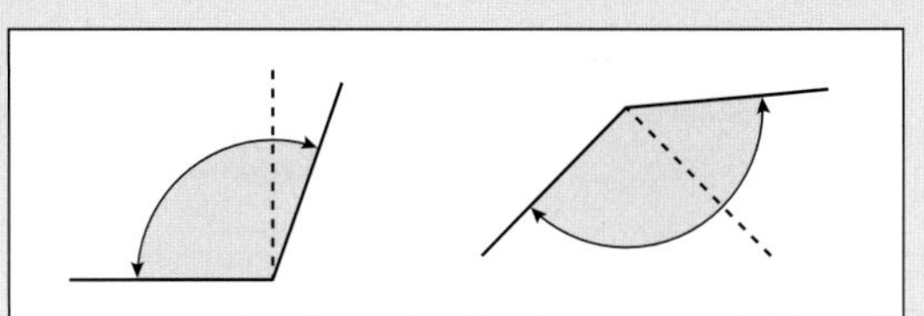

Exercise 3

Write whether each angle is **acute**, **right** or **obtuse**.
The dotted blue line shows you the **right angle**.

1 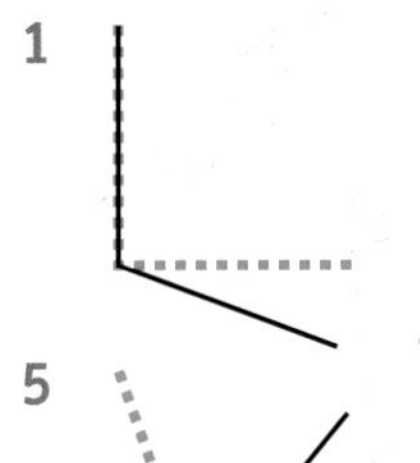

2 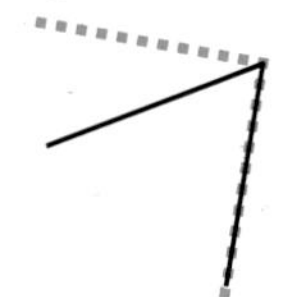

3 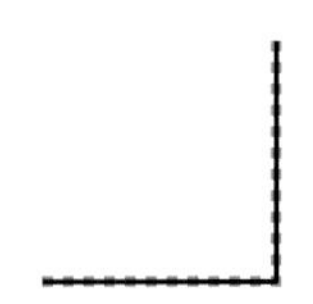

4 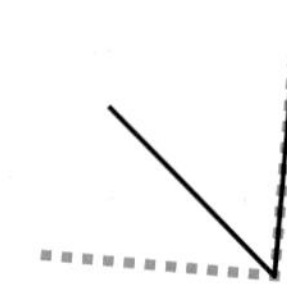

5

6 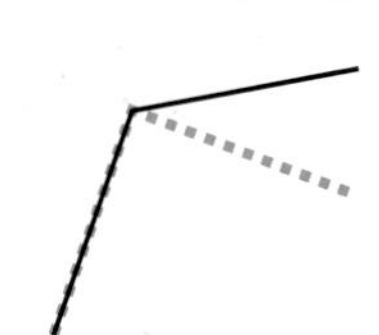

7 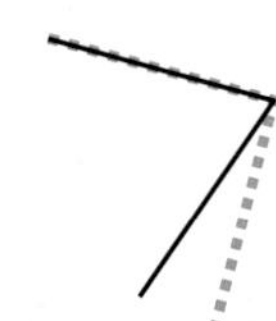

8 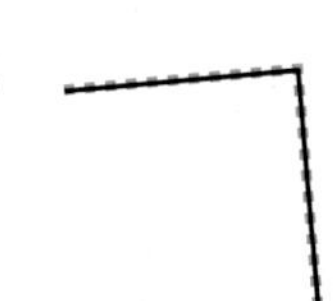

Exercise 4

Write whether each angle is **acute**, **right** or **obtuse**.
There are no blue lines to guide you!

1 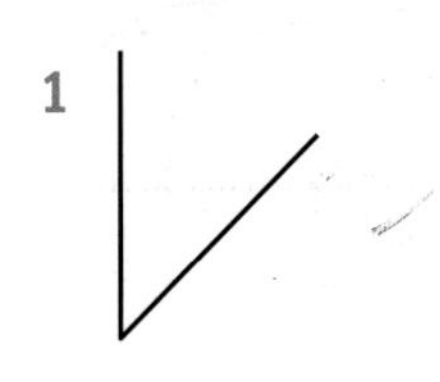

2 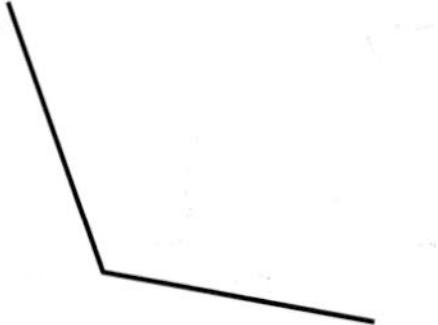

3 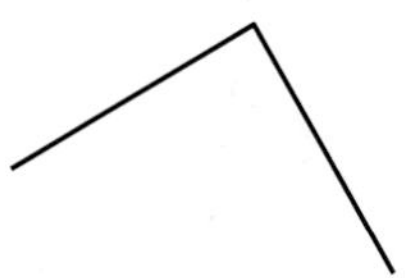

4 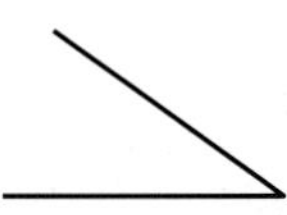

5

6 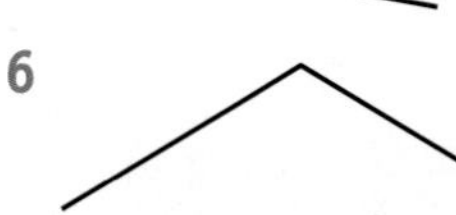

7 

8 

When an angle makes a half turn, it forms a **straight line**.

When an angle turns beyond a straight line, it makes a **reflex angle**.

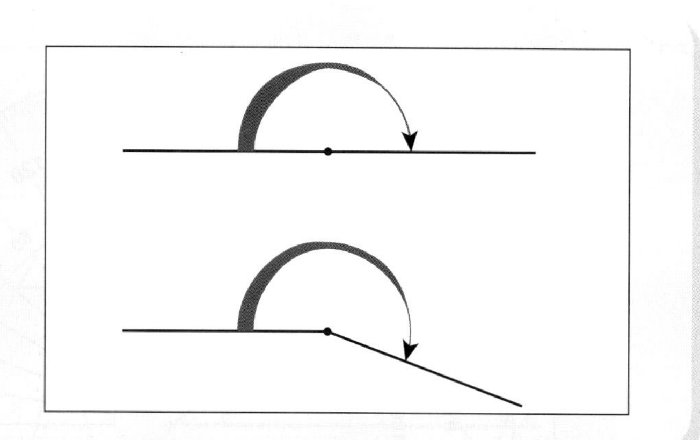

Exercise 5

Name the type of angle in each picture. Write **acute**, **right**, **obtuse**, **straight** or **reflex angle**.

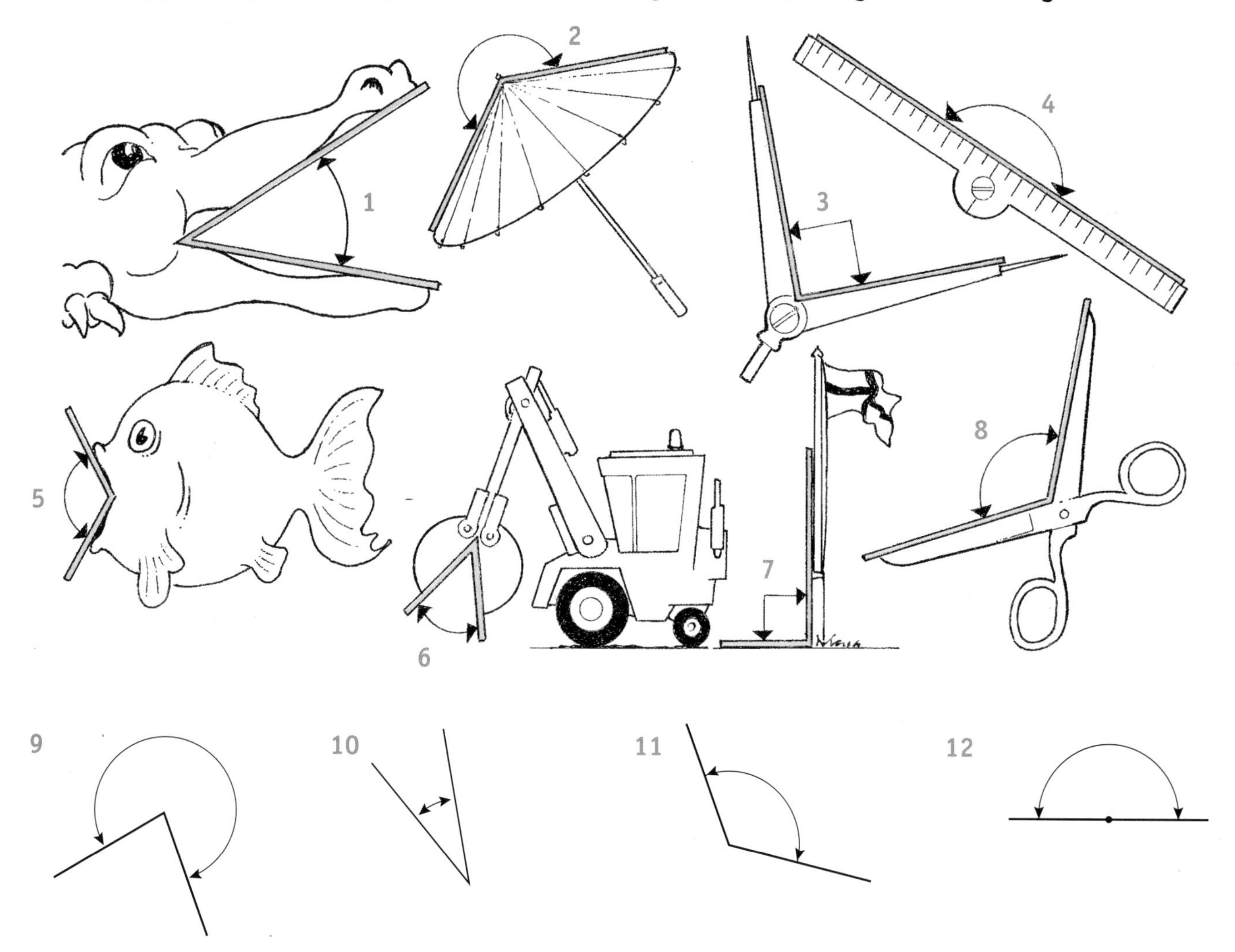

Exercise 6

1 Draw an **acute angle** and label it.

2 Draw a **reflex angle** and label it.

3 Draw an **obtuse angle** and label it.

4 Draw a **right angle** and label it.

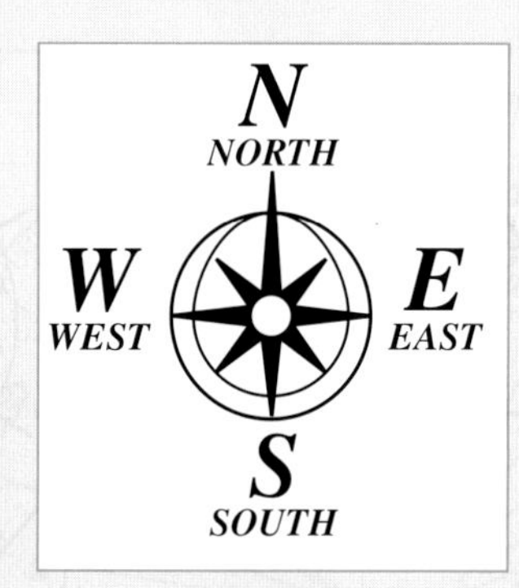

This is a **compass rose.**
It shows the four main points of the compass: **North**, **South**, **East** and **West**.

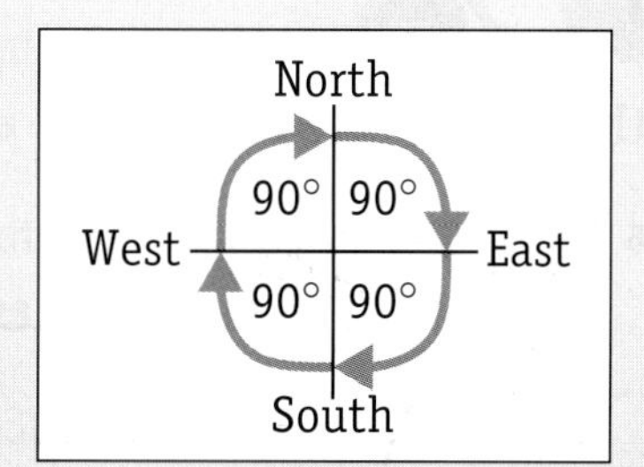

If you start by facing **North** and turn 90° you will have turned through one **right angle.** You will now be facing **East.** There are other **right angles** (90°) between **East** and **South**, **South** and **West**, and **West** and **North.**

Exercise 12

Look at the drawings and answer the questions.

1

Joe is facing North.

(a) What will Joe see if he looks East?

(b) What will he see if he looks West?

(c) In which direction is he looking if he can see the church?

2

Asha is facing East.

(a) What will Asha see if she looks West?

(b) What will she see if she looks South?

(c) In which direction is she looking if she can see a tree?

Exercise 13

Answer these questions. Each turn you make should be **clockwise** (the same direction that the hands of a clock turn).

1 How many **right angles** will you turn through if you turn from **North** to **South**?

2 How many **right angles** will you turn through if you turn from **North** to **West**?

3 If you are facing **North** and make one complete turn so that you are facing **North** again, how many **right angles** will you have turned through?

4 If you are facing **South** and turn through 90°, which direction will you be facing?

5 If you are facing **East** and turn through 90°, which direction will you be facing?

Exercise 14

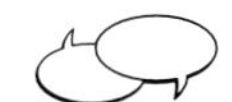

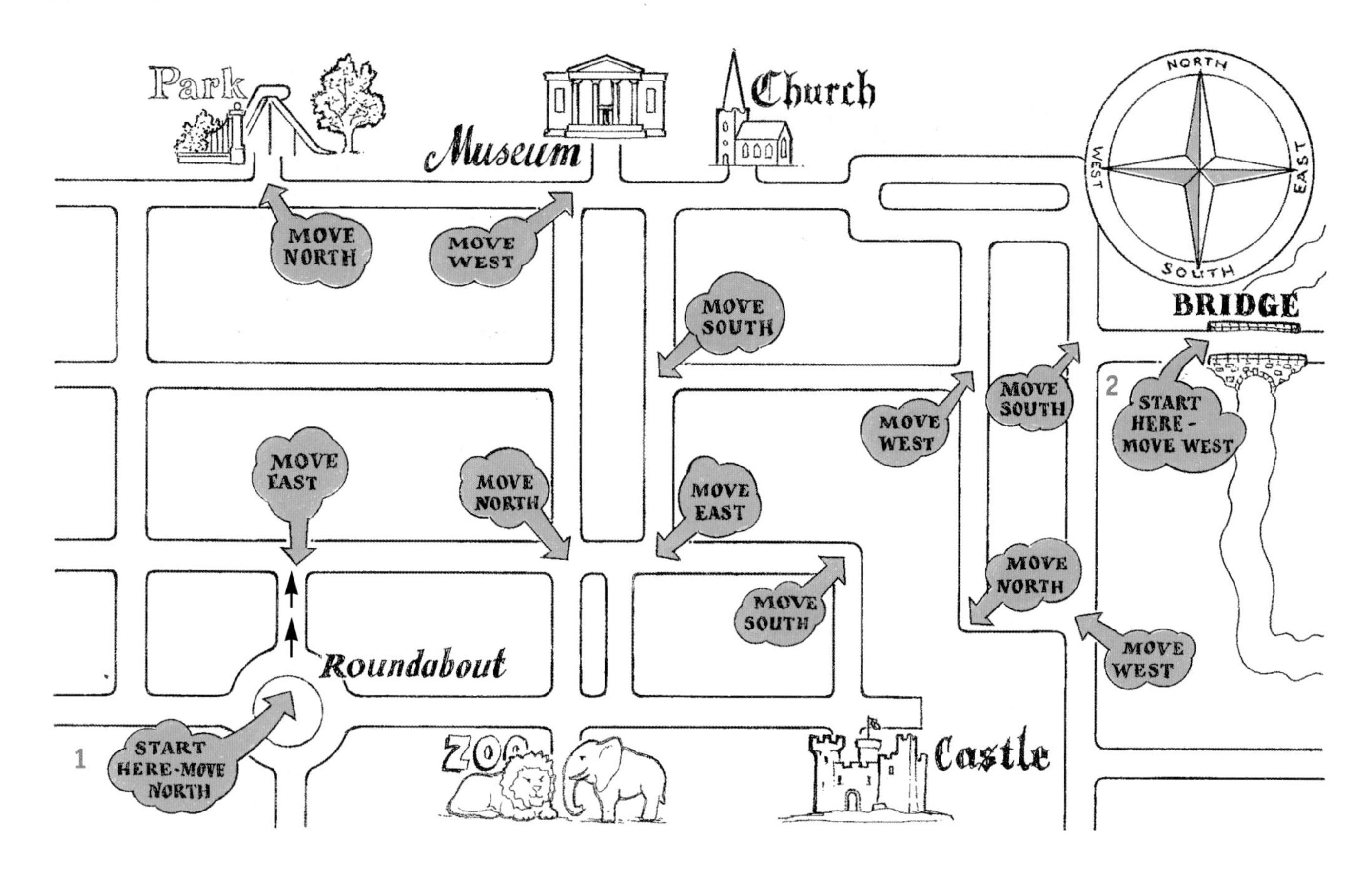

1 Uzma starts her journey at the roundabout. Where does her journey end?

2 If Uzma starts her journey at the bridge, where will her journey end?

3 Give directions for a journey from the church to the zoo.

Key ideas

The family of angles is:
- **acute angle** – more than 0°, but less than a right angle;
- **right angle** – exactly 90°;
- **obtuse angle** – more than a right angle, but less than half a turn;
- **straight line** – half a turn;
- **reflex angle** – more than half a turn, but less than a complete turn.

An angle measures the amount of turn. The unit that is used is a **degree** (which is written as a small circle like this: 60°). A right angle is **90°** of turn.

The four main points of the **compass** are **North**, **South**, **East** and **West**.

Chapter 8 Work Out 1 The Youth Club Trip

Members of the Axford Youth Club are going to Adventure Camp for the weekend.
They get into the minibus, and start the journey.

A The journey

Here is a map of the journey from **Axford** to **Adventure Camp**.

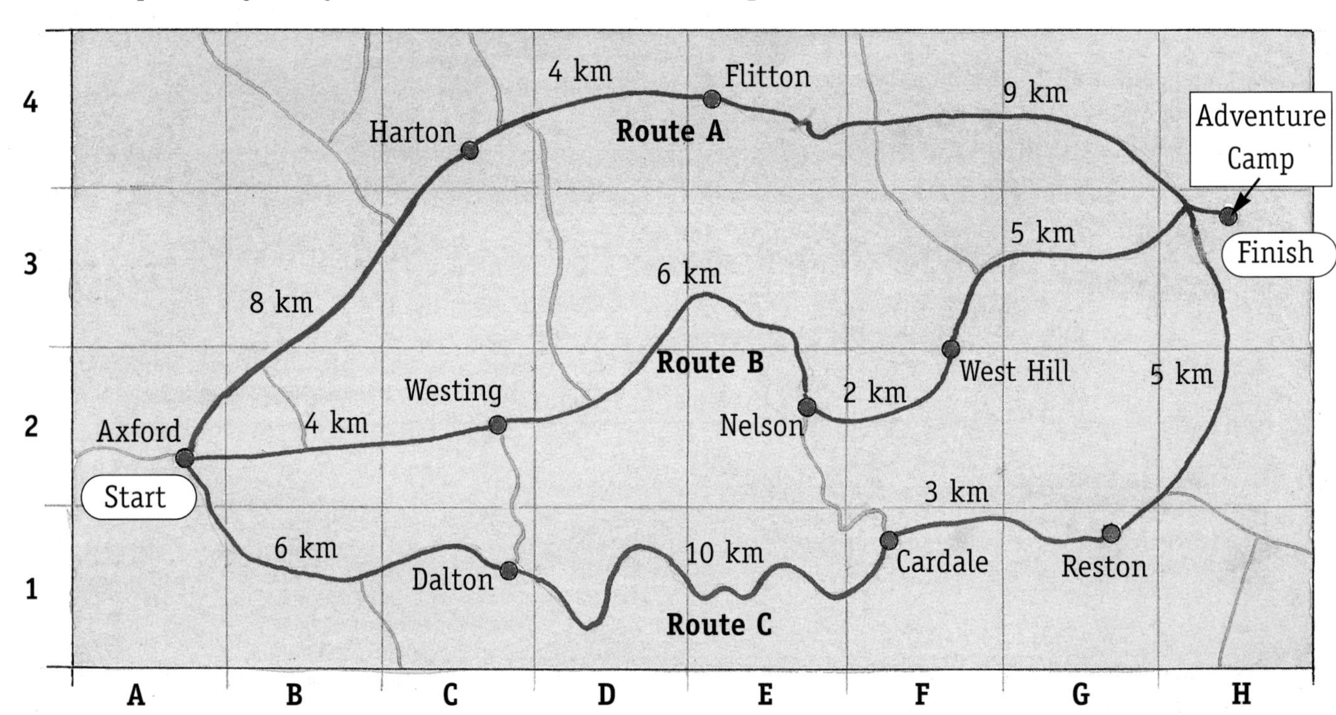

1 How many **kilometres** is it from Axford to Harton?

2 How many **kilometres** is it from Dalton to Reston (route C)?

3 There are three routes to the Adventure Camp.
(a) What is the total distance by route A?
(b) What is the total distance by route B?
(c) What is the total distance by route C?

4 Which town will you find at (C, 2)?

5 Which town will you find at (E, 2)?

6 What are the **co-ordinates** for the camp?

7 What are the **co-ordinates** for Axford?

8 What are the **co-ordinates** for Flitton?

9 What are the **co-ordinates** for Reston?

10 Through which **co-ordinates** does the road from Dalton to Cardale pass?

B Arrival

When the group arrive at Adventure Camp they see that the site is huge. Jenny the Youth Worker has to give them directions to get to their tents.

Here is a plan of the campsite. Follow Jenny's directions and work out which tent each person has been given.

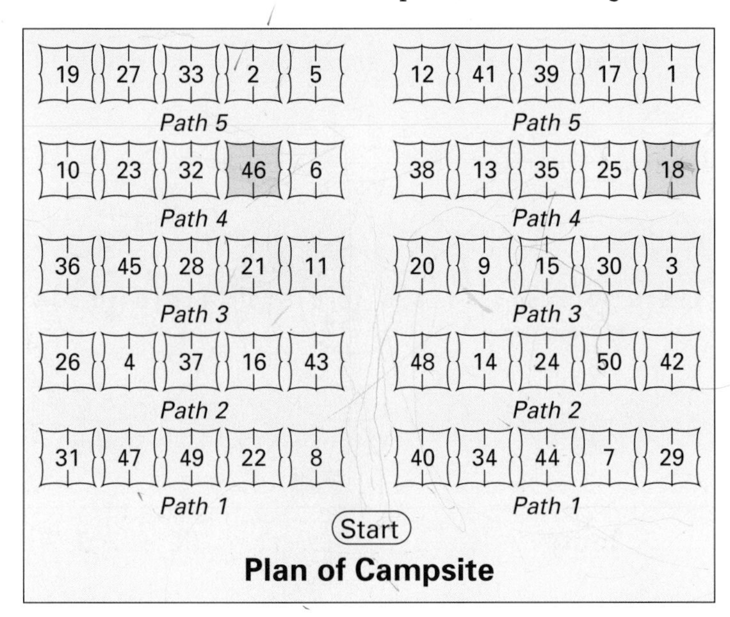

Jack and Carl. To find your tent, walk along to the 4th path. Turn left. It is the 3rd tent on your right.

1 Jack and Carl are in tent number **?** .

Sophie and Beth. Turn right at the 2nd path. Your tent is the 4th on the left.

2 Sophie and Beth are in tent number **?** .

Kenny and Hamad. Go to the 5th path. Turn right. Your tent is 5th on the left.

3 Kenny and Hamad are in tent number **?** .

Gemma and Kate. Take the 3rd path on your left. Your tent is 2nd on the right.

4 Gemma and Kate are in tent number **?** .

5 Jenny the Youth Worker is put in tent 18. Give directions for her to find the tent.

6 Sam the minibus driver is put in tent 46. Give directions for him to find his tent.

7 Give directions so that Jack and Carl can find their way to Kenny and Hamad's tent.

8 Give directions so that Gemma and Kate can find their way to Sophie and Beth's tent.

C Archery 

The group start the day with an archery competition.
Here are the targets of each member of the Axford Youth Club.

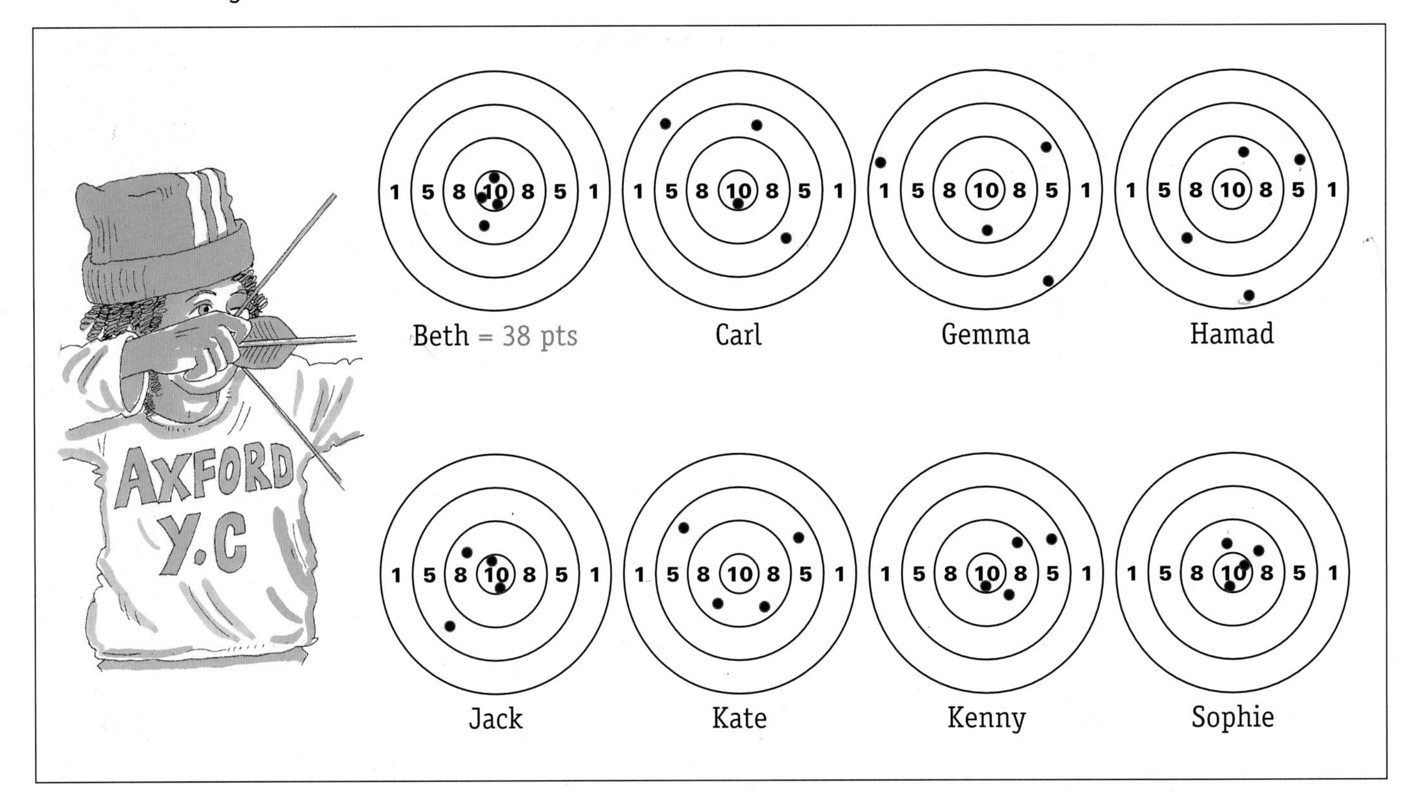

1 With her four arrows, Beth scored 38 points.
Work out the scores for the other members of the group.

2 Who came **(a)** 1st, **(b)** 2nd, **(c)** 3rd, and **(d)** 4th in the competition?

D Indoor soccer

Axford take part in a soccer competition. They play four games.
The table below shows the results.
Each team earns **3 points** if they win,
1 point if they draw and **0 points** if they lose.

1 Work out how many points each team earned.
2 Put the teams in order, 1st to 5th.

Team	Games won	Games drawn	Games lost	Points total
Axford	3	0	1	?
Bentley	3	1	0	?
Carlton	0	1	3	?
Reddington	0	2	2	?
St Patrick's	1	2	1	?

E Orienteering

In the afternoon the group go on an orienteering trip.

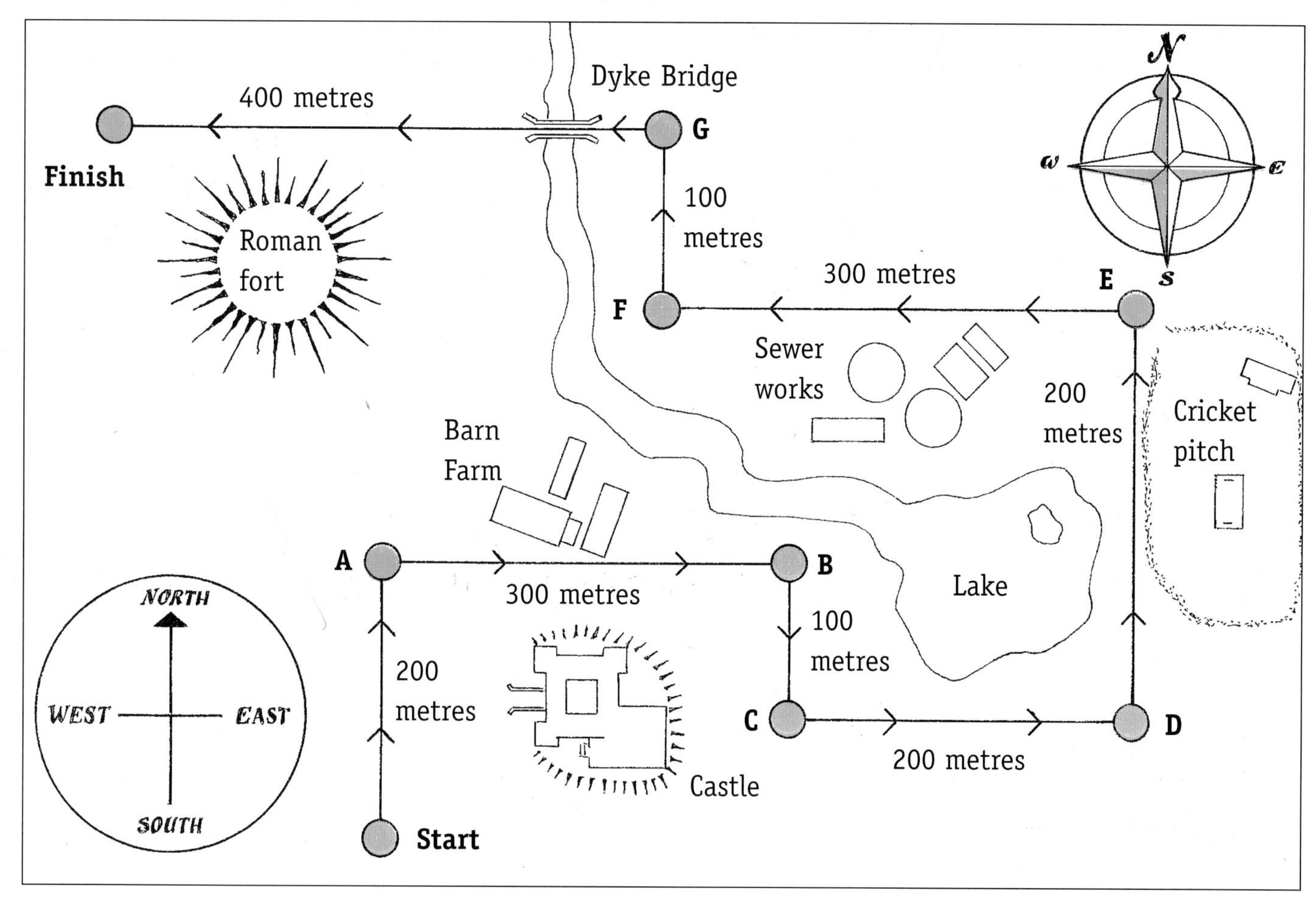

1 How far is it from the start to checkpoint A?

2 How far is it from checkpoint B to checkpoint E?

3 How far is it from checkpoint E to the finish?

4 What is the direction of travel between the start and checkpoint A? (North, South, East or West.)

5 What is the direction of travel between checkpoint G and the finish?

6 What would you see on your left between checkpoints E and F?

7 What would you see on your right between checkpoints D and E?

8 How do you cross the river between checkpoint G and the finish?

9 What do you see on your left as you get near the finish?

10 Copy and complete the table.

Stage	Direction of travel	Distance (metres)
Start to A	North	200
A to B	East	300
B to C	?	?
C to D	?	?
D to E	?	?
E to F	?	?
F to G	?	?
G to Finish	?	?

F The beach study 

The Axford group are exploring a rock pool.
They are studying the wildlife and taking measurements.

1 Record the name and measurement of each creature.

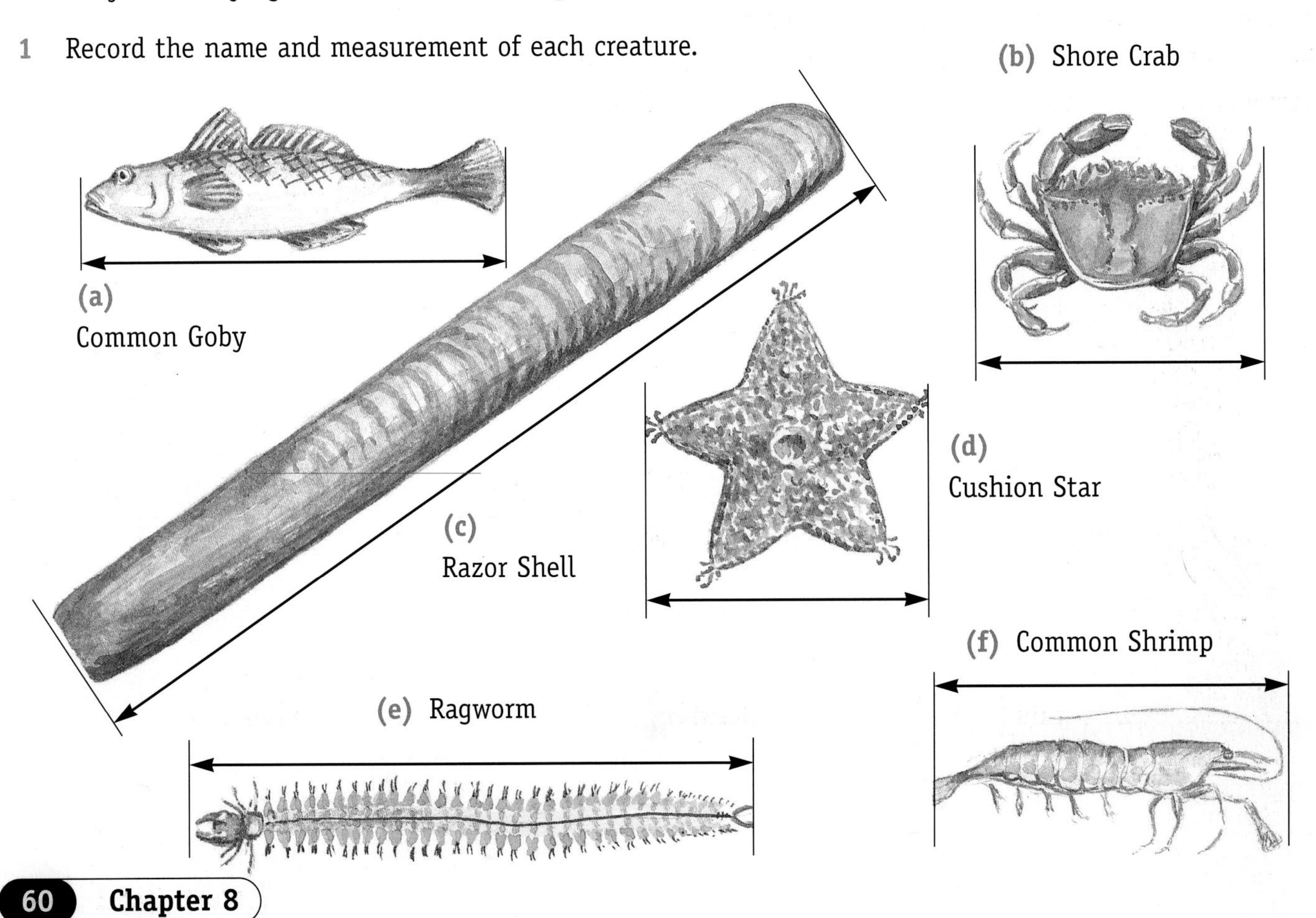

2 The group then collect shells and measure them.
Record the name and measurement of each shell.

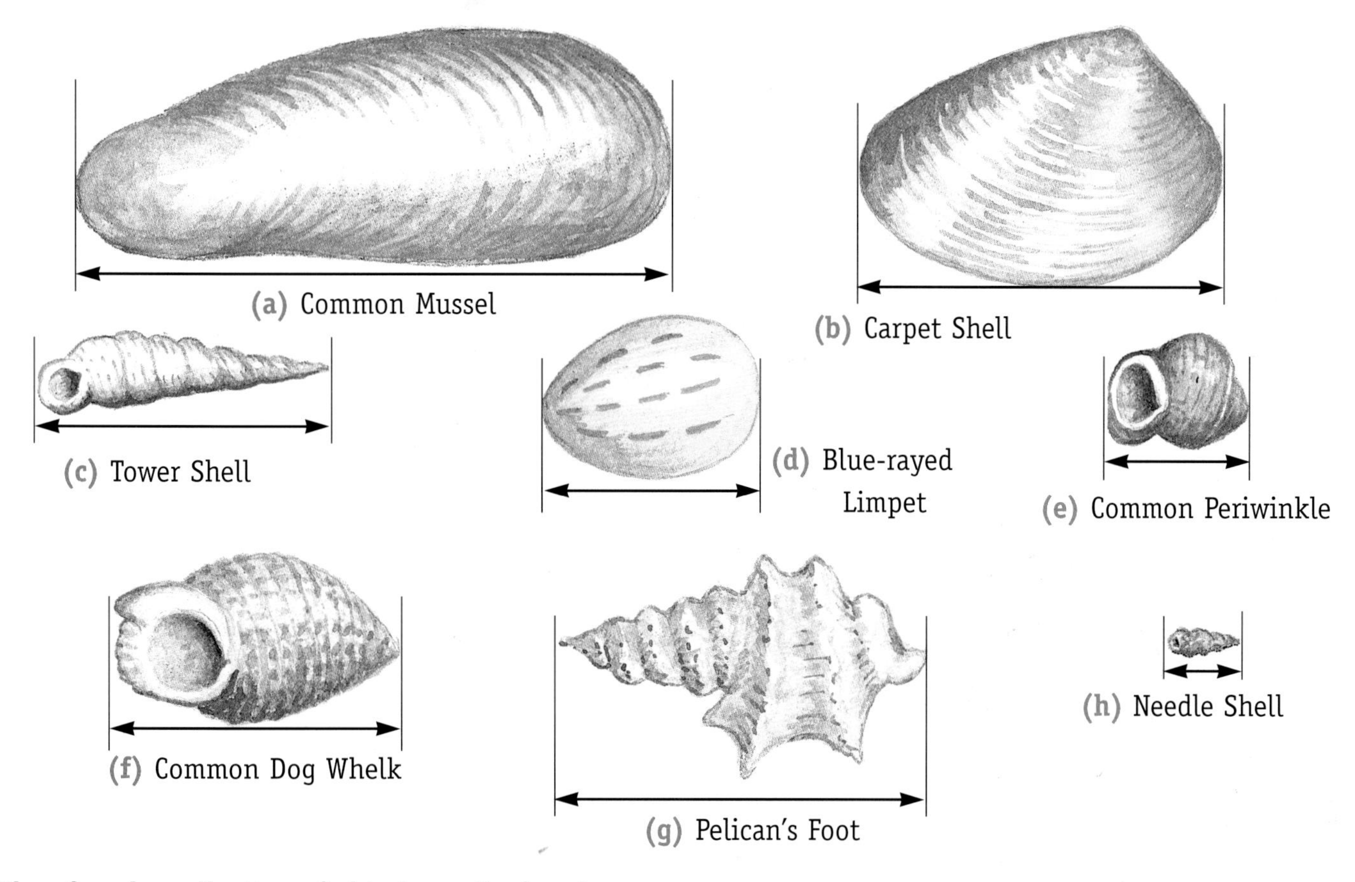

3 They found a collection of objects on the beach.
Some of the objects are **symmetrical**. Look at the group's collection below.
How many lines of symmetry could be drawn on each object?

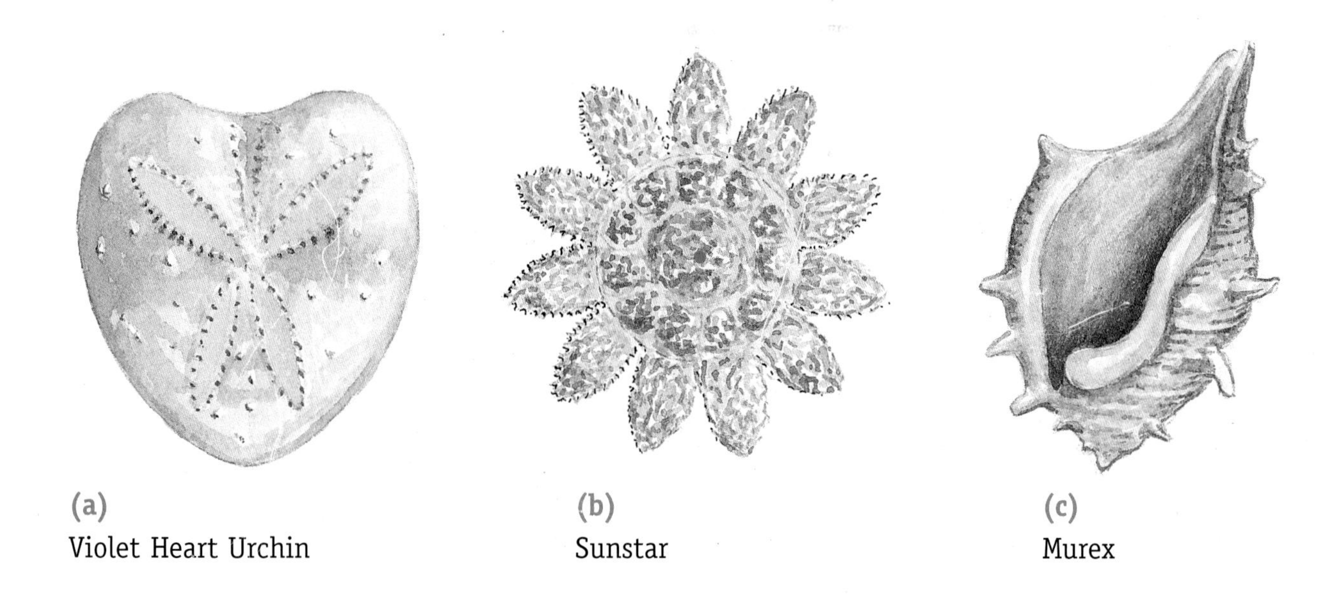

(a)
Violet Heart Urchin

(b)
Sunstar

(c)
Murex

G The rock climbing trip

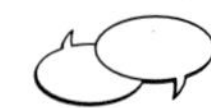

1 On some of the climbs the ropes make an angle.
Write whether each lettered angle is **acute**, **right** or **obtuse**.

Using the scale on the **left** of the picture, **estimate** an answer to these questions.

2 Kenny is about ? metres below Kate.

3 Carl is about ? metres from the summit (top).

4 Kate is about ? metres away from Beth.

5 Jack is about ? metres above the ground.

6 Sophie is about ? metres away from Gemma.

7 Hamad is about ? metres above the ground.

8 The rock face is about ? metres high.

H Awards

Jenny kept a record of the achievement points awarded to each member of the group. Here are the scores.

Name: Beth

Activity	Score
Camp craft	8
Archery	10
Orienteering	7
Beach study	4
Rock climbing	10
Conduct	8
Total	?

Name: Carl

Activity	Score
Camp craft	8
Archery	3
Orienteering	10
Beach study	8
Rock climbing	10
Conduct	7
Total	?

Name: Gemma

Activity	Score
Camp craft	10
Archery	2
Orienteering	10
Beach study	10
Rock climbing	9
Conduct	9
Total	?

Name: Hamad

Activity	Score
Camp craft	9
Archery	2
Orienteering	10
Beach study	10
Rock climbing	8
Conduct	8
Total	?

Name: Jack

Activity	Score
Camp craft	3
Archery	6
Orienteering	3
Beach study	3
Rock climbing	4
Conduct	4
Total	?

Name: Kate

Activity	Score
Camp craft	6
Archery	4
Orienteering	6
Beach study	7
Rock climbing	10
Conduct	6
Total	?

Name: Kenny

Activity	Score
Camp craft	4
Archery	5
Orienteering	10
Beach study	5
Rock climbing	7
Conduct	7
Total	?

Name: Sophie

Activity	Score
Camp craft	5
Archery	8
Orienteering	3
Beach study	5
Rock climbing	7
Conduct	4
Total	?

1 Work out the total score for each person.

2 Who got the highest total?

3 Who scored 10 on three activities?

4 Who scored 39 points in total?

5 Who got the lowest total?

6 Which two people got the same total?

7 Who scored 8 on rock climbing?

8 Who scored 8 for archery?

9 How many points did Kate score on camp craft?

10 Who scored 5 for archery?

Chapter 9 Multiplication and Division

Step-up Multiplication

The friendly aliens come from … *beyond!*
There are three types: Gips, Spogs, Runner Beings.

A

Profile
Name: Gips
Arms: 4
Eyes: 3

B

Profile
Name: Spogs
Arms: 3
Eyes: 4

C

Profile
Name: Runner Beings
Arms: 5
Eyes: 2

Answer these questions.

1. How many eyes can you see in each picture?
2. How many arms are there in each picture?
3. Imagine that there were 5 aliens in each picture, and answer questions 1 and 2 again.

These aliens also have **3** eyes. To work out how many eyes there are altogether between **5** you can add **3**, five times.
$3 + 3 + 3 + 3 + 3 = 15$
If you know your multiplication tables you could remember that $5 \times 3 = 15$.

4. Do you know what…
   (a) 4×2 is? (b) 2×5 is? (c) 5×3 is?
   (d) 5×5 is? (e) 3×4 is? (f) 4×4 is?

Exercise 1

Use your memory of multiplication tables or your own calculations, to answer these questions.

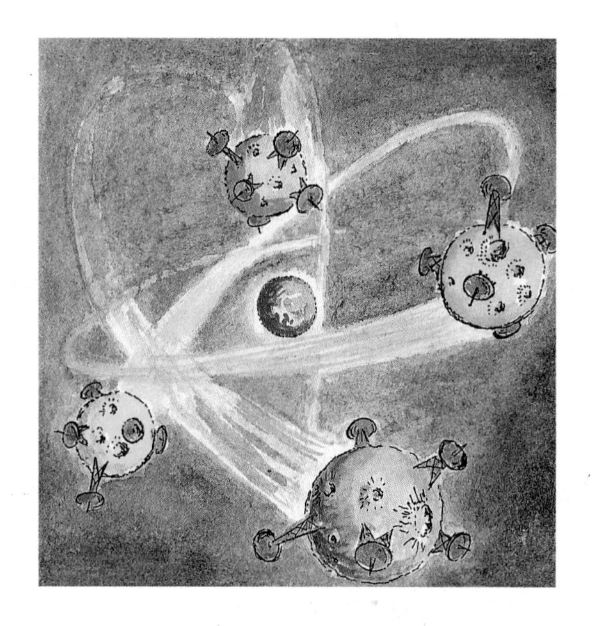

In the aliens' galaxy each planet has **4 moons.**
Each moon has **5 radio stations.**

1 How many radio stations will there be on all 4 moons together?

Each radio station is run by **2 aliens.**

2 How many aliens are needed to run the radio stations of one moon? (Check with your teacher or on a calculator that you answered question 2 accurately.)

3 How many aliens will be needed to run the radio stations on **2 moons**?

×	**1**	**2**	**3**	**4**	**5**
1	1	2	3	4	5
2	2	4	6	8	10
3	3	6	9	12	15
4	4	8	12	16	20
5	5	10	15	20	25

The **multiplication** table can be used to save you counting or adding.
For example, to find the number of aliens needed to run the radios on one moon you could add:
2 + 2 + 2 + 2 + 2 aliens or ... you can find 5 **lots** of 2 on the table. **5 lots of 2 = 10.**

For example, the number of moons around 5 planets is:
4 + 4 + 4 + 4 + 4 or using the table:
5 lots of 4 = 20 moons.

Use the table to check your answers to questions 1 to 3.

Exercise 2

Use the multiplication table to answer these problems or to check your answers.

1 3 lots of 5 = **?**

2 4 lots of 4 = **?**

3 3 lots of 3 = **?**

4 5 lots of 3 = **?**

5 4 lots of 5 = **?**

6 4 lots of 2 = **?**

We can use this sign '×' instead of writing 'lots of'.

7 $1 \times 5 =$ **?**

8 $2 \times 3 =$ **?**

9 $5 \times 5 =$ **?**

10 Is this true or false? '3 × 4 is the same as 4 × 3'.

11 Is this true or false? '2 lots of 5 = 5 × 2'.

This astronaut can make long leaps.

In the diagram below she is leaping 2 metres at a time. To travel 10 metres she needs to make 5 leaps. Check this on the multiplication table.

(5 lots of 2 is 10, $5 \times 2 = 10$)

If she makes 3 leaps, how far will she travel?
How did you get your answer?

0 1 2 3 4 5 6 7 8 9 10 11 12 13 14 15 16 17 18 19 20 21 22 23 24 25 26 27 28 29 30

Exercise 3

Work out how far the astronaut will travel if she takes these numbers of leaps.
You can use the table for some of the problems, or the number line. Start from zero each time.

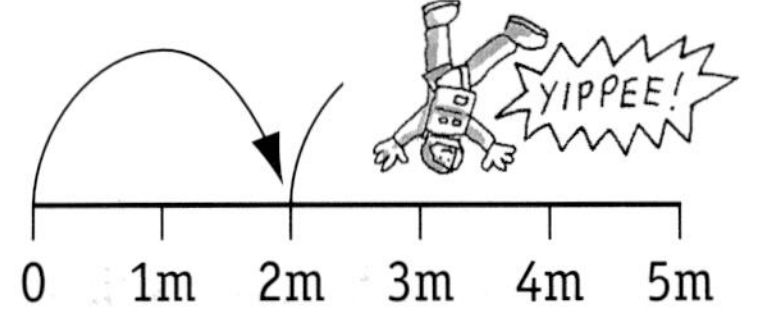

1. 4 leaps
2. 1 leap
3. 3 leaps
4. 6 leaps
5. 8 leaps
6. 7 leaps
7. 9 leaps
8. 10 leaps
9. The 2 times table on page 65 ends at 10.
   Write out the 2 times table as far as 10×2.

Exercise 4

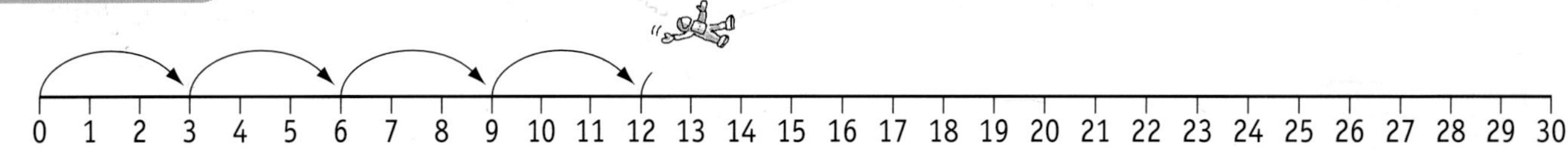

She now makes leaps of 3 metres. How far will she travel if she takes these numbers of leaps?

1. 2 leaps
2. 4 leaps
3. 1 leap
4. 3 leaps
5. 5 leaps
6. 7 leaps
7. 10 leaps
8. 6 leaps
9. 9 leaps
10. Write out the 3 times table as far as 10×3.

Exercise 5

0 1 2 3 4 5 6 7 8 9 10 11 12 13 14 15 16 17 18 19 20 21 22 23 24 25 26 27 28 29 30

Use this number line to answer these multiplication problems.

1. $3 \times 2 =$?
2. $4 \times 3 =$?
3. $1 \times 5 =$?
4. $5 \times 3 =$?
5. $4 \times 4 =$?
6. $6 \times 4 =$?
7. $5 \times 2 =$?
8. $3 \times 6 =$?
9. $4 \times 5 =$?
10. $7 \times 3 =$?
11. $5 \times 5 =$?
12. $8 \times 2 =$?

You will need to think beyond the number line to answer some of these.

13. $10 \times 2 =$?
14. $10 \times 3 =$?
15. $10 \times 4 =$?
16. $10 \times 5 =$?

Multiplication by groups

Here are five alien space ships.

Z2 has a crew of two.

Z1 carries one alien.

Z5 will carry five aliens.

Z4 has a crew of four aliens.

Z3 carries three aliens.

So: In two Z4 ships there will be eight crew members, because $2 \times 4 = 8$

Exercise 6

How many aliens will these numbers of ships hold:

1 three Z2 ships?
2 five Z2 ships?
3 four Z4 ships?
4 three Z3 ships?
5 three Z5 ships?
6 four Z5 ships?
7 six Z3 ships?
8 seven Z3 ships?
9 nine Z1 ships?
10 five Z3 ships?
11 ten Z2 ships?
12 eight Z2 ships?

Exercise 7

Rewrite the questions above as multiplication problems.
Use the '×' sign. The first one is done for you.

three Z2 ships:
$3 \times 2 = 6$ crew members.

Exercise 8

1 Work out how many aliens you will need to crew these groups of ships.
You can copy this table.

Ships in the group	**two Z2 and one Z3**	**three Z2 and two Z3**	**three Z4 and one Z5**	**four Z2 and three Z1**	**five Z4 and two Z5**
Total number of crew members	?	?	?	?	?

2 What combination of ships could you use to move:
(a) 7 aliens? (b) 12 aliens?

Step-up 1 Division

The Yates Family are building a shed.
The truck arrives with bags of cement.

Each member of the family carries an equal number of bags.

There are 12 bags of cement.

There are four people in the Yates family.

Mr Yates has carried 3 bags.
Mrs Yates has carried 3 bags.

Lucy has carried 3 bags.
Joe has carried 3 bags.

The Yates family have shared 12 cement bags into 4 piles. 12 'shared' by 4 = 3.

1 Make a table like this one. Find the number of bags each member of the family will have to carry.
Fill in the spaces.
There are not always 4 people in each family.

Number of bags	Number of people	Number of bags in each pile
12	4	3
15	3	?
10	2	?
16	4	?
20	4	?
15	5	?

Step-up 2 Division

The timber arrives next, but Mr Yates is left on his own to carry the wood to the garden.

There are 18 pieces of wood on the truck. Mr Yates can carry 3 pieces at a time.

To move all the timber, he will have to carry 6 loads.

This drawing shows how Mr Yates has to **divide** the loads of timber.
There are 18 pieces of wood.

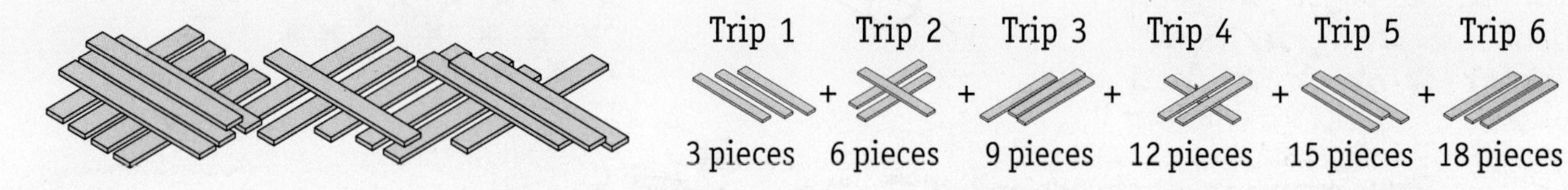

Mr Yates carries 3 pieces each load until he has finished. He needs 6 loads.

2 How many trips will Mr Yates have to make to carry these loads to his garden?
Make simple drawings like this to help you.

(a) There are 12 pieces of timber to move. He can carry 6 pieces each trip.

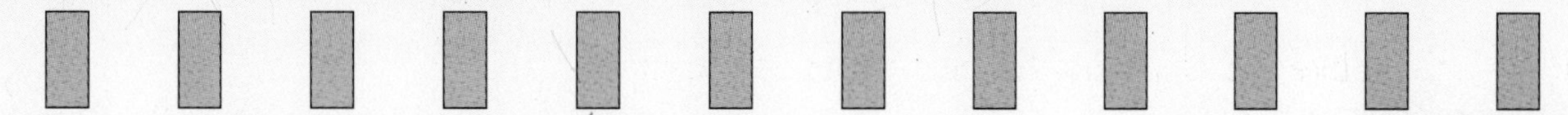

(b) He has to move 30 bags of sand. He can carry two bags each trip.

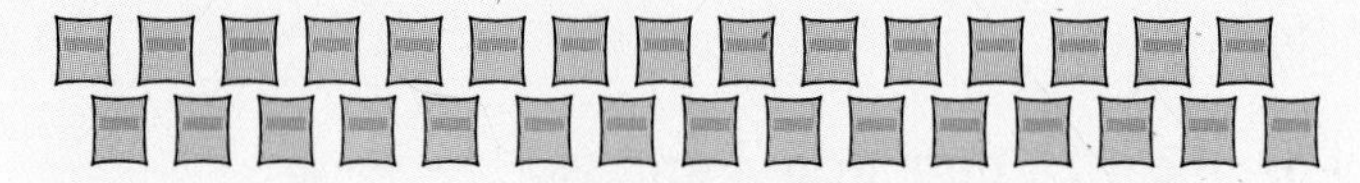

(c) There are 8 rolls of felt. He can carry 4 rolls each trip.

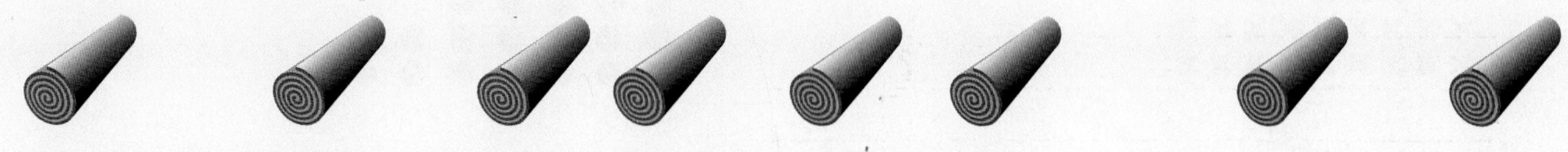

(d) The lorry delivers forty slabs. He can carry five at a time.

How many groups are there?

How many groups of **5** can you make from **15**?

You can make **3 groups of 5** from **15**.

15 ÷ 3 = 5

Exercise 1

Use drawings to complete these divisions.

1 Divide 12 dots into groups of 4.

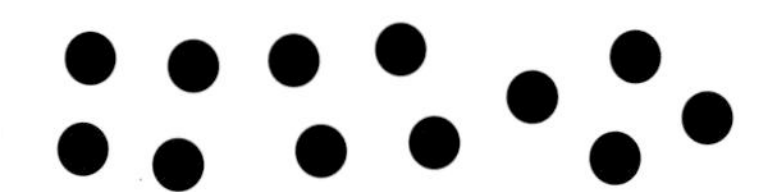

2 Divide 15 crosses into groups of 5.

3 Divide 20 stars into groups of 5.

4 Divide 18 crosses into groups of 9.

How many in each group?

Divide 10 into 5 groups.

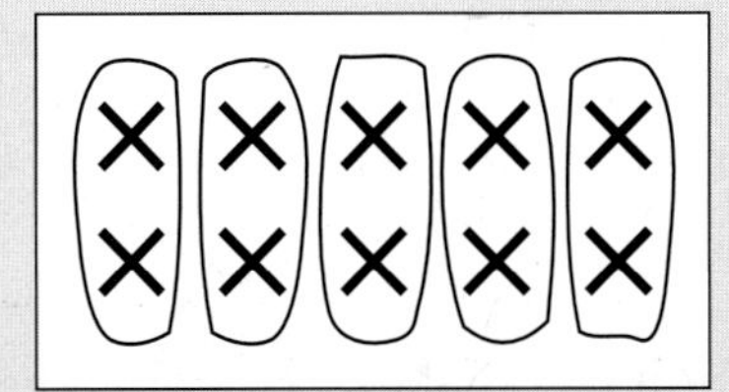

There are **2** in each of the **5** groups.

10 ÷ 5 = 2

Exercise 2

Use drawings to complete these divisions.

1 25 crosses into 5 groups.

2 24 dots into 3 groups.

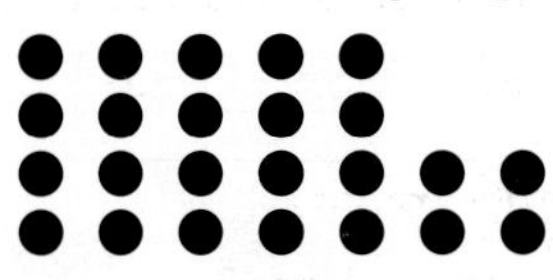

3 21 circles into 7 groups.

4 18 squares into 9 groups.

×	**1**	**2**	**3**	**4**	**5**	**6**
1	1	2	3	4	5	6
2	2	4	6	8	10	12
3	3	6	9	12	15	18
4	4	8	12	16	20	24
5	5	10	15	20	25	30
6	6	12	18	24	30	36
7	7	14	21	28	35	42
8	8	16	24	32	40	48

This multiplication table can be used to help you with **division** problems.

To **share** or **divide** 30 into groups of 5, look along the **'5'** row until you come to **30**. This is the **6** column.

There are 6 groups of 5 in 30.

$30 \div 5 = 6$

Exercise 3

How many will there be in each group when you divide?
Use the table above to help you.

1 Share 18 into groups of 3.

2 Share 24 into groups of 6.

3 Share 24 into groups of 3.

4 Share 21 into groups of 3.

5 Share 35 into groups of 7.

6 Share 16 into groups of 4.

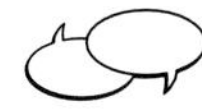

24 cards are dealt out.

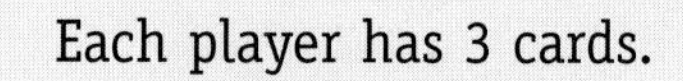

Each player has 3 cards.

How many players are there?

To find the answer you need to divide or share. Find 24 on the 3 column.
The answer is 8. **$24 \div 3 = 8$**

Exercise 4

Use the table at the top of this page to help you to divide.

1 30 cards are dealt. There are 6 cards for each player.
How many players are there?

2 There are 5 players. 40 cards are dealt.
How many cards will each player have?

3 Egg boxes hold 6 eggs. There are 42 eggs to be packed.
How many boxes are needed to pack the eggs?

4 Each 'in-line' skate has 4 wheels.
How many **pairs** of skates can be made if you have 32 wheels?

Dividing with remainders

13 cakes are put into boxes.
Each box holds **4 cakes.**

The cakes fill 3 boxes. There is 1 cake remaining unpacked. This is called the **remainder.**

13 ÷ 4 = 3 (**remainder 1**)

Exercise 5

Divide to find how many boxes are needed to pack these numbers of cakes. Each box holds 4 cakes. Copy the table and fill in the empty columns.

Number of cakes	Number of boxes	Unpacked cakes (remainder)
9	?	?
14	?	?
7	?	?
18	?	?
25	?	?

Investigate!

Look at the numbers on the doors.

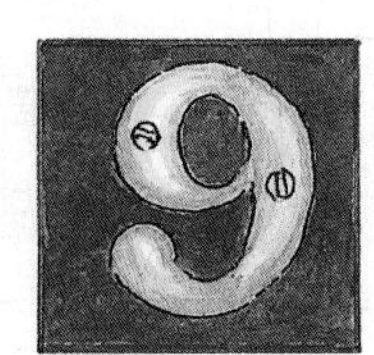

1 Divide each door number by **2**.

2 What do you notice about the blue door numbers when you divide by 2?
Begin: 'The numbers on the blue doors … '

3 What do you notice about the red door numbers when you divide by 2?
Begin: 'The numbers on the red doors … '

When a number is divided by 2, and it leaves a remainder of 1, it is called **odd**.
When a number is divided by 2, and there is no remainder, the number is called **even**.

4 Using the numbers below, try to find a short-cut for deciding whether a number **is odd or even.**

24 25 9 27 10 20 33 36 19 231 222

Begin: 'I have noticed that **even** numbers have an … number in the units place.'
'I have noticed that **odd** numbers have an … number in the units place.'

5 There is a party at James's house! No-one knows his door number. Everyone is given the same clues:

Start at any door. If the number is even, then halve it. If it is an odd number, add 1 to it. Keep doing this until you find my door number.

Delroy starts at number 19. Kerry starts at number 30. Ashley starts at number 21. List all of the door numbers they have to visit on the way to James's party.

Key ideas

× this sign means multiply   ÷ this sign means divide

Multiplication saves you having to keep adding numbers together, like this:
4 + 4 + 4 + 4 + 4 can be written as 5 × 4 = 20

Division is a way to share out numbers equally, like this:
Share 12 Easter eggs between 4 children.
12 − 4 = 8
8 − 4 = 4
4 − 4 = 0 We have had to take away 4, three times. 12 ÷ 4 = 3

When you divide an **odd** number by 2, it will leave a remainder of 1.
When you divide an **even** number by 2, it will **not** leave a remainder.

Chapter 10 Flat Shapes

Step-up

These are **solid** shapes.
They have **thickness**.

These are **flat** shapes.
They have **no thickness**.

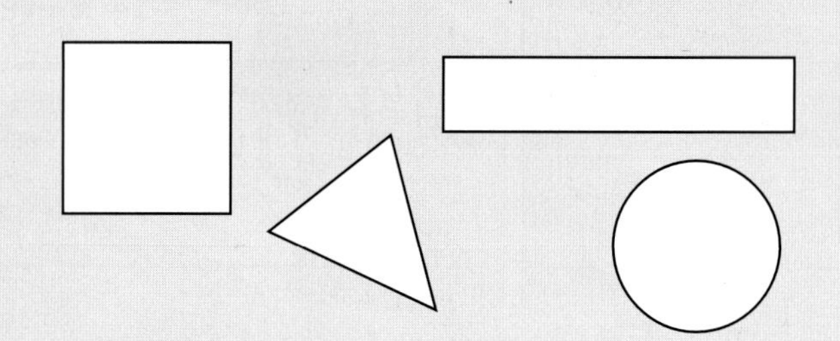

Sort these shapes into **flat** shapes and **solid** shapes.
Write: 'These shapes are flat shapes – B, …'
'These shapes are solid shapes – A, …'

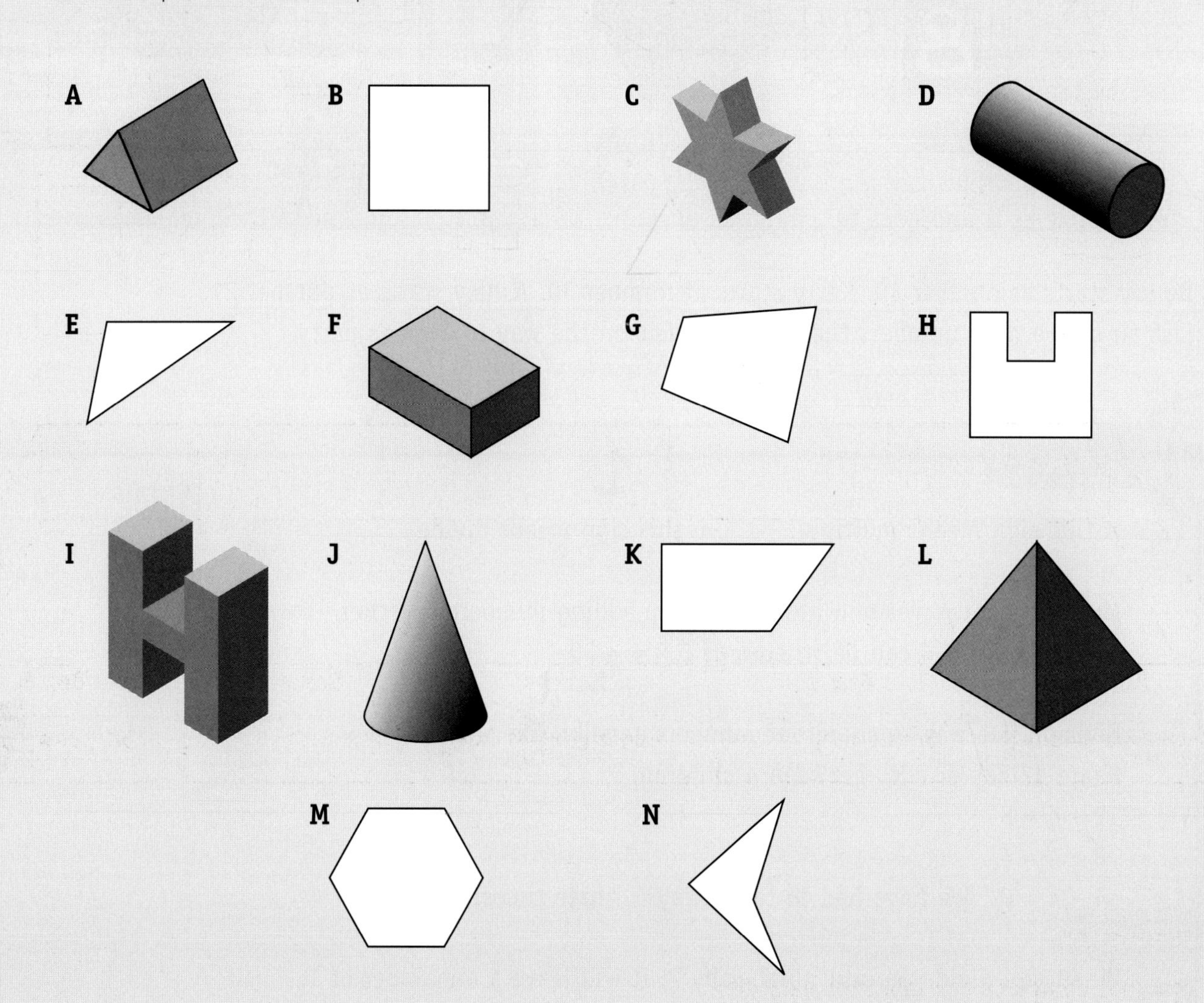

These flat shapes are being sorted into five boxes.

Exercise 1

Finish sorting the shapes into their correct boxes.
Write: '*These shapes belong in box 1 – D, L, ...*', and so on.

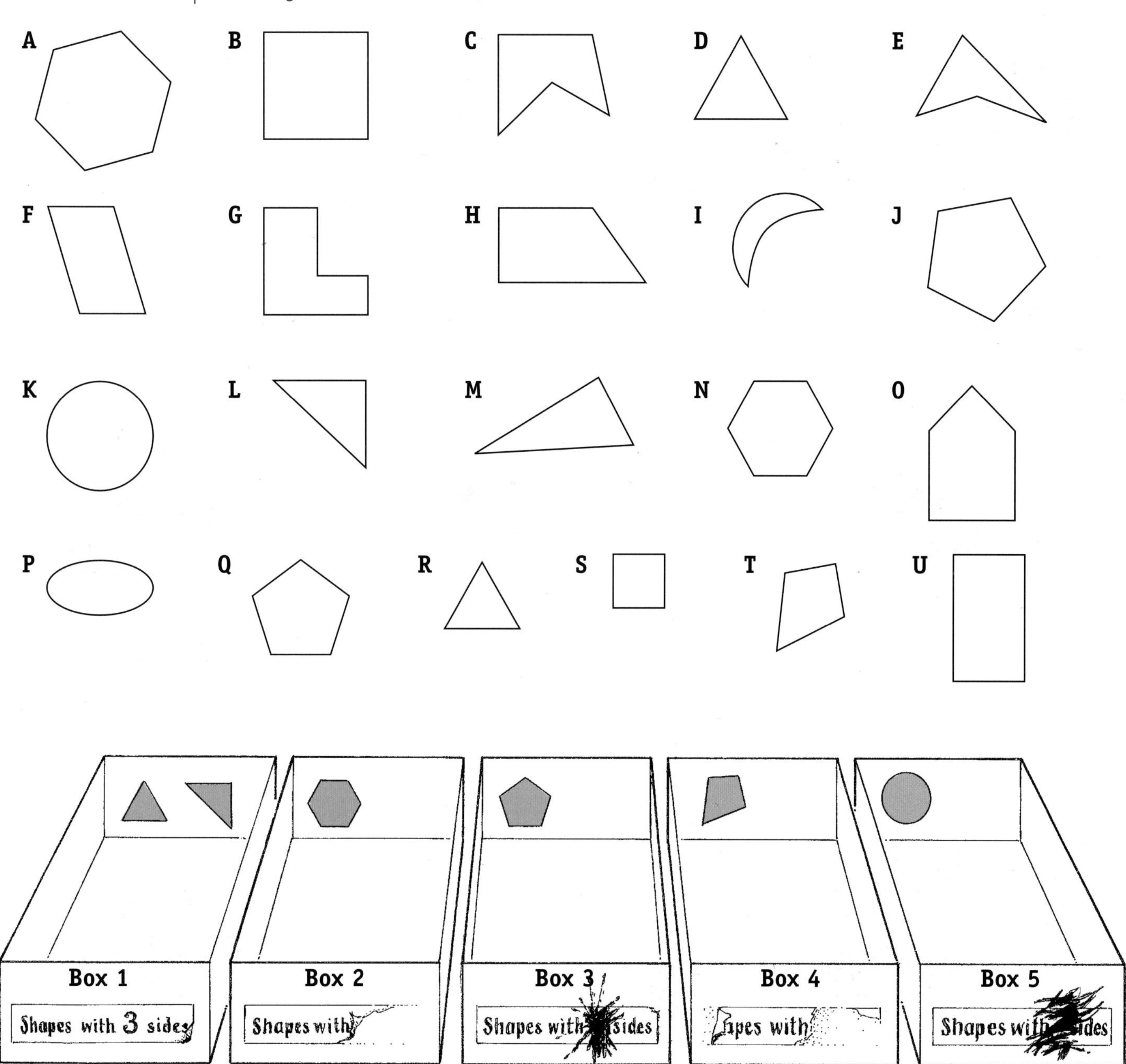

Exercise 2

Copy and complete the label for each box.
Write: '*Box 1 label reads Shapes with 3 sides*' and so on.

These shapes have **3** straight sides.
They are called **triangles**.
'**Tri**' means **3**.

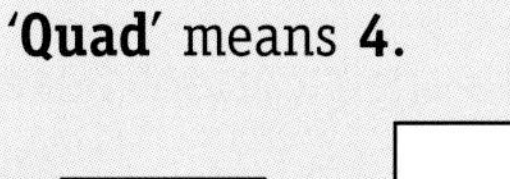

These shapes have **4** straight sides.
They are called **quadrilaterals**.
'**Quad**' means **4**.

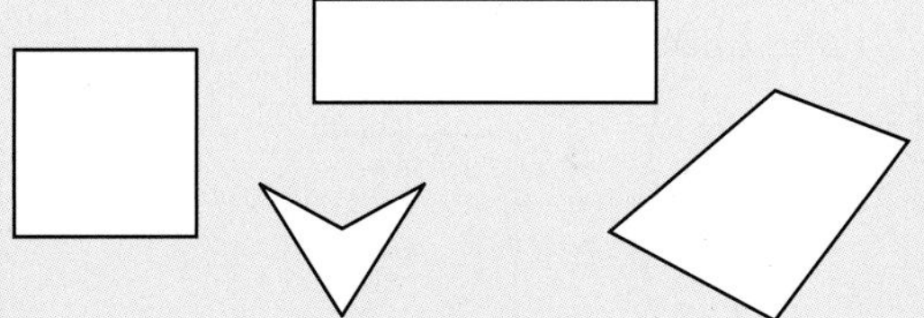

These shapes have **5** straight sides.
They are called **pentagons**.
'**Penta**' means **5**.

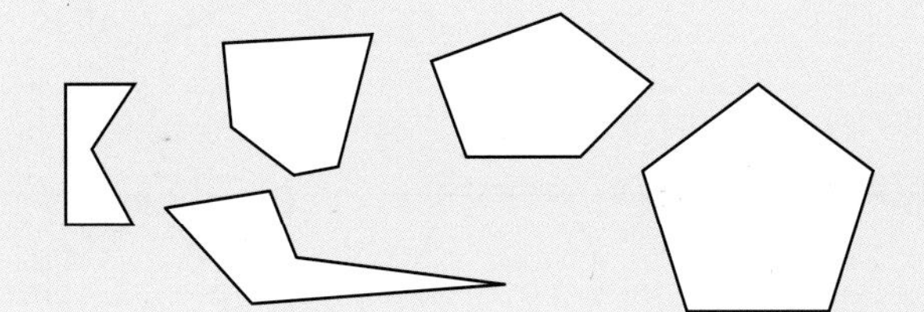

These shapes have **6** straight sides.
They are called **hexagons**.
'**Hexa**' means **6**.

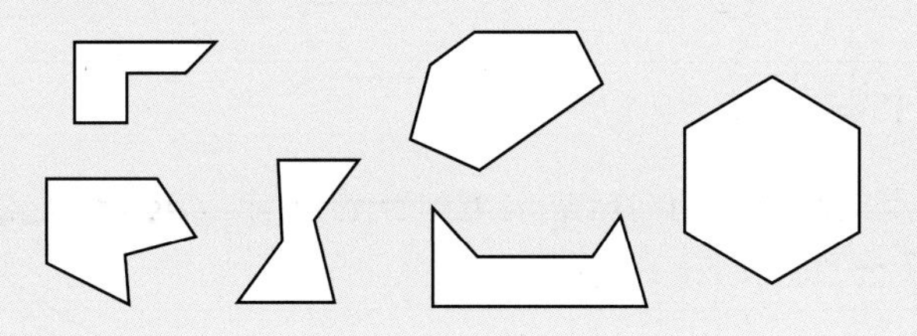

Exercise 3

Use the four names: **triangles**, **quadrilaterals**, **pentagons**, **hexagons** to label each box below.
Write: '*The label on the yellow box is ...*'

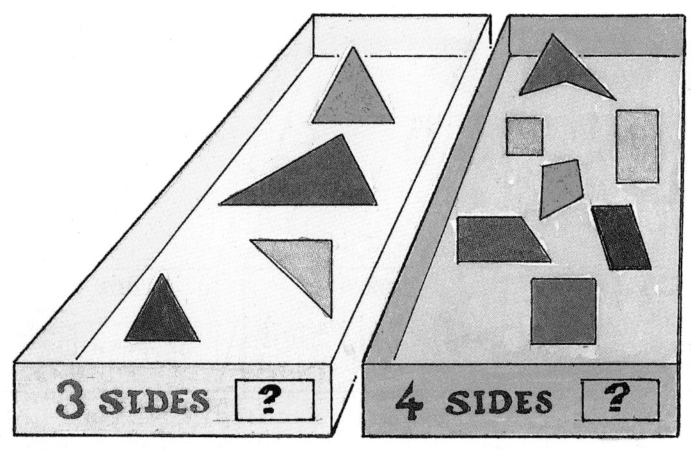

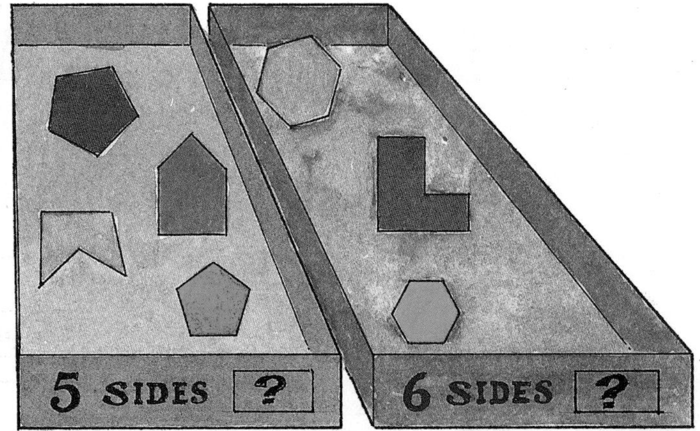

Exercise 4

Using a ruler, draw two more shapes to go in each box.
Draw **your own** shapes – do not copy the shapes above.

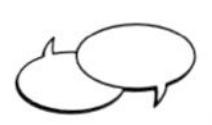

These shapes are both **hexagons**.
They each have six sides, but there is a difference between them.

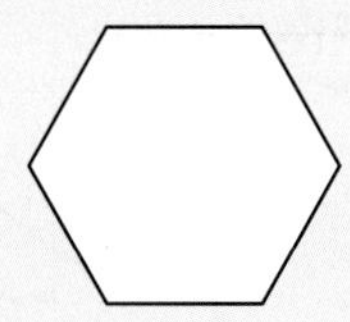

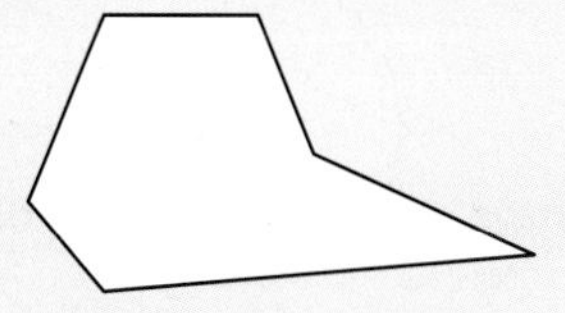

This shape is **regular**.
Its sides are all the same length.
Its angles are all the same size.

This shape is **irregular**.
Its sides are **not** all the same length.
Its angles are **not** all the same size.

Exercise 5

Look into the boxes and list which shapes are **regular** and **irregular**.
Write: 'Yellow box: regular …
irregular …'

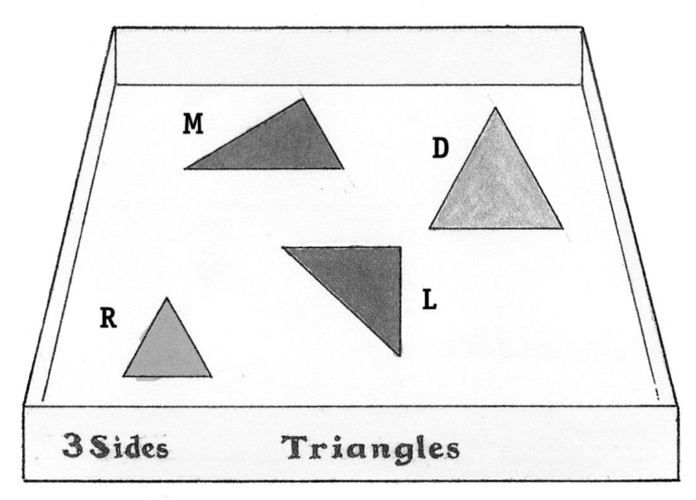

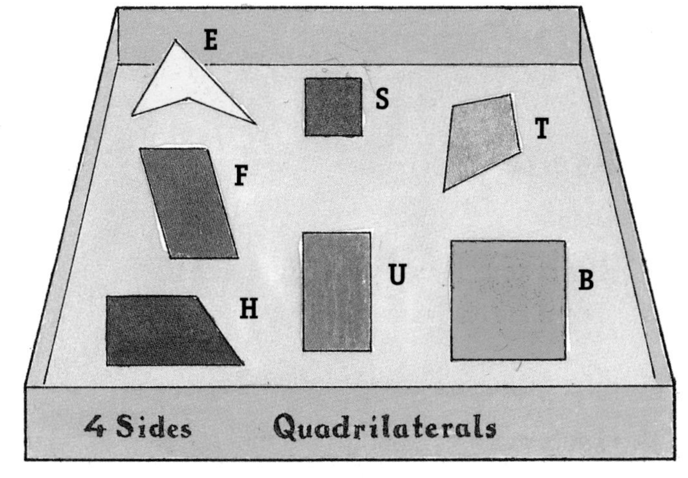

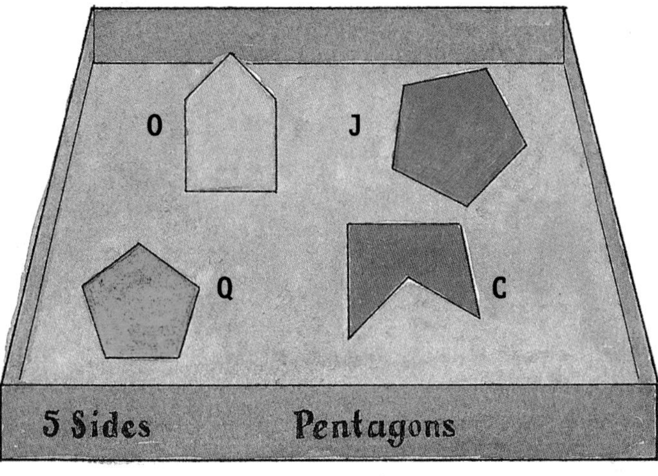

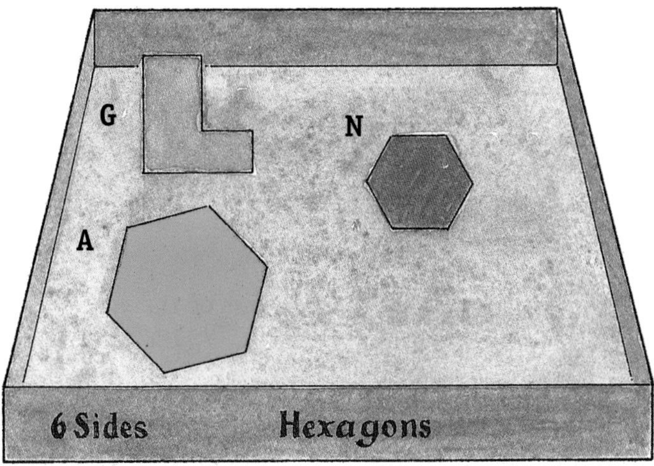

Here are some flat shapes that you can see around you daily.

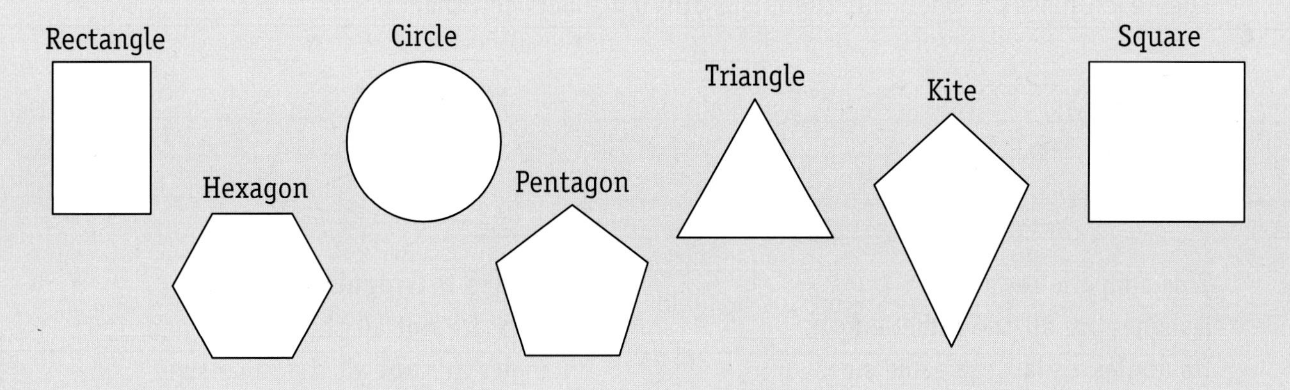

Exercise 6

Use the drawings above to help you complete these sentences.

1. A ? has 5 straight sides.
2. A ? has 4 equal sides and 4 right angles.
3. A rectangle has 4 ? angles.
4. A ? has no straight sides.
5. A ? has 6 sides and ? angles.
6. A kite has 2 pairs of equal sides. It has ? angles.

Exercise 7

Look at the picture on the opposite page.
Use it to complete these sentences.

1. There are ? circles.
2. The drawing has ? kites.
3. There are ? regular hexagons.
4. There are ? irregular hexagons.
5. There are ? regular pentagons.
6. There are ? irregular pentagons.
7. I can find ? squares.
8. I have counted ? regular triangles.
9. There are ? irregular triangles.
10. The drawing has ? rectangles.

Exercise 8

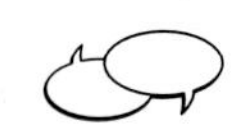

Look around the room or out of the window. How many of these shapes can you see:
rectangles? triangles? pentagons? circles? squares? kites? hexagons?
Write a list.

Investigate!  

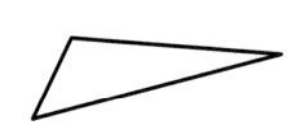

Irregular triangle. Has **no** lines of symmetry.

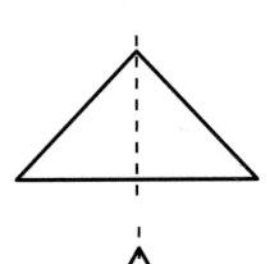

Irregular but has symmetry. Has **1** line of symmetry.

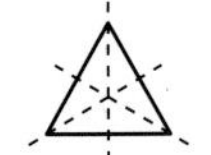

Regular triangle. Has **3** lines of symmetry.

Investigate **lines of symmetry** in **regular** and **irregular** shapes.
Use Worksheet 37 and work with your partner.
Complete the table on the worksheet by counting
the lines of symmetry for:

- the quadrilaterals;
- the pentagons;
- the hexagons.

Quadrilaterals

Irregular

Irregular but symmetrical

Regular and symmetrical

Pentagons

Irregular

Irregular but symmetrical

Regular and symmetrical

Hexagons

Irregular

Irregular but symmetrical

Regular and symmetrical

What have you noticed?

When you have finished your investigation,
write down what you have noticed or found out.
You can start like this:

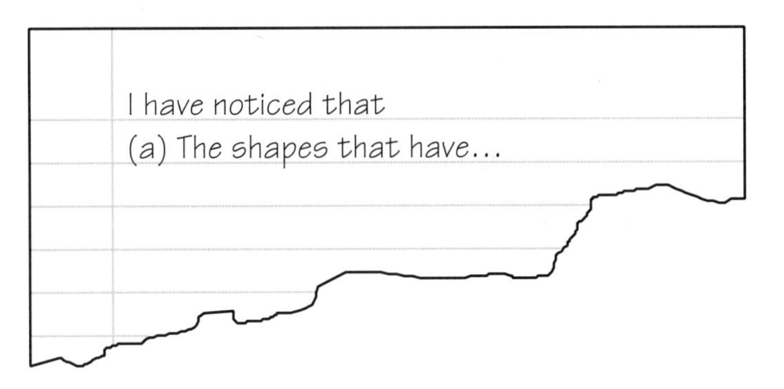

Words like: **if**, **when**, **found out**, **might**, could be useful.

Write what you have noticed about:

- which type of shapes (irregular, symmetrical, regular) have the most lines of symmetry;
- the number of sides of regular shapes, and the number of lines of symmetry;
- whether or not all regular shapes are symmetrical.

Key ideas

Flat shapes are not solid. They do not have any thickness or depth.
Flat shapes can be sorted into different groups, in different ways:

regular: shape with all its sides the same length and all its angles the same size.

irregular: shape with sides of different lengths and angles of different sizes.

symmetrical: shape that has one or more lines of symmetry.

They can be sorted by the number of sides:

3 sides – triangles (tri means 3);

4 sides – quadrilaterals (quad means 4);

5 sides – pentagons (penta means 5);

6 sides – hexagons (hexa means 6).

Chapter 11 Fractions

Jean and Roger are twins. They share the same birthday, and the same cake!

The cake was cut into two parts but Roger's piece was too small, so ... he was not happy!

The cake should be cut into **2 equal** pieces ($\frac{1}{2}$) so that Jean and Roger each have a fair share.

Exercise 1

1 Which cakes show 2 equal pieces ($\frac{1}{2}$)?

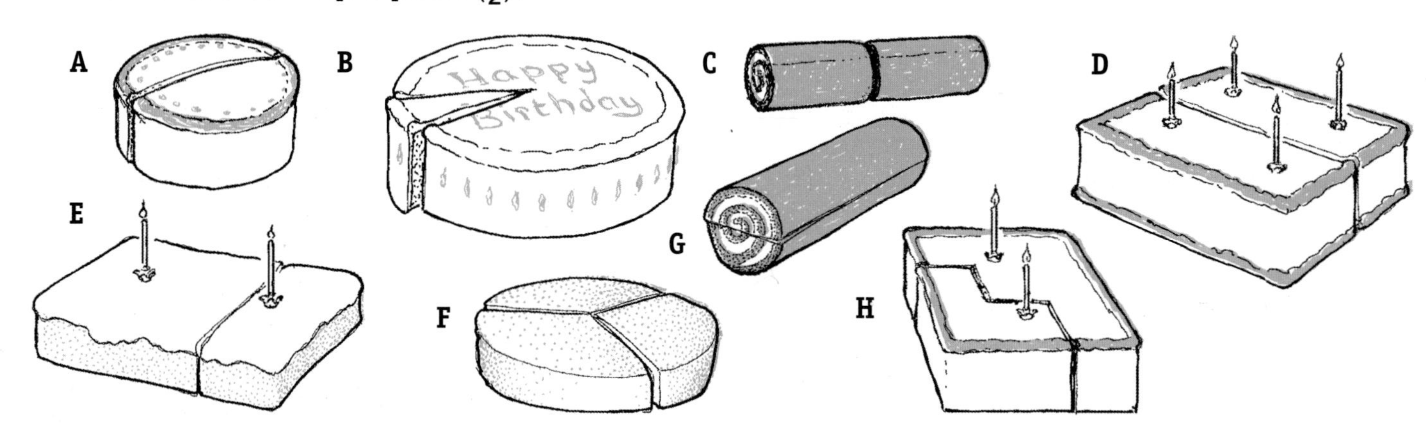

2 Which drawings show the food and drinks have been shared fairly into halves ($\frac{1}{2}$)?

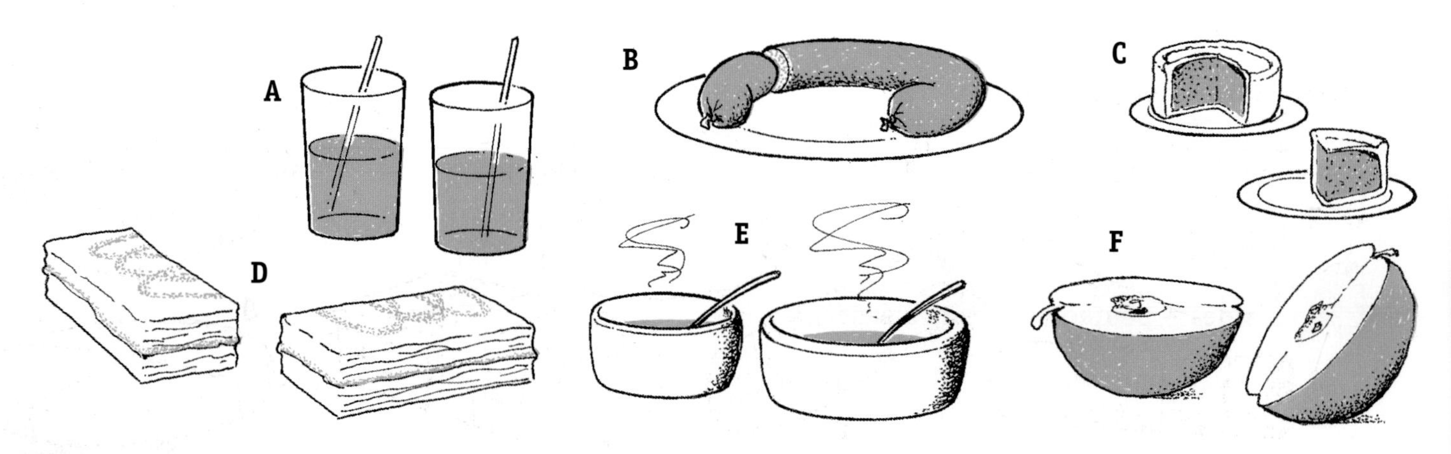

Jenny, Penny and Wendy are triplets.

When they share their birthday cake, it has to be divided into **3 equal** pieces.

They will each get $\frac{1}{3}$ of the cake.

Exercise 2

Which cakes show equal thirds ($\frac{1}{3}$)?

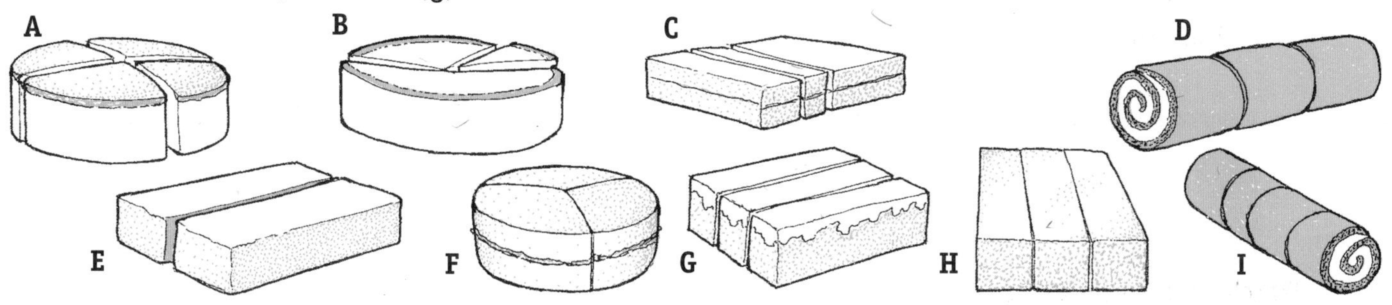

Holly, Polly, Tim and Jim are quadruplets.

When they share they have **4 equal** parts.

They will each get $\frac{1}{4}$ of the cake.

Exercise 3

Which cakes show equal quarters ($\frac{1}{4}$)?

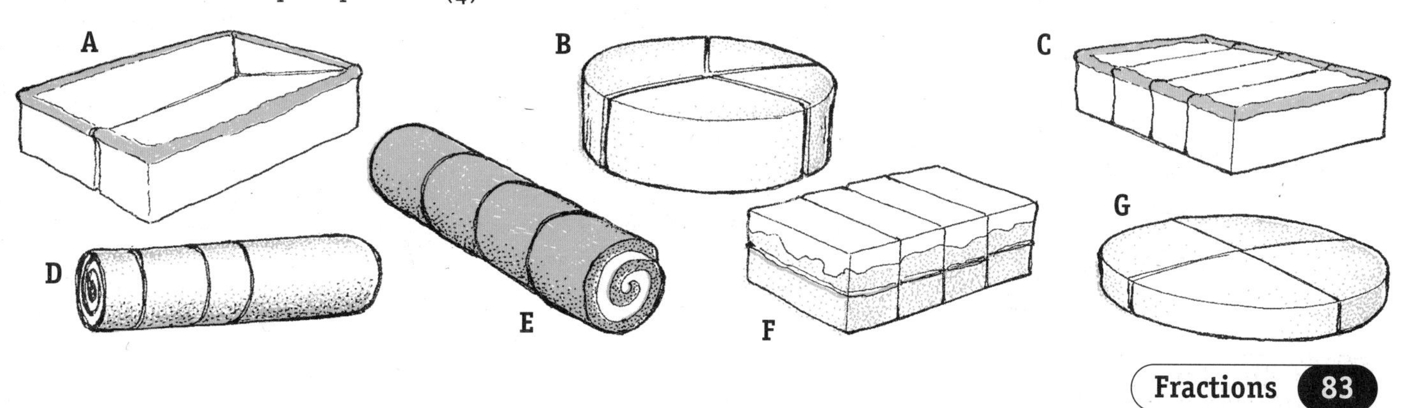

Exercise 4

Complete the three statements about **each** shape.
The first one has been completed for you.

1 

(a) This shape has been cut into **2** parts.
(b) **1** part out of **2** is shaded.
(c) The fraction shaded is $\frac{1}{2}$.

2 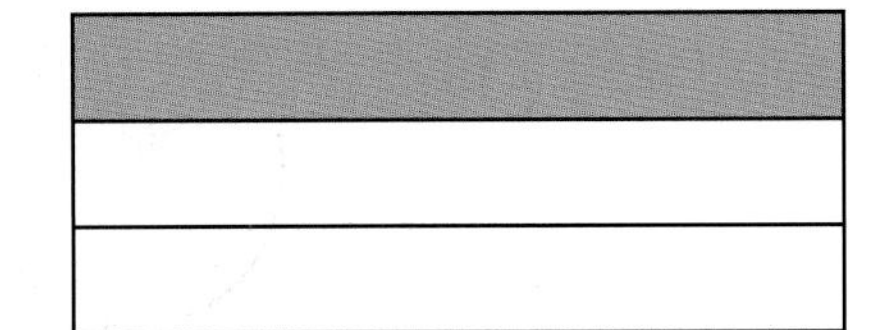

3 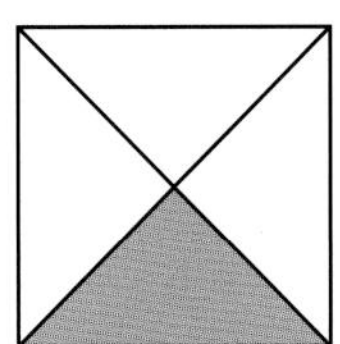

4 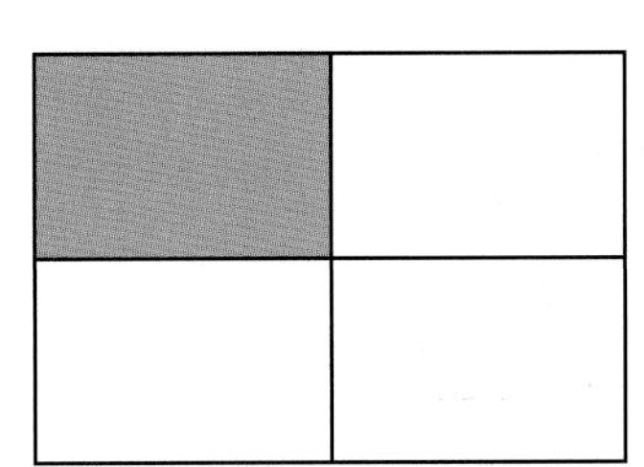

5 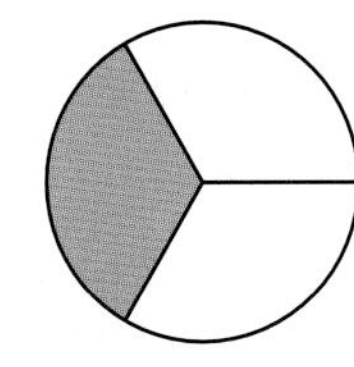

6 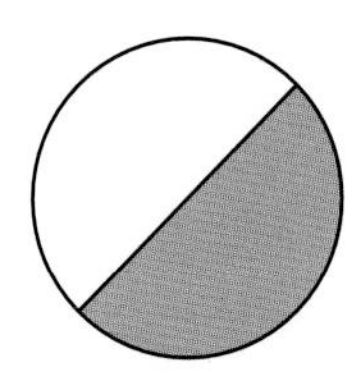

7 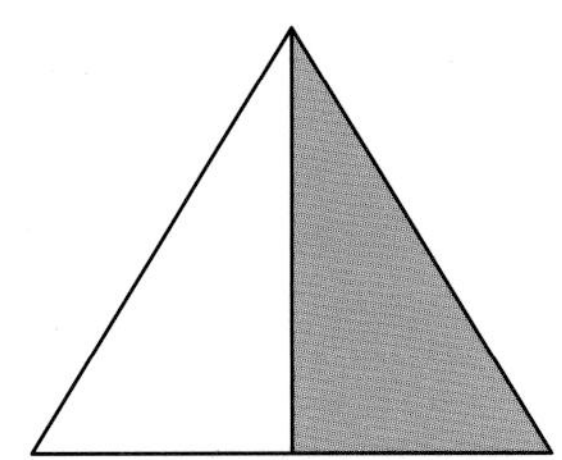

Exercise 5

Use $\frac{1}{2}$, $\frac{1}{3}$, or $\frac{1}{4}$ to complete these statements.

1 This glass is [?] full.

2 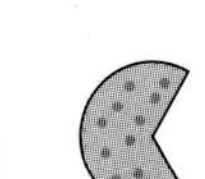 About [?] of this cake has been eaten.

3 About [?] of this drink is left.

4 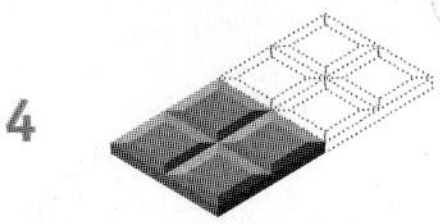 About [?] of this chocolate bar has been eaten.

Exercise 6

Match each drawing with its fraction.

$\frac{1}{2}$
$\frac{1}{3}$
$\frac{1}{4}$

1 

2 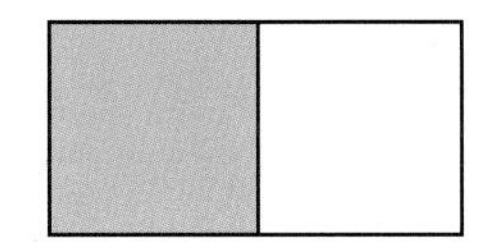

3 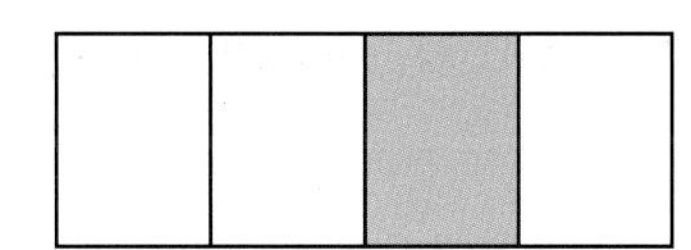

Exercise 7

Match each drawing with its fraction.

$\frac{1}{3}$
$\frac{1}{2}$
$\frac{1}{4}$

1 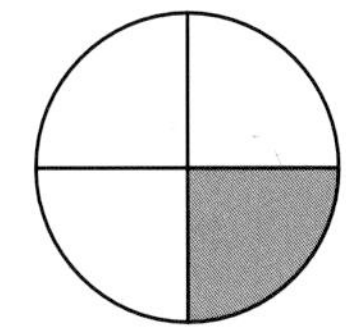

2 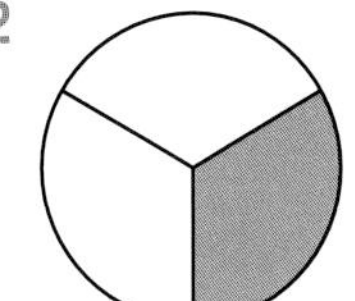

3 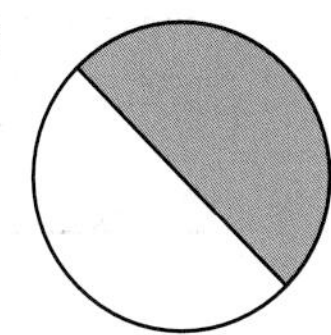

Exercise 8

What fraction of each shape is shaded?

1 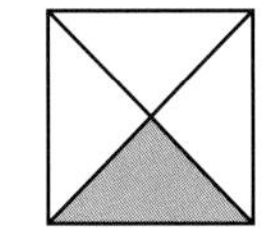

2 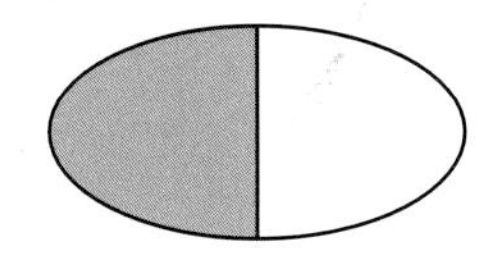

3 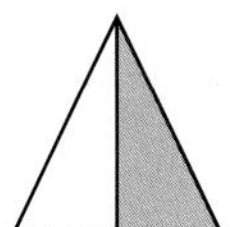

4 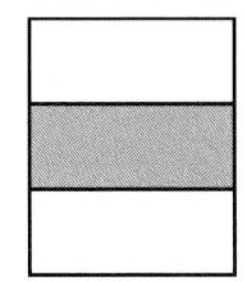

5 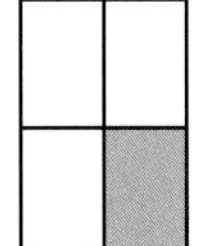

6 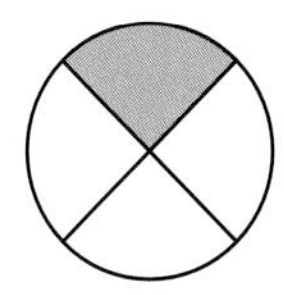

Exercise 9

Answer **yes** or **no** to each of these questions.

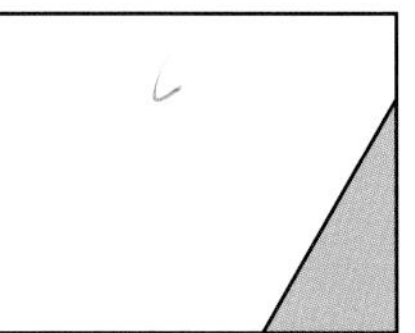
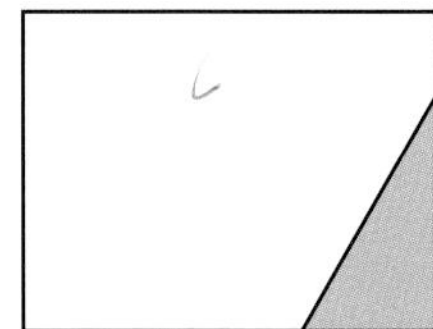

1 Is $\frac{1}{2}$ shaded?

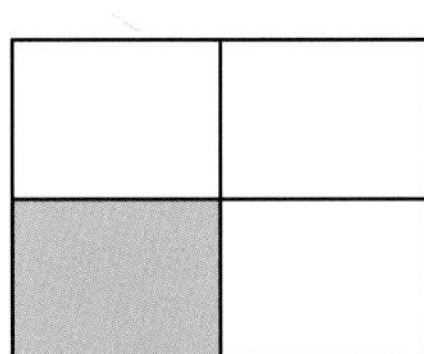

2 Is $\frac{1}{4}$ shaded?

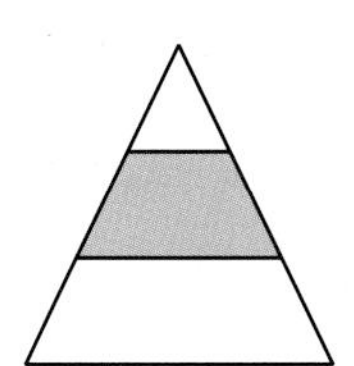

3 Is $\frac{1}{3}$ shaded?

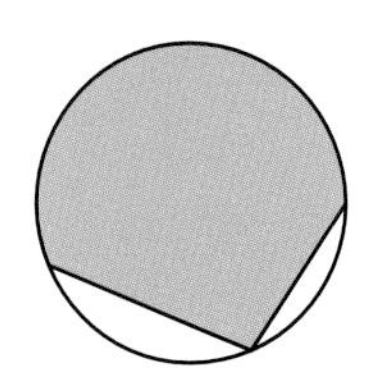

4 Is $\frac{1}{3}$ shaded?

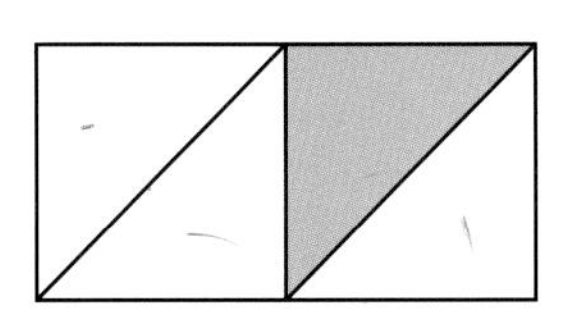

5 Is $\frac{1}{4}$ shaded?

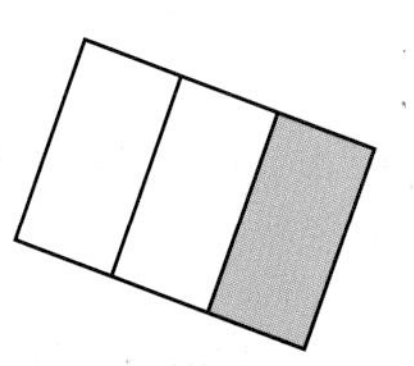

6 Is $\frac{1}{3}$ shaded?

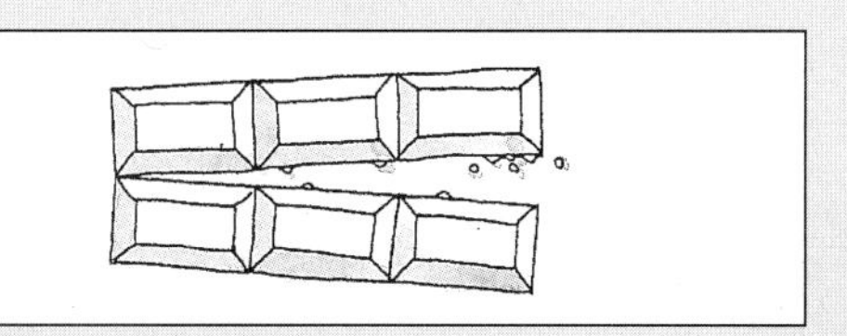

When this bar of chocolate is broken in $\frac{1}{2}$, **each half has 3 pieces.**

So $\frac{1}{2}$ of 6 = 3.

Exercise 10

When these bars of chocolate are broken in half, how many pieces will be in each half?
Write: $\frac{1}{2}$ *of this bar has* **4** *pieces.*

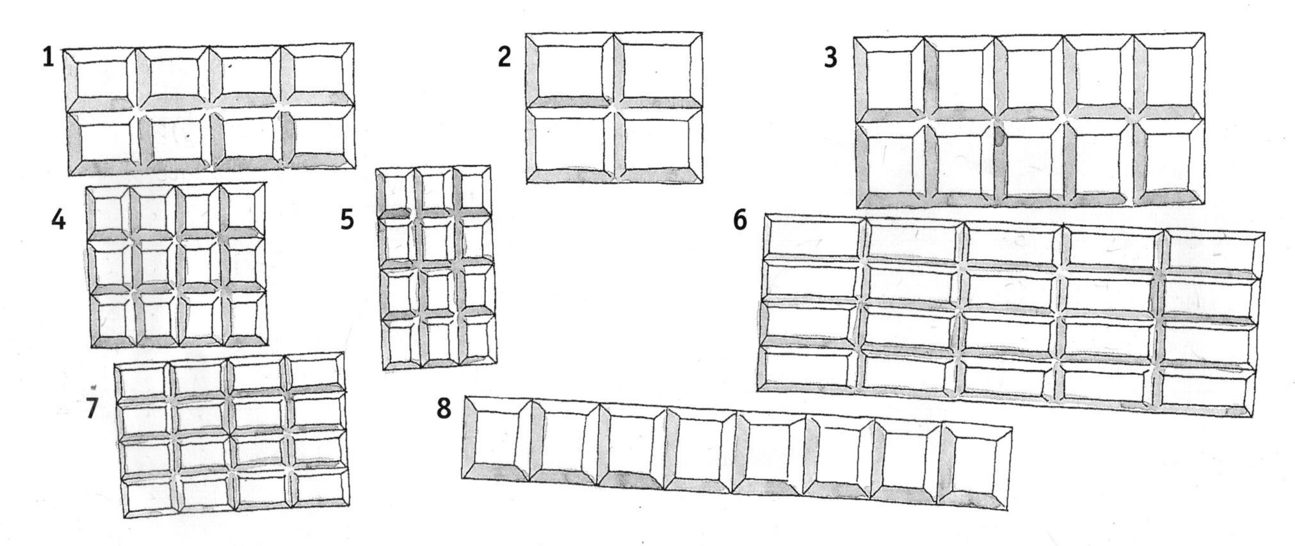

Exercise 11

Which of these bars do not break **exactly** into halves?

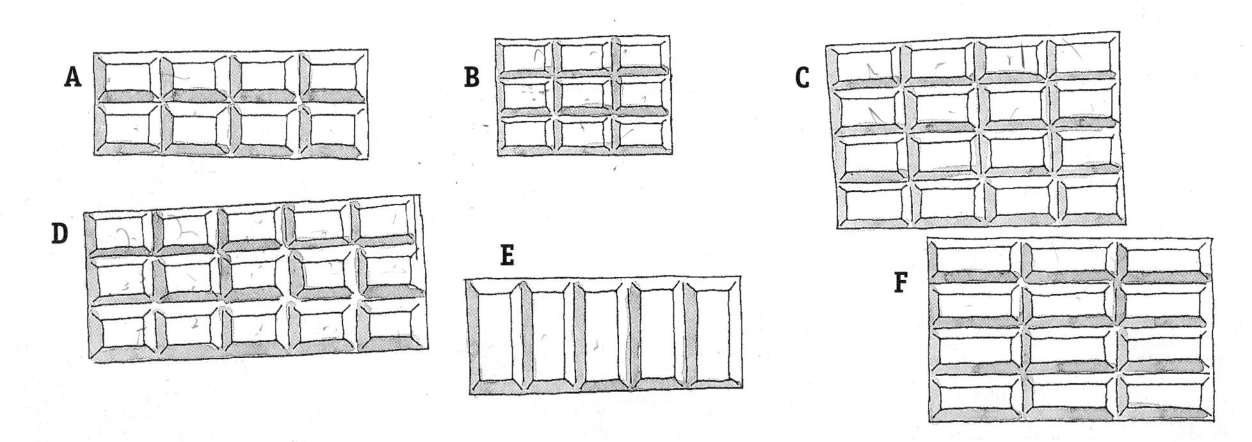

Exercise 12

Draw some more bars that will not break **exactly** into halves.

Roger and Jean have to learn to share groups of objects.
They share 6 crayons.

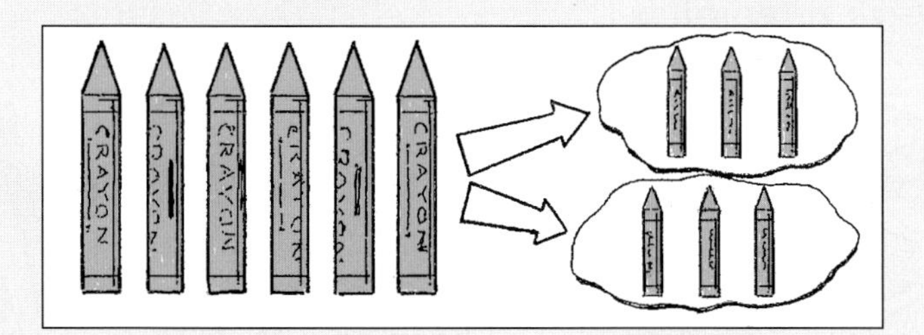

3 is half ($\frac{1}{2}$) of 6.

Exercise 13

The twins decide to share their presents. Which items have been shared exactly in half ($\frac{1}{2}$)?

Write: *The pencils have been shared into two halves*, or *The goldfish have not been shared into two halves*.

1 Goldfish

2 Pencils

3 £1 coins

4 Chocolates

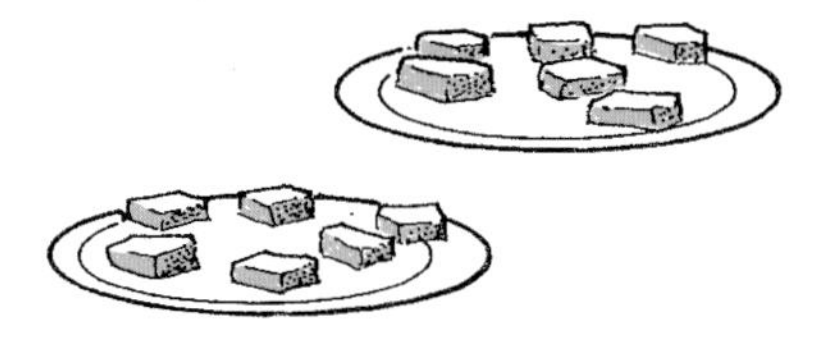

5 Cards

6 Balloons

Exercise 14

Share these items into halves. How many in each half?

1 Marbles

2 Boxes

3 Tennis balls

4 Bicycles

5 Pounds

6 Cards

7 (a) Suggest some amounts that will not share into halves.
(b) Explain how you chose the amounts.

Exercise 15

The groups of items below will be shared between the three sisters.
Complete each sentence to show how many each sister will get.

1 $\frac{1}{3}$ of 6 boxes is **2**.

2 $\frac{1}{3}$ of 9 pens is [?].

3 $\frac{1}{3}$ of 3 bottles is [?].

4 $\frac{1}{3}$ of 15 pound coins is [?].

5 $\frac{1}{3}$ of 12 sweets is [?].

6 When you find $\frac{1}{3}$ of an amount you share the amount into [?] equal parts.

Exercise 16

Share these items between 4 brothers. How many in each quarter ($\frac{1}{4}$)?

1 $\frac{1}{4}$ of these balloons is [?].

2 $\frac{1}{4}$ of these pencils is [?].

3 $\frac{1}{4}$ of these marbles is [?].

4 $\frac{1}{4}$ of these cakes is [?].

5 $\frac{1}{4}$ of these ice-creams is [?].

6 (a) Suggest 3 more amounts which can be divided exactly into $\frac{1}{4}$s.

(b) Explain how you chose the amounts.

Exercise 17

Find fractions of these amounts.

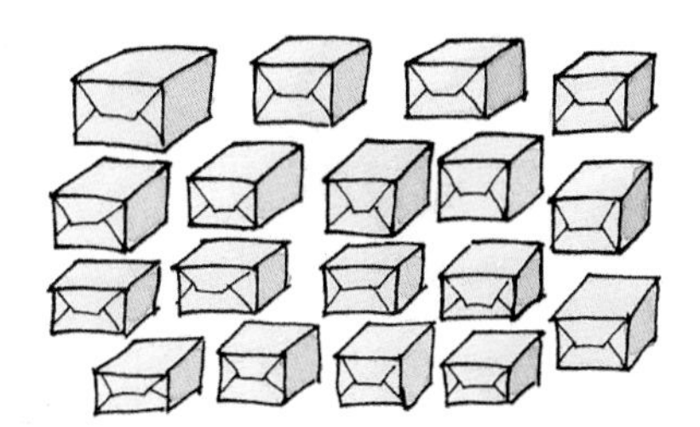

1 $\frac{1}{2}$ of these boxes are taken. How many are left?

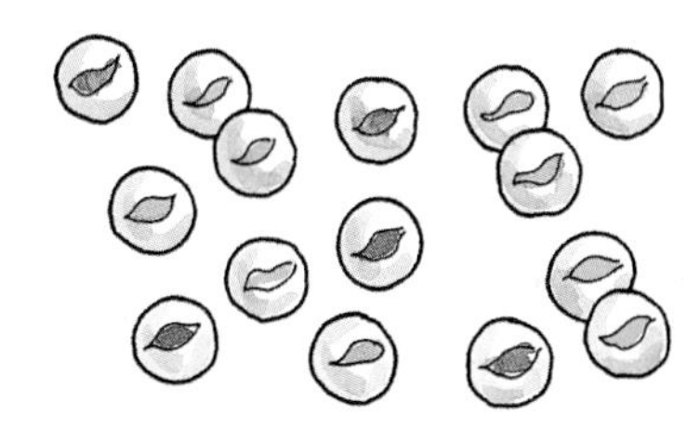

2 $\frac{1}{3}$ of these marbles belong to John. How many marbles belong to John?

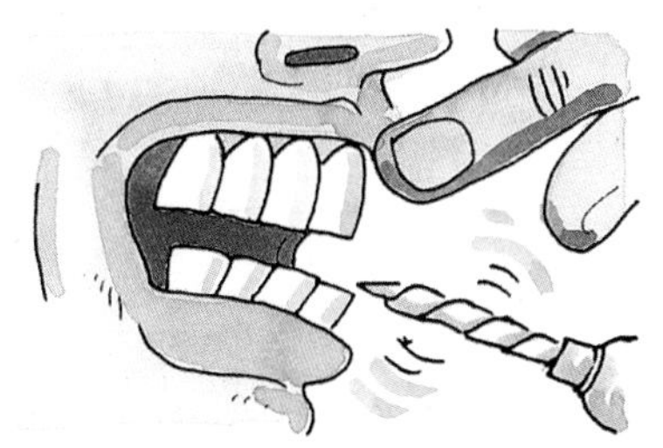

3 Roy has $\frac{1}{4}$ of these teeth filled. How many teeth are not filled?

4 $\frac{1}{2}$ of these radios do not work. What number of radios do not work?

5 $\frac{1}{3}$ of these candles get blown out. How many are left alight?

6 $\frac{1}{4}$ of these cakes are eaten. How many are left?

7 Think of some numbers that can be divided into half ($\frac{1}{2}$), exactly.

8 Find a number that can be divided into $\frac{1}{2}$s and into $\frac{1}{3}$s.

9 Find the missing numbers below. When you add each pair of numbers, $\frac{1}{3}$ of their total is **2**.

1	?

2	?

3	?

0	?

Key ideas

A **fraction** is an **equal** part of one or more items, for example 3 is one half of 6.

Writing fractions: $\frac{1}{3}$ means 1 ÷ 3 or 1 of 3 equal parts

$\frac{1}{4}$ means 1 ÷ 4 or 1 of 4 equal parts

We can find a fraction of an amount by dividing: half of 6 means 6 ÷ 2.

Chapter 12 Measurement (2)

Step-up

1 These children are doing tasks about measurement.
What sort of things are they measuring?

2 Do you think that the measurements below will be correct?

(a) (b) (c) (d)

3 How could you improve the accuracy of these measurements?

Measuring weight

Here are some units of weight.

Gram (g). Grams are used to measure very light objects.

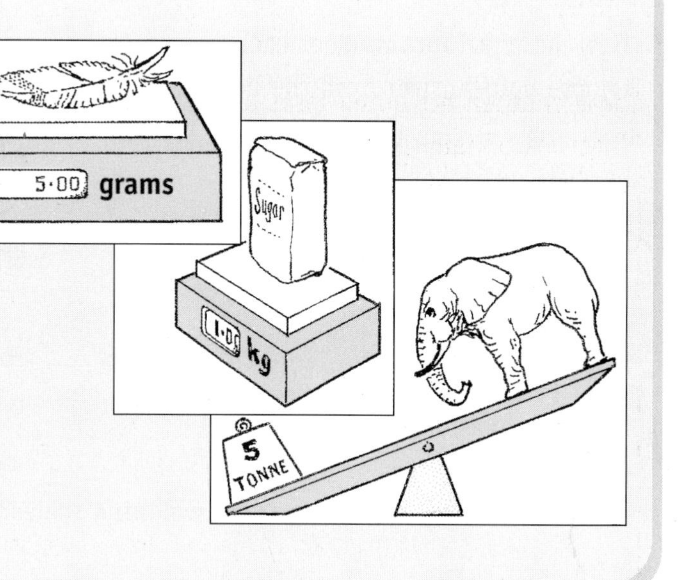

Kilogram (kg). 1000 grams = 1 kilogram.
Kilograms are used to weigh heavier objects.
A bag of sugar usually weighs 1 kilogram.

Tonne. 1000 kilograms = 1 tonne.
Very heavy objects are measured in tonnes.

Exercise 1

The weight of a product is often shown on the packaging.
Answer the questions about these products.

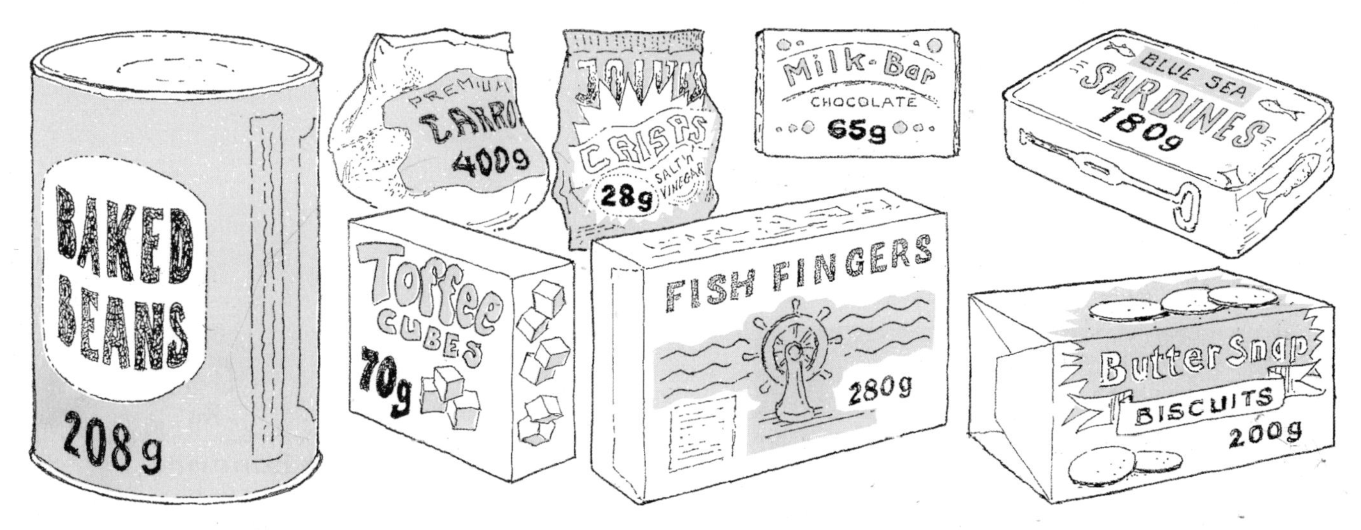

1. How many grams do the fish fingers weigh?
2. How much does the chocolate bar weigh?
3. How many grams do the biscuits weigh?
4. How much does the tin of beans weigh?
5. Which product weighs 400 g?
6. Which product weighs 70 g?
7. Which product is the heaviest?
8. Which product is the lightest?
9. Find the weight of two packs of carrots.
10. How much will half a pack of biscuits weigh?
11. A plastic carrier bag can hold 1 kg before it tears. Using the products above, how many different ways can you find to pack the bag without tearing it?
    Each time put as much as you can into the bag and list the products and their total weight.

Exercise 2

How many **kilograms** does each person weigh?
Choose your answer from the list below.

59 kg
110 kg
21 kg
385 kg

Sumo Sam Tom Jane Roy

Exercise 3

What weights are shown on these weighing scales?

1

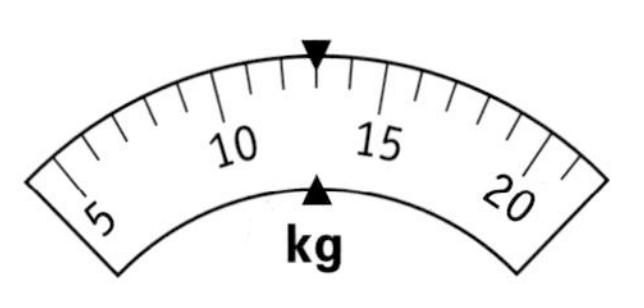

2

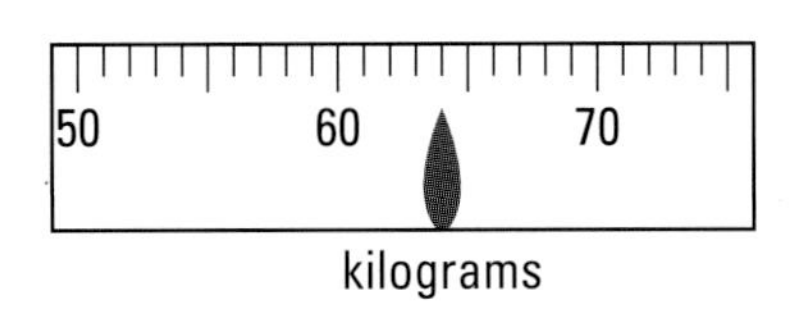

3

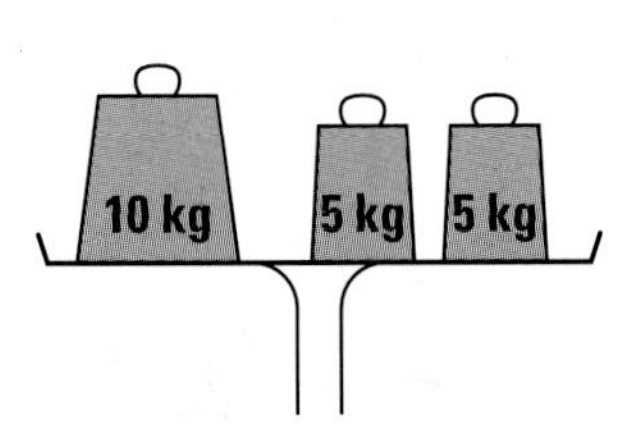

4

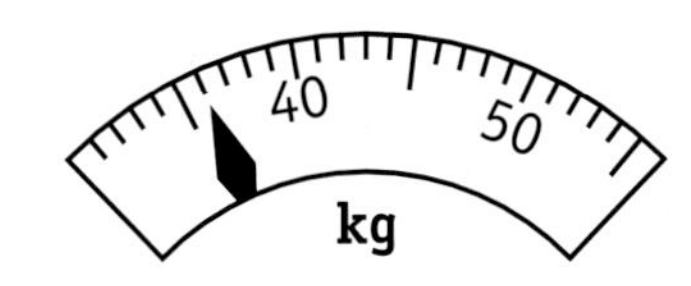

Exercise 4

Answer the questions about this shop display.

1 How much does **1 kilogram** of carrots cost?

2 How much would **2 kilograms** of carrots cost?

3 How much does **1 kilogram** of tomatoes cost?

4 How much does each bag of coal weigh?

5 How much would **2 kilograms** of bananas cost?

6 How much does each bag of onions weigh?

7 How much does **1 kilogram** of peppers cost?

8 What could you buy for **exactly** £1.00?

All of these amounts weigh **1000 grams** which is the same as **1 kilogram**.

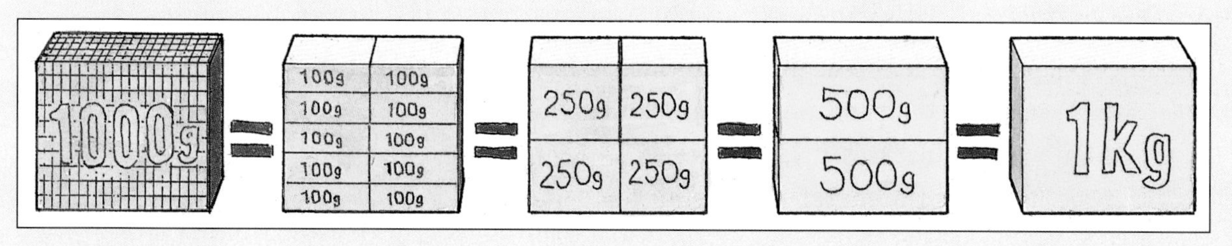

Exercise 5

How many grams have to be added to balance the scales?

1

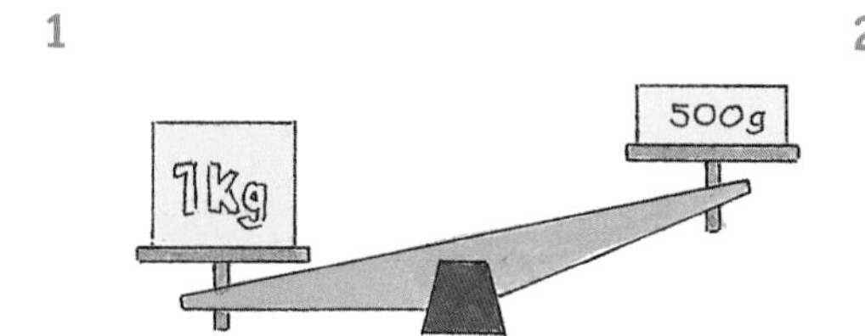

2

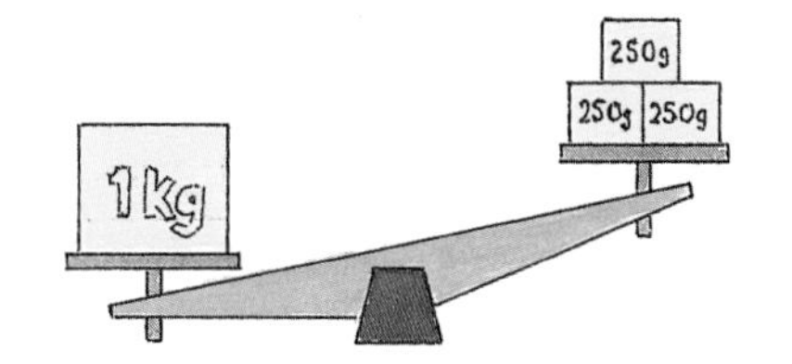

3

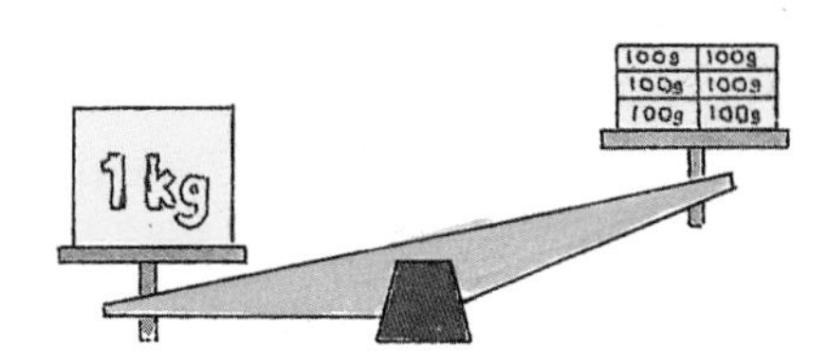

4

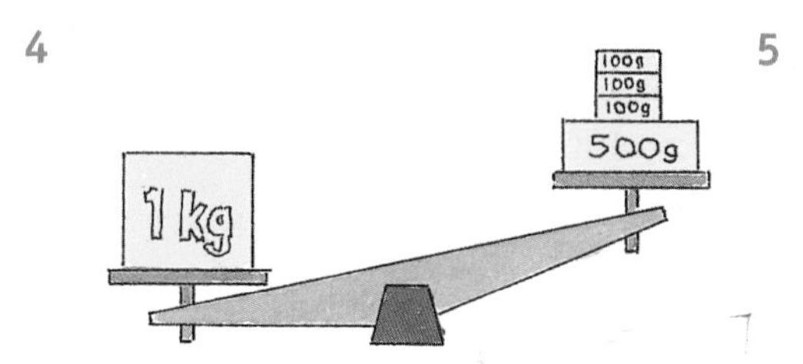

5

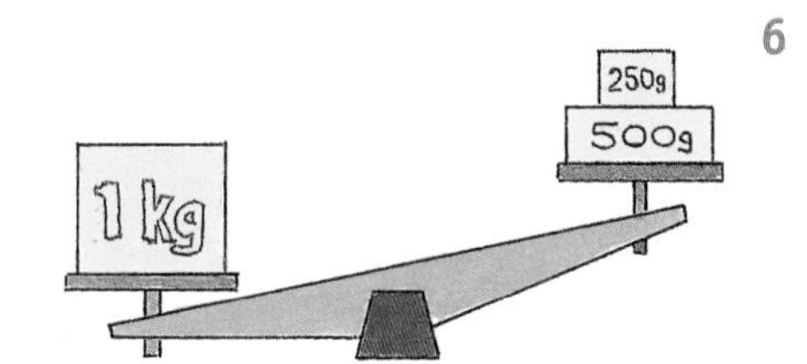

6

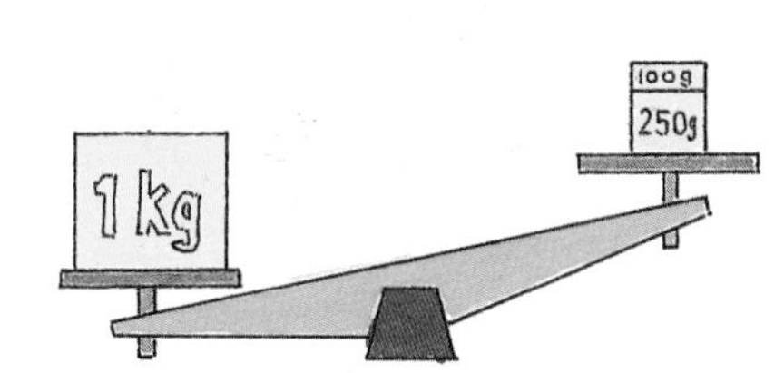

Exercise 6

How much does the unmarked box weigh in each of these?

1

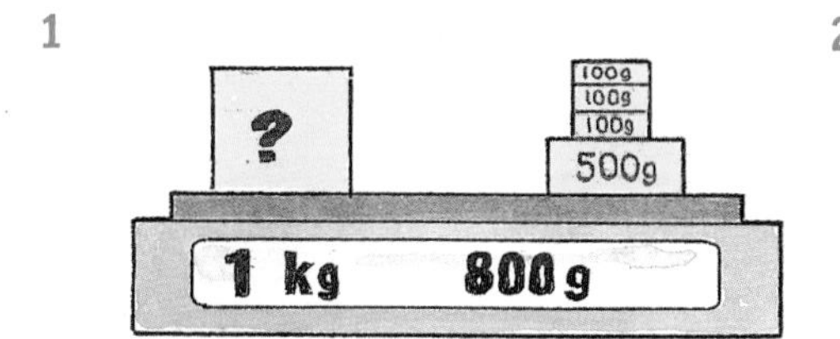

2

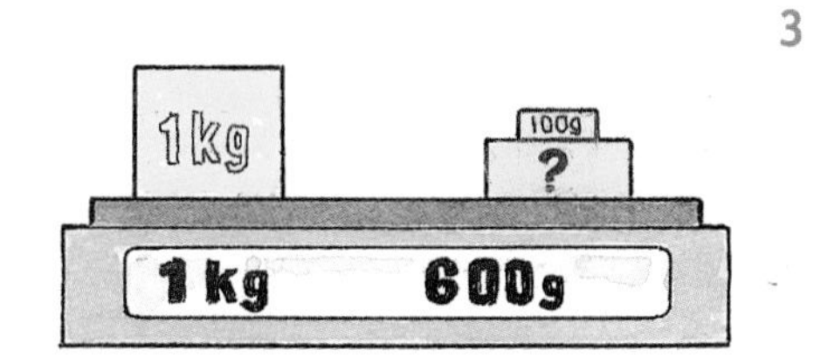

3

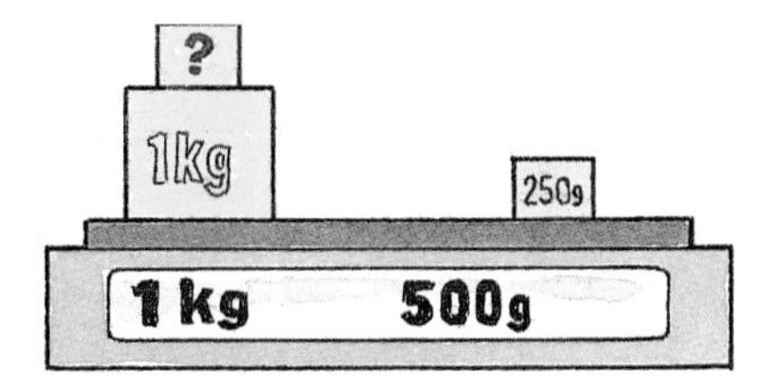

4

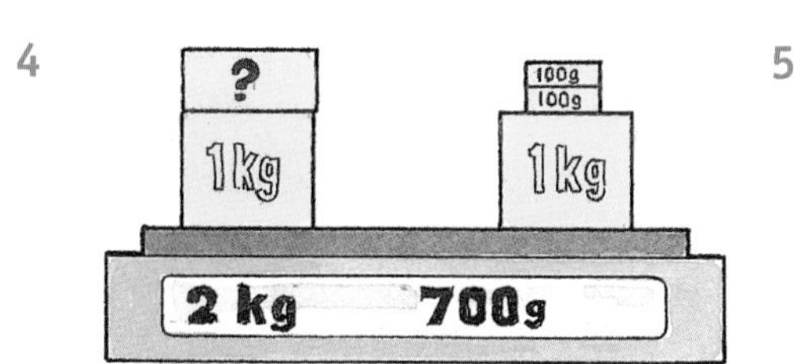

5

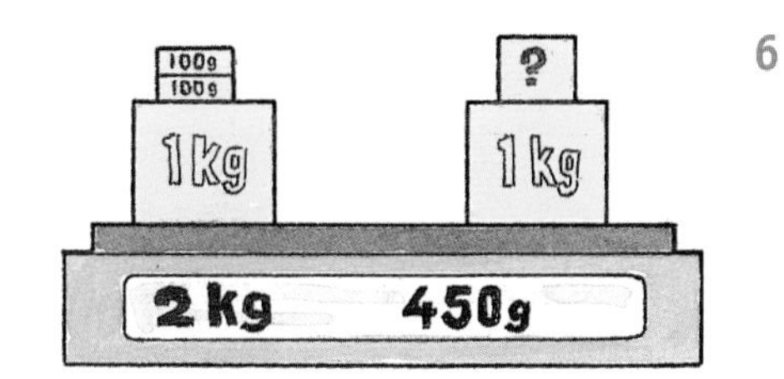

6

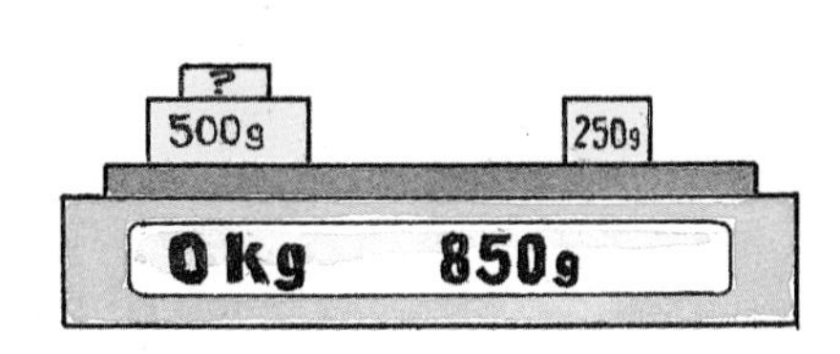

Measuring temperature

Temperature is a measurement of heat – how hot or cold it is.
We measure temperature in **degrees Celsius.**
We write it like this: **°C.**
We use a **thermometer** to measure temperature.

Using degrees Celsius we know that at 100 °C water boils, and at 0 °C water freezes.

Exercise 7

Here is a thermometer.
It is numbered in 10-degree intervals.
Each small division line on the scale stands for one degree.

1 What is the temperature at **A**?
2 What is the temperature at **B**?
3 What is the temperature at **C**?
4 What is the temperature at **D**?
5 What would happen to water at 0 °C?
6 What would happen to water at 100 °C?

Exercise 8

Match the correct temperature to each picture. Here are the four temperatures:
A $^{-}5$ °C (5° below zero) **B** 8 °C **C** 45 °C **D** 100 °C

1 

2 

3 

4 

Normal body temperature is about 37 °C.

If your temperature is a few degrees higher than this you have a fever.

If it is a few degrees lower you have hypothermia (your body is dangerously cold).

Exercise 9

1 Which of these thermometers show temperatures **above** 37 °C?

2 Which of these thermometers show temperatures **below** 37 °C?

A B C D E F

Exercise 10

The weather report shows the temperatures in six places around the world.
Which city goes with which thermometer?

1

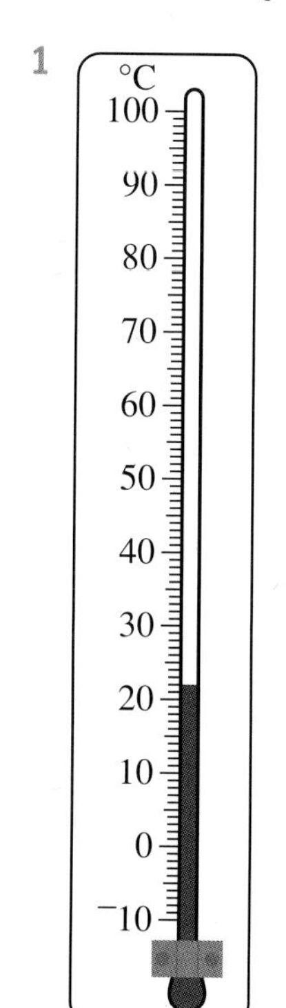

2

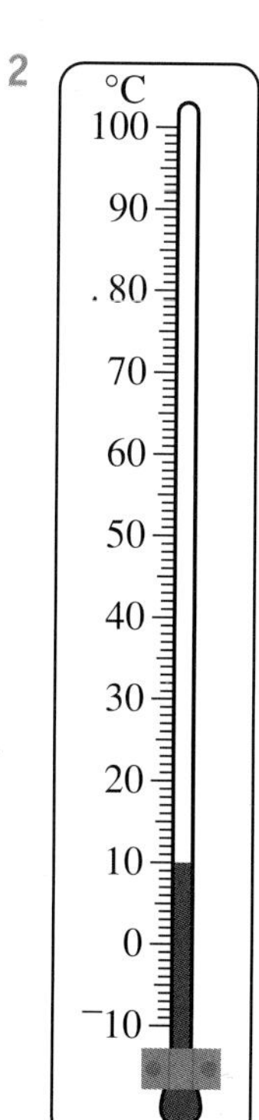

3 4

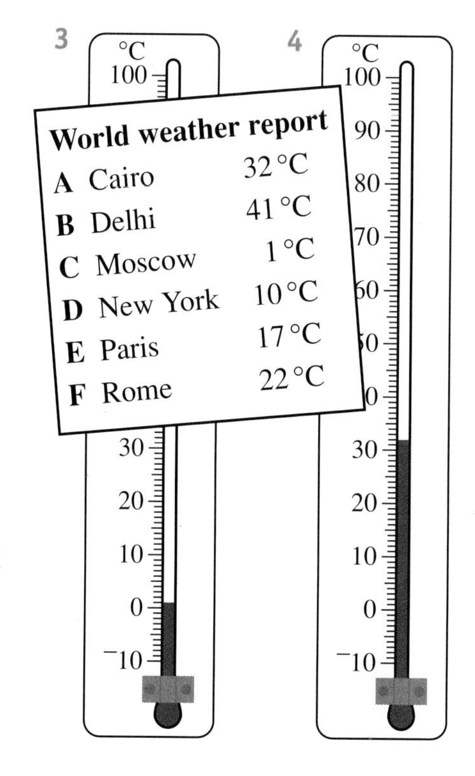

World weather report

A	Cairo	32 °C
B	Delhi	41 °C
C	Moscow	1 °C
D	New York	10 °C
E	Paris	17 °C
F	Rome	22 °C

5

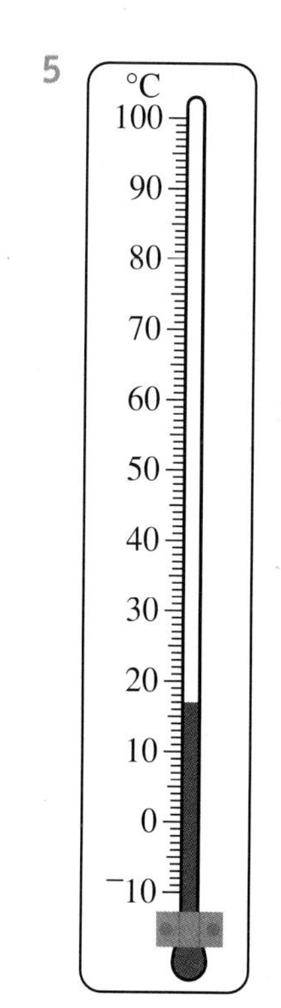

6

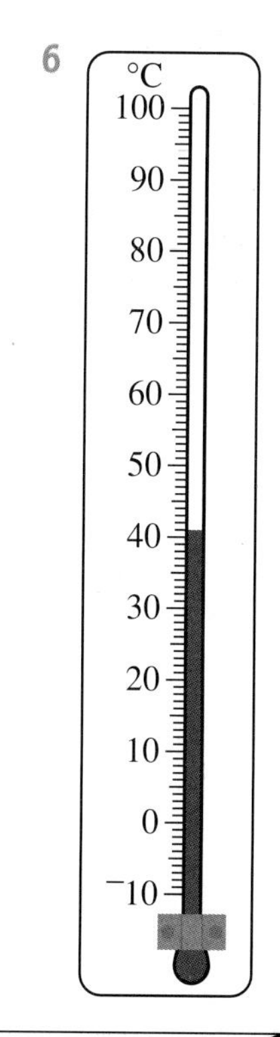

Exercise 11

Here are 10 temperature readings from a thermometer.
Write the temperatures shown. Remember to use **°C**.

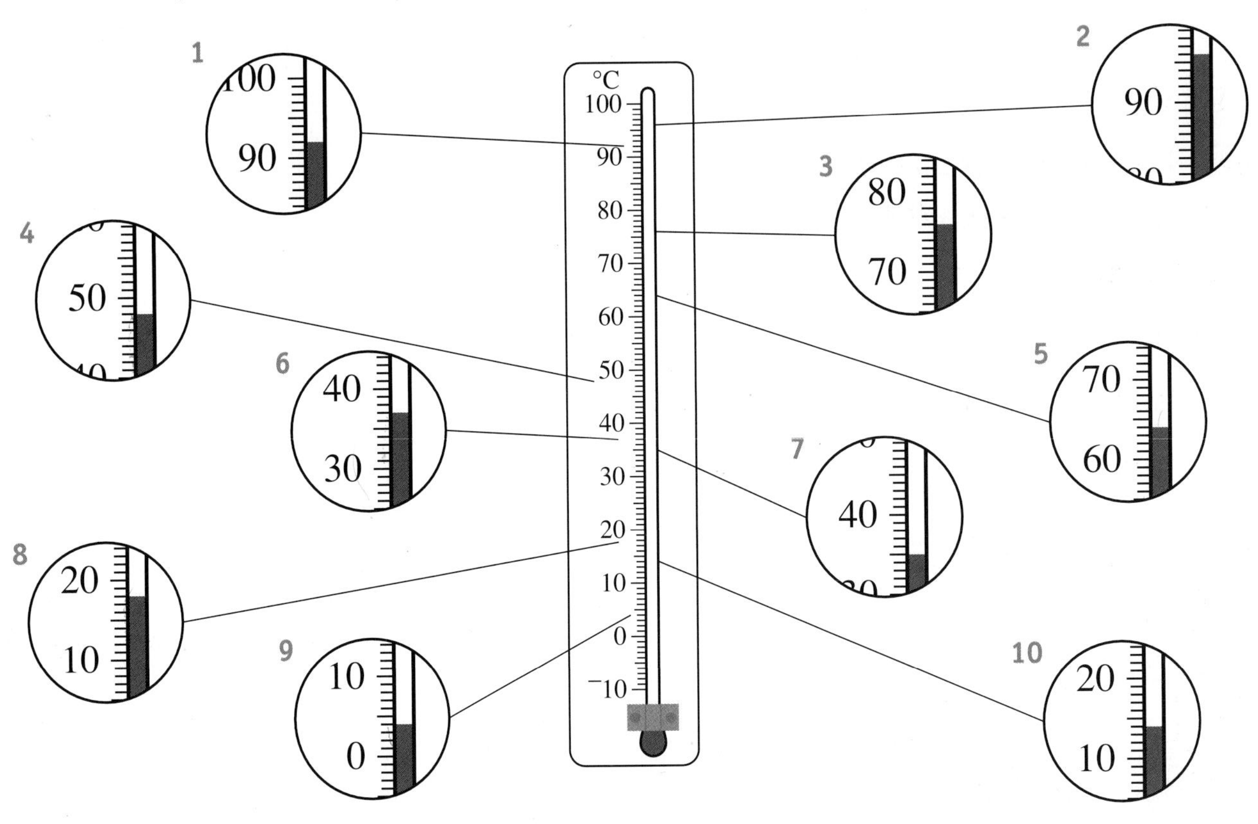

Exercise 12

Answer these questions.

1 The temperature is 10 °C. It goes **up** by 4 degrees. What is the new temperature?

2 The temperature is 21 °C. It goes **up** by 7 degrees. What is the new temperature?

3 The temperature is 15 °C. It goes **down** by 5 degrees. What is the new temperature?

4 The temperature is 11 °C. It goes **down** by 6 degrees. What is the new temperature?

5 It is 22 °C in Paris and 31 °C in Rome. What is the difference in temperature?

6 Write these temperatures in order. Start with the coldest.

15 °C **27 °C** **2 °C** **37 °C** **19 °C** **11 °C**

7 What happens to water when its temperature drops below 0 °C?

8 (a) Put these words in order. Start with the coldest.

cool **hot** **freezing** **mild** **sweltering** **cold**

(b) Now match these temperatures to the words above.

−5 °C **40 °C** **18 °C** **3 °C** **10 °C** **30 °C**

Measuring time

There are many different units used for measuring time. Here are some of them:

seconds **minutes** **hours** **days** **weeks** **years**

Exercise 13

Choose the best unit to measure each of these.

1 Your age. (seconds – days – years)

2 The length of your summer holiday. (hours – weeks – years)

3 The time taken to boil an egg. (seconds – minutes – hours)

4 The time taken to run a 100 metre sprint. (seconds – minutes – hours)

5 The amount of time you sleep each night. (minutes – hours – days)

Clocks are used to measure time.

The long hand on this clock is the **minute hand**. It counts the **minutes.** When it goes once around the clock face then 60 minutes (or one hour) have passed by.

Each small division line is one minute.

The shorter hand is the **hour hand**. It counts the **hours.** When it goes once around the clock face then 12 hours have passed by.

The numbers show the hours.

Exercise 14

Match the correct time to each clock. Here are the eight clock times.

A	three o'clock	**B**	eight o'clock	**C**	five o'clock	**D**	two o'clock
E	six o'clock	**F**	ten o'clock	**G**	one o'clock	**H**	nine o'clock

1 

2 

3 

4 

5 

6 

7 

8 

Past the hour ... to the hour

The minute hand is $\frac{1}{4}$ of the way around the clock face.
It is $\frac{1}{4}$ **past the hour**.

The minute hand is $\frac{1}{2}$ way around the clock face.
It is $\frac{1}{2}$ **past the hour**.

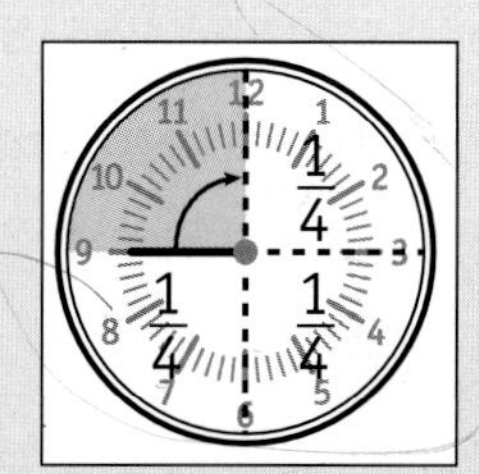

The minute hand is $\frac{1}{4}$ of a turn away from the hour.
It is $\frac{1}{4}$ **to the hour.**

Exercise 15

Copy and complete each sentence.

1 It is $\frac{1}{4}$ [?] 12.

2 

It is $\frac{1}{4}$ [?] 6.

3 

It is [?] past 2.

4 

It is [?] to 3.

5 

It is [?] 8.

6 

It is [?] 4.

7 

It is [?] 5.

8 

It is [?] 9.

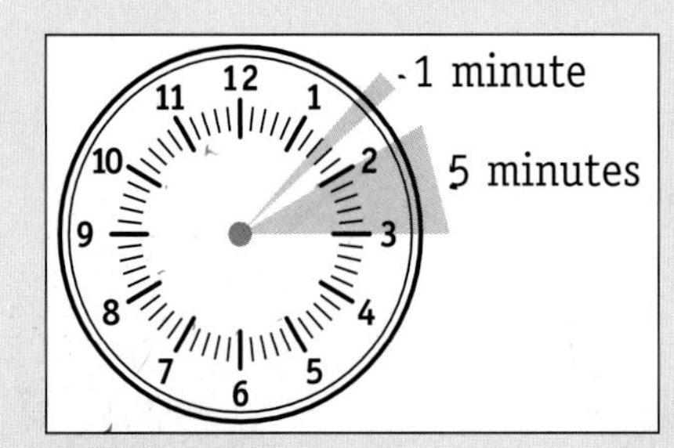

When the minute hand passes one small division then 1 minute has passed by.

When the minute hand passes from one number to another then 5 minutes have passed by.

Exercise 16

How many minutes **past** the hour does each minute hand show?

1 

2 

3 

4 

Exercise 17

How many minutes **to** the hour does each minute hand show?

1 

2 

3 

4 

Exercise 18

Answer these questions.

1 

How many minutes **past** 6 is it?

2 

How many minutes **past** 9 is it?

3 

How many minutes **to** 3 is it?

4 

How many minutes **to** 7 is it?

5 

How many minutes **past** 12 is it?

6 

How many minutes **to** 5 is it?

7 

How many minutes **past** 8 is it?

8 

How many minutes **to** 10 is it?

Exercise 19

How many minutes **to** six, or **past** six does each clock show?

1 

2 

3 

4 

5 

6 

7 

8 

Danny is going to meet Sarah at 8 o'clock.
But will they meet at 8 o'clock in the **morning**, or 8 o'clock in the **evening**?
She tells him, "We'll meet at **8 am**."
This means **8 o'clock in the morning.**

The hours from **12 midnight** to **12 midday** are described as **am**.

The hours from **12 midday** to **12 midnight** are described as **pm**.

Exercise 20

1 Record the times shown on this time line using **am** or **pm**.
Write: '(a) 3.00 am'

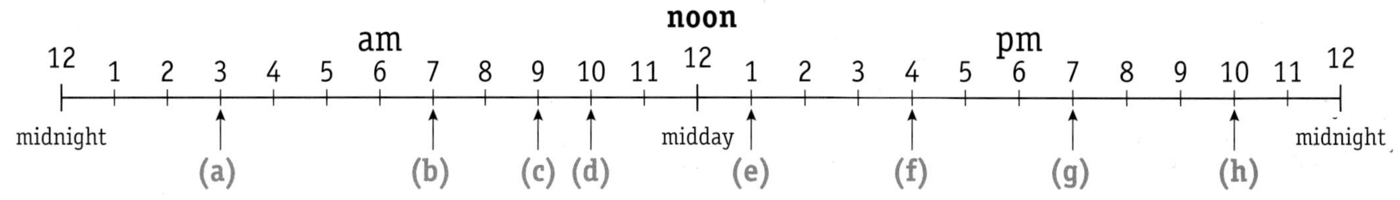

2 Would you usually be awake or asleep at:
(a) 2 pm? (b) 3 am? (c) 5 pm?

Exercise 21

Answer these questions. Use **am** or **pm** in your answers.

1 What time do you get up in the morning?

2 What time do your school lessons end each day?

3 What time do you go to bed at night?

4 What time does school start each day?

5 What time does lunch break start at school?

Exercise 22

Here are some moments from Liz's day at a holiday camp.

1 Are these events taking place **am** (morning) or **pm** (afternoon and evening)?
   (a) Breakfast (b) Go-karting (c) Horse riding
   (d) Dancing (e) Brushing teeth (f) Big Dipper

2 What is Liz doing at:
   (a) 8 am? (b) 8 pm? (c) 11 am? (d) 11 pm?

3 Write the time, using **am** or **pm**, that Liz is:
   (a) go-karting (b) having breakfast (c) waking up (d) on the Big Dipper

4 How many hours is it between Liz waking up and Liz horse riding?

5 How many hours is it between Liz having her breakfast and Liz dancing?

Key ideas

We measure weight in **grams (g)**, **kilograms (kg)** and **tonnes**.
(1000 g = 1 kg and 1000 kg = 1 tonne.)

We measure temperature in **degrees Celsius (°C)**. Water boils at 100 °C and freezes at 0 °C.

We measure time using many units – **seconds**, **minutes**, **hours**, **days**, **weeks**, **years**.
The hours between **midnight** and **midday** (night and morning) are called **am**.
The hours between **midday** and **midnight** (afternoon and evening) are called **pm**.

Chapter 13 Data Handling

Sorting and grouping

The oak tree goes into group **B**, because it belongs with the plants.

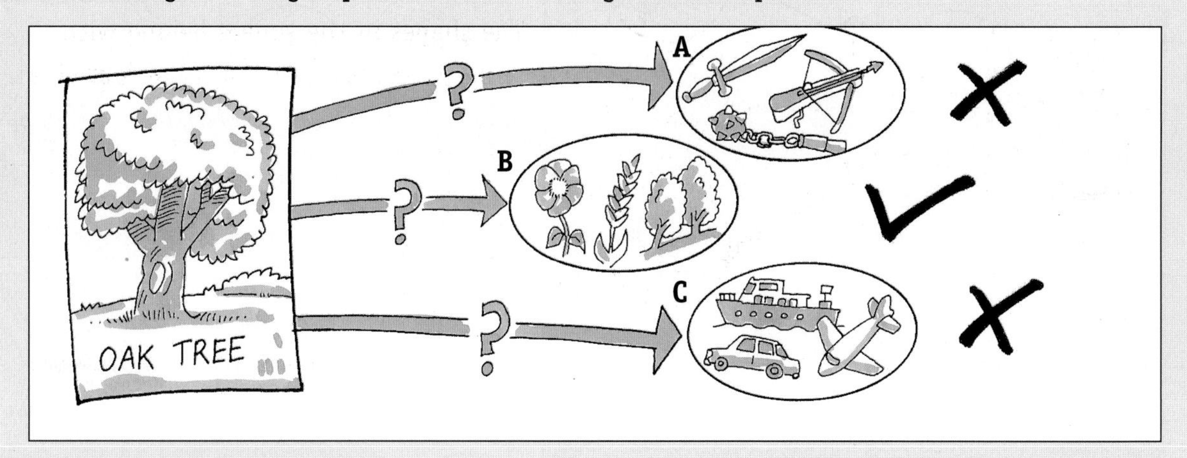

Exercise 1

Sort each object into the best group.

Write: '*The football belongs in group ...*'

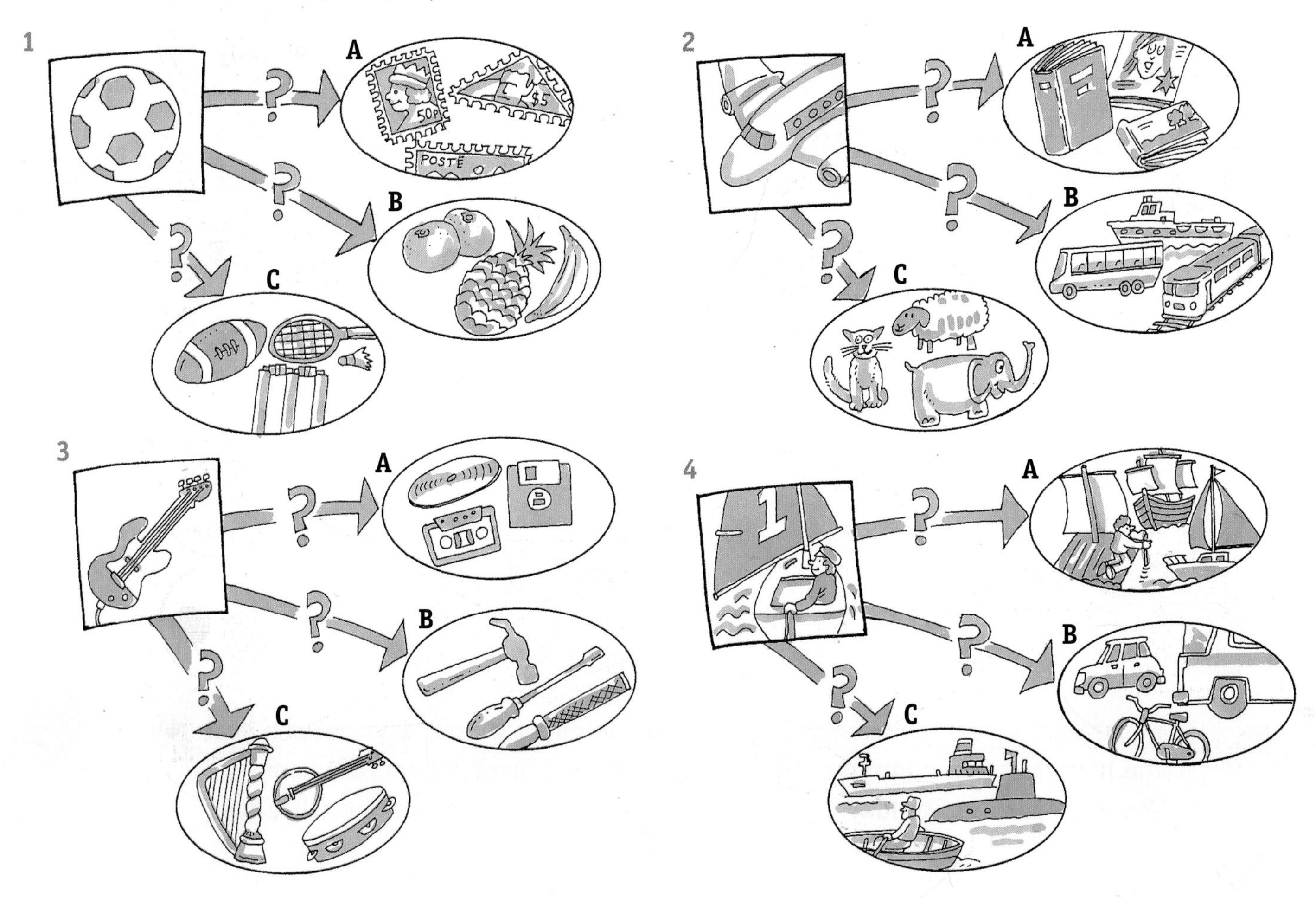

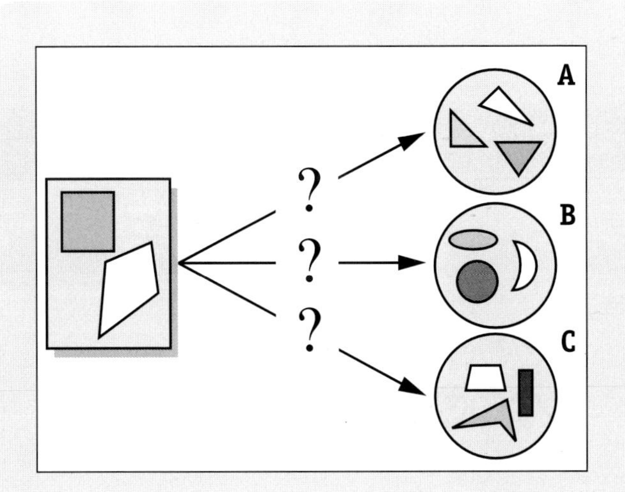

The shapes in the square belong with group **C**, because they all have four sides.

Exercise 2

Sort these shapes into groups.

Write why you think you have chosen the best groups.

Write: '*The shapes go into group … , because they …*'

1

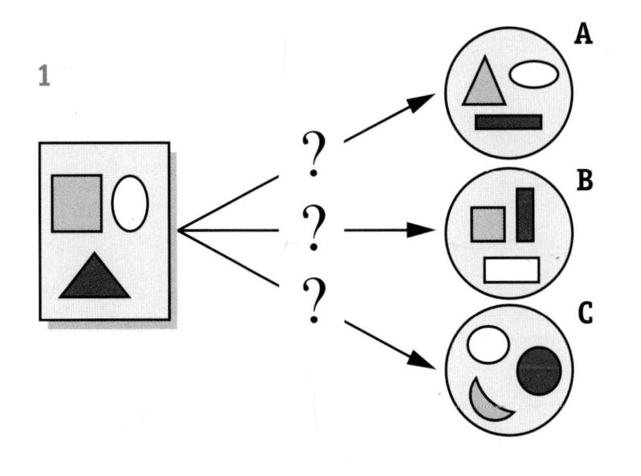

2

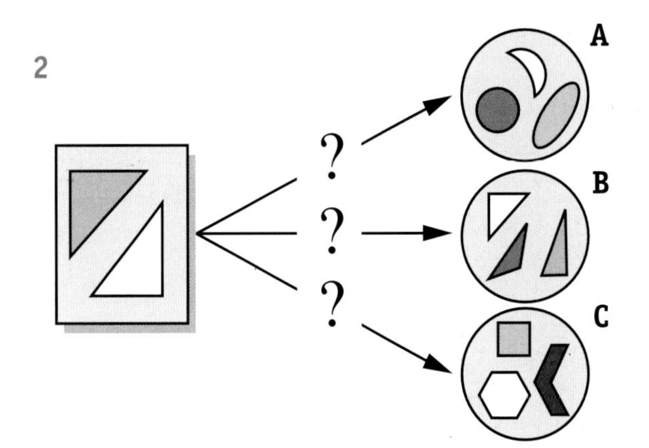

3

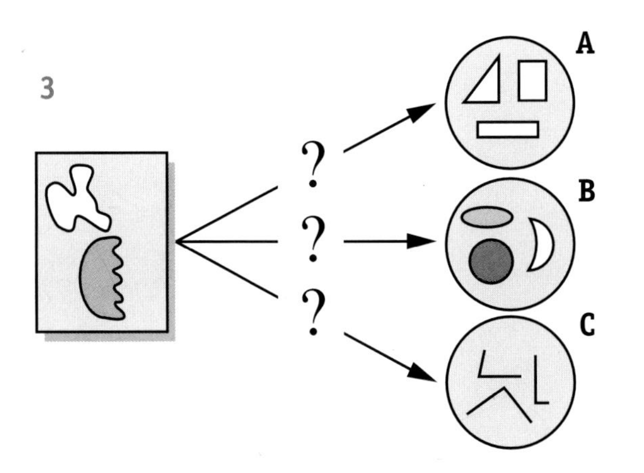

4

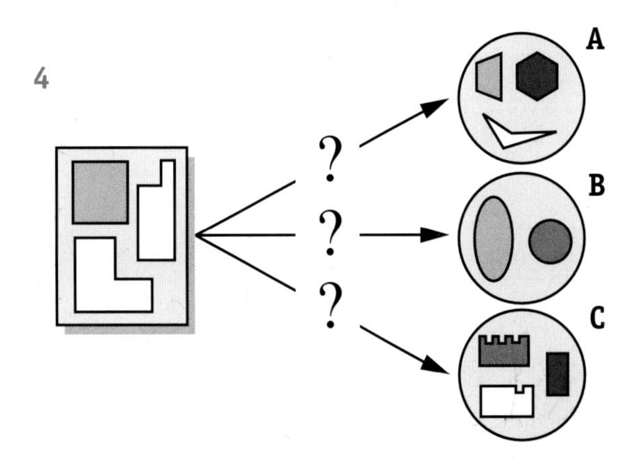

Counting groups

As we count objects, we can quickly note our results using a **five-bar gate**.

(3 sheep) = |||	(5 sheep) = 𝍸
(7 sheep) = 𝍸 ||	(10 sheep) = 𝍸 𝍸

Exercise 3

Here are 12 dots. As we count each dot we record it by putting one line on the **five-bar gate**. ● ● ● ● ● ● ● ● ● ● ● ● = 𝍸 𝍸 ||

Notice – when you record the fifth item you draw a line across the other four: 𝍸

Copy this table, and make a **tally** of the shapes on the left. The first one is done for you.

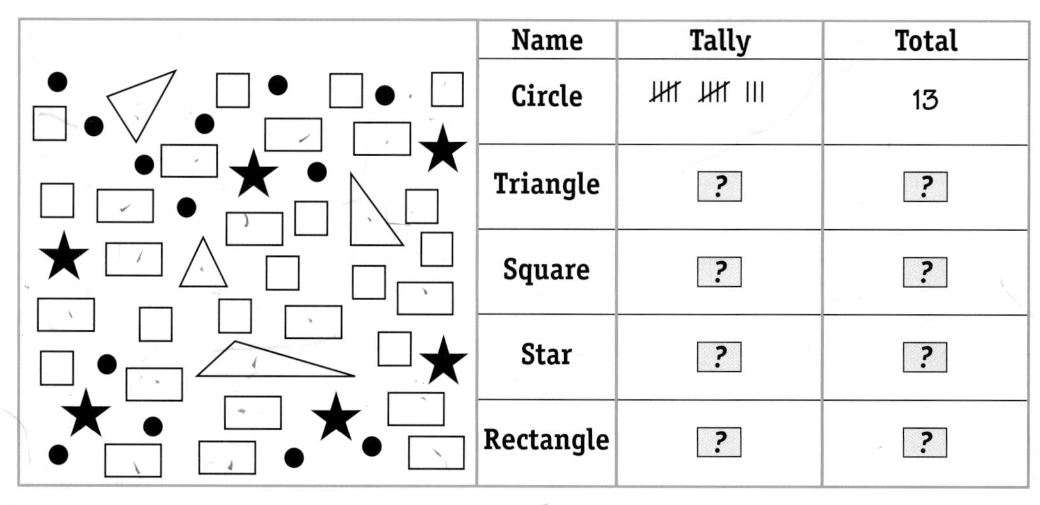

Name	Tally	Total
Circle	𝍸 𝍸 |||	13
Triangle	?	?
Square	?	?
Star	?	?
Rectangle	?	?

Exercise 4

Write these tallies as numbers.

1 𝍸 ||
2 𝍸 𝍸
3 𝍸 𝍸 |||
4 𝍸 𝍸 𝍸 ||
5 𝍸 𝍸 ||
6 𝍸 𝍸 𝍸 𝍸 ||||
7 𝍸 𝍸 𝍸 ||||
8 𝍸 𝍸 𝍸 𝍸 𝍸

Exercise 5

Show these numbers as tallies using 'five-bar gates'.

1 8
2 12
3 16
4 25
5 18
6 9
7 23
8 29

Exercise 6

Chris is ill with chickenpox! He decides to do some maths so that he does not fall behind in his work. Using a **tally chart** he records items from the picture below.

Copy and complete the tally chart.

Item	Tally	Frequency (total)
People	?	?
Birds flying	?	?
Doors	?	?
Windows	?	?

Exercise 7

He then looks around the kitchen and makes a tally of the items below.
Draw and complete a tally chart for these items: cups, jugs, plates, pictures.

Shelly has to sort out this pile of box files. She decides to group them by colour.

She then makes a tally chart.

Tally of box files		
Colour	**Tally**	**Frequency (total)**
Black	𝍸	5
Grey	𝍸 I	6
Blue	II	2
White	IIII	4

When she has sorted them by colour and piled them up, the box files look like this.

Next Shelly draws a **bar chart** to record and display the box files. The bar chart shows that there are **5 black** files, **6 grey** files, **2 blue** files and **4 white** files.

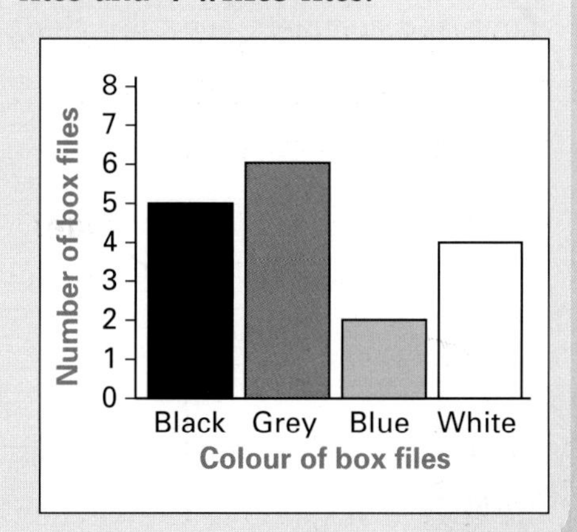

Shelly notices that the biggest group are the **grey** files. There are more **grey** files than any other colour. We call this the **mode**.

Exercise 8

Here is a bar chart for another group of box files. Answer the questions about this bar chart.

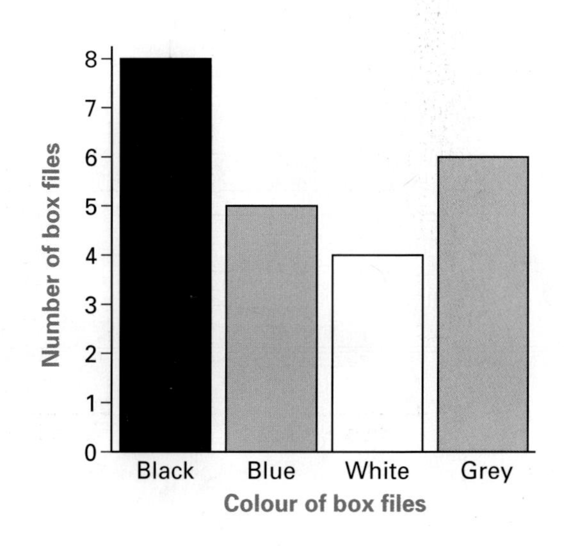

1 How many black files are there?

2 How many white files are there?

3 There are five files in one group. What colour are these files?

4 How many white **and** grey files are there altogether?

5 How many files are there altogether?

6 Which colour of file is the **mode**?

Exercise 9

Shelly has sorted out another group of box files. This time she has drawn a **stick diagram**.

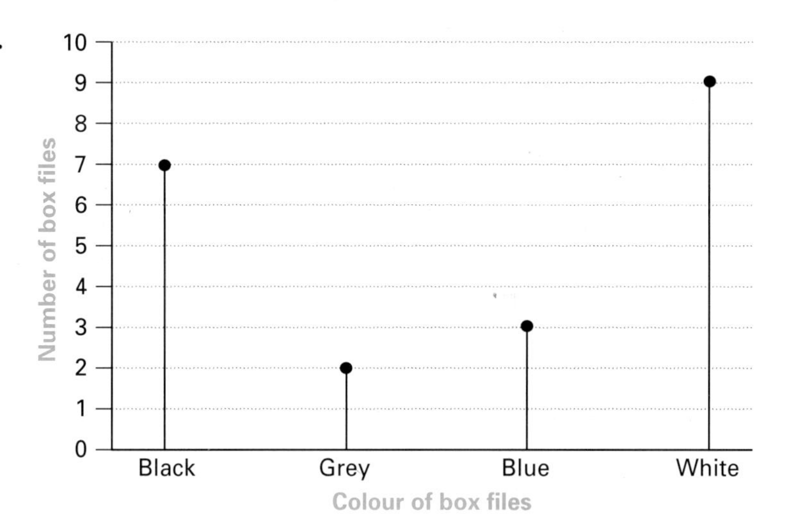

1 How many white files are there?

2 How many blue files are there?

3 There are three files in one group.
What colour are these files?

4 Which column (pile) has the most files?

5 Which column (pile) has the fewest files?

6 Which colour of file is the **mode**?

Exercise 10

1 Carefully copy the grid below.
On the **horizontal axis** (across the page) write the colours of the files.
Then number the **vertical axis** (up the page).
Draw the bar chart for this pile of box files.

2 Which colour of file is the **mode**?

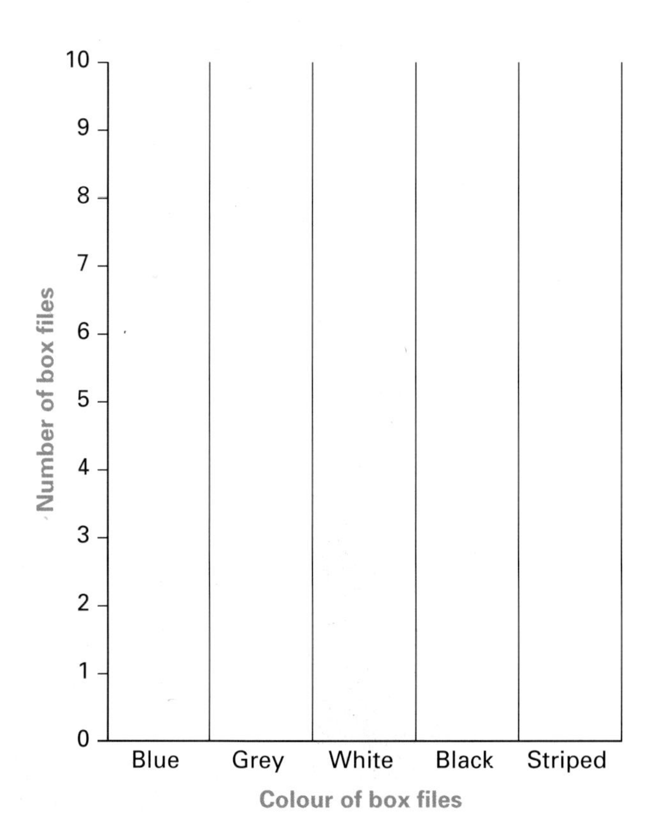

Exercise 11

Here is a bar chart which displays the number of pupils in each class of Shelly's year group.
Answer the questions about the bar chart.

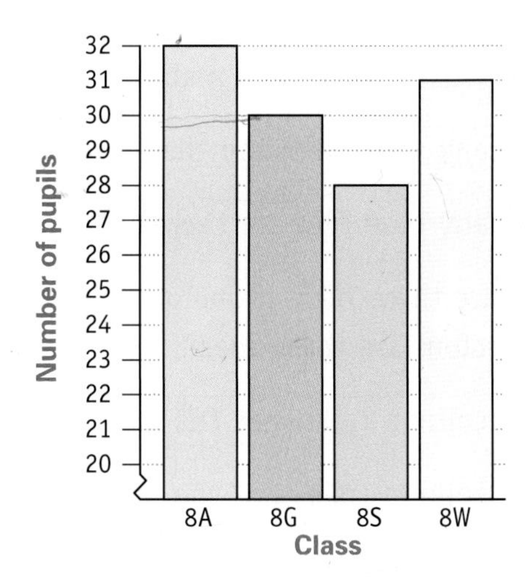

1. How many classes are there?
2. Which class has 28 pupils?
3. How many pupils are there in 8G?
4. Which class has the fewest pupils?
5. How many pupils are there in 8W?
6. Which class group is the mode?

Exercise 12

Use a **stick diagram** or a **bar chart** to display this information.

A survey of favourite foods	
7 people like burgers.	6 people like curry.
3 people like pizza.	9 people like Chinese food.

Exercise 13

Use a **stick diagram** or **bar chart** to display this information.

	A survey of favourite sports	
10 people like basketball.	9 people like hockey.	7 people like rugby.
4 people like tennis.	13 people like soccer.	2 people like swimming.

Exercise 14

1. Using this **stick diagram**, make a list of the ways that pupils come to school.
   Write: *8 pupils cycle to school* .
2. Which type of transport is the mode?

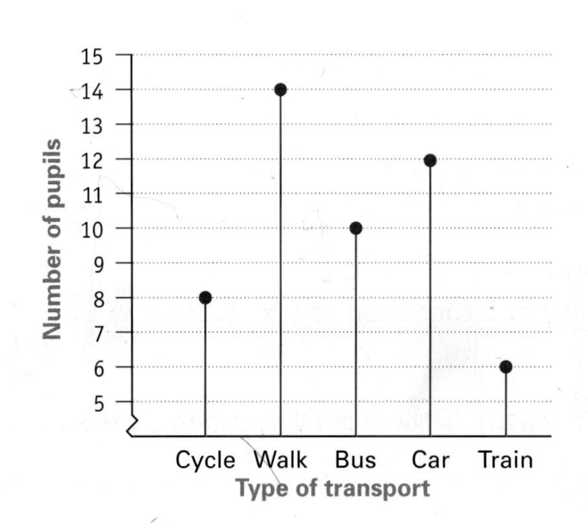

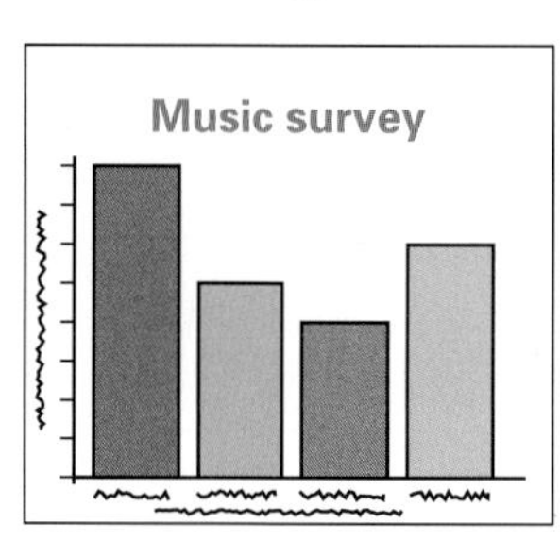

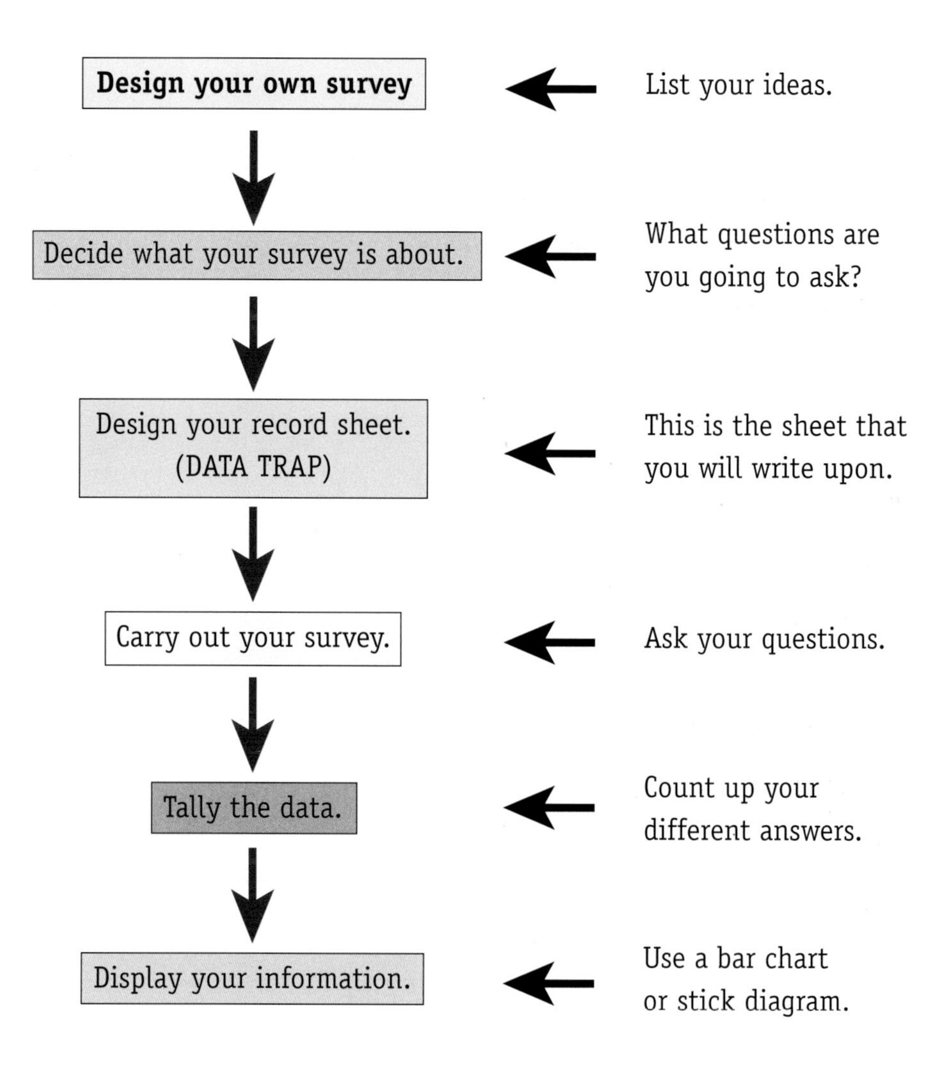

Key ideas

When you **sort** or **group** objects together, you find something that they have in common. You can have groups which have more than one thing in common.

When you **tally** you count in groups of five, like this: 𝍸𝍸𝍸 This is 15 counted.

Display is the way information is shown. Graphs show information quickly and easily.

Bar charts show how often something happens, or how often something is chosen.

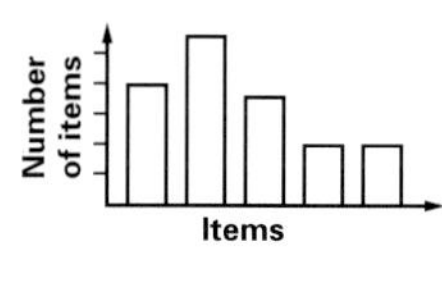

Stick diagrams show the same type of information as bar charts.

The **mode** is the biggest group in a collection.

Chapter 14 Ten Times Bigger

Step-up

Ten Singles or One Ten

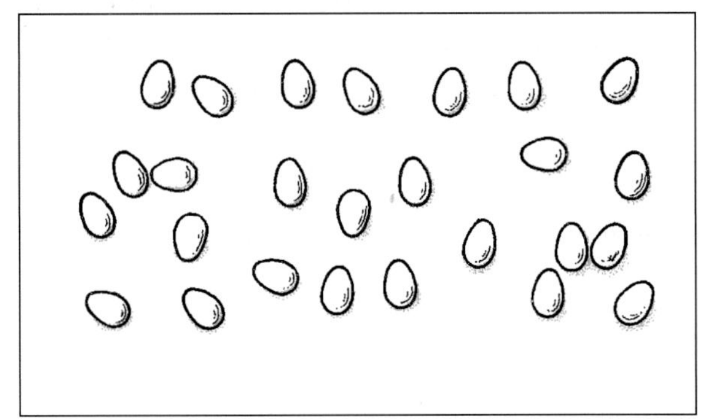

There are 26 single eggs in this pile.
They are packed into '**10s boxes**'.

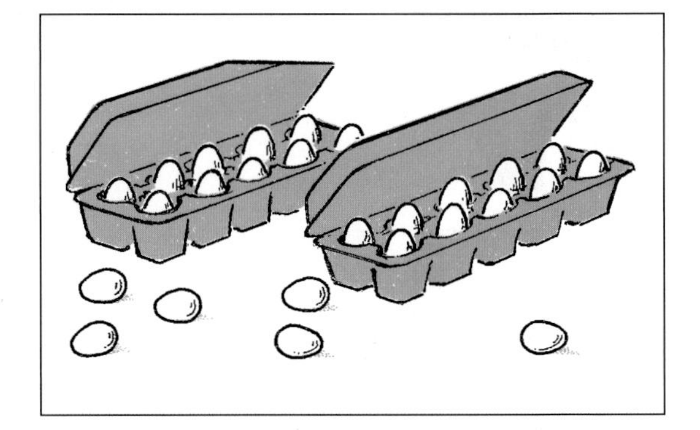

Two '**10s boxes**' are needed.
There are 6 single eggs left over.

Sort these eggs into boxes of ten. Draw **simple** drawings like the example below to show the '**10s boxes**' and the **single** eggs left over. The first one has been done for you.

26 eggs [10] [10] 0 0 0 0 0 0

1	26 eggs	2	32 eggs	3	41 eggs	4	13 eggs	5	66 eggs
6	20 eggs	7	50 eggs	8	39 eggs	9	17 eggs	10	99 eggs

Hundreds	Tens	Units	
2	3	**6**	The **6** stands for **6**; it is placed in the **units** column.
7	**2**	1	The **2** stands for **20**; it is placed in the **tens** column.
4	5	7	The **4** stands for **400**; it is placed in the **hundreds** column.

Write how much the **bold** figure is worth in each number.

1	1**3**	2	**7**9	3	**5**5	4	8**6**	5	**6**2
6	**3**32	7	**7**90	8	**5**51	9	**1**86	10	**6**62

Counting in Tens

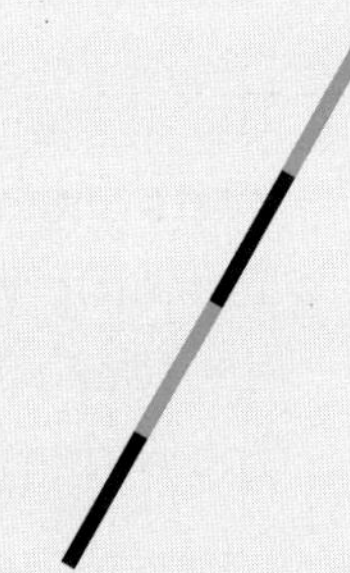

Mick has made a square by using 4 straws. Each straw is 10 cm long.

If Mick put 4 straws into a straight line they would measure 40 cm.

10 + 10 + 10 + 10 = 40

Exercise 1

Each straw is 10 cm long. What will be the length of each line?
Draw the lines into your book and write how long they would be.

1

2

3

4

5

6

Exercise 2

Mick has made these shapes using the straws. If he places the straws into straight lines, how long will each line be? Remember, each straw is 10 cm long.

1 

2 

3 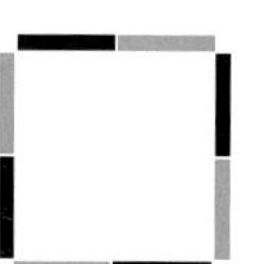

4 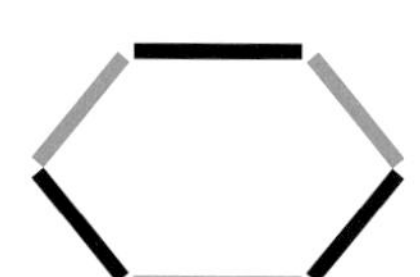

5 

6 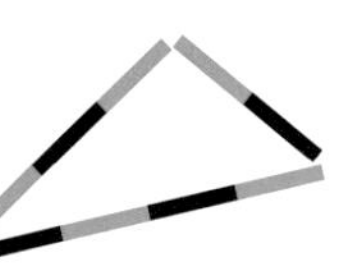

7 

Laid end-to-end, the straws in the box would measure 150 cm.
How many straws are there in the box?

8 Draw some shapes like the ones above.
If the straws were laid end-to-end to make lines,
what would be the length of each line?

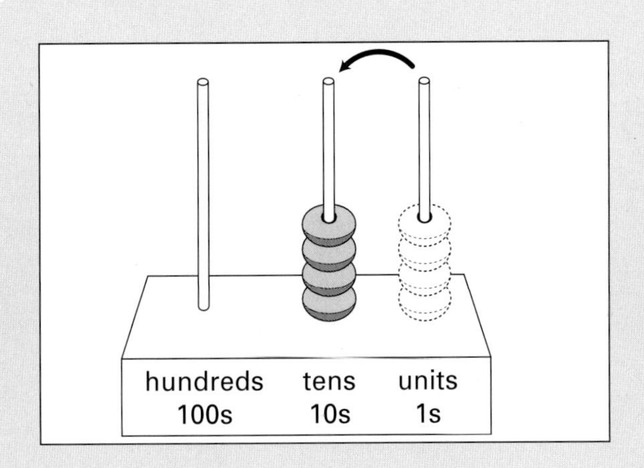

This is an abacus. It is used for counting and calculating.

The abacus was showing **4** rings on the **units** spike.
To multiply **4** by **10**, we moved the rings onto the **tens** spike.
The **4** rings now count as **40.**

Exercise 3

Multiply these numbers by ten. Re-draw each abacus to show your answer.
The first question has been done for you.

1

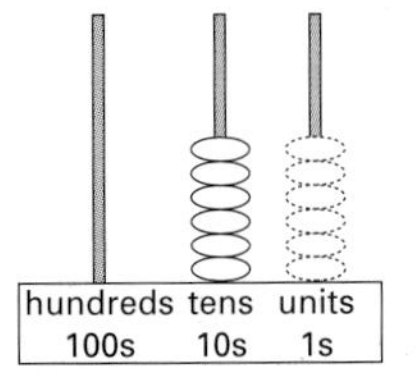

6 × 10 = 60

2

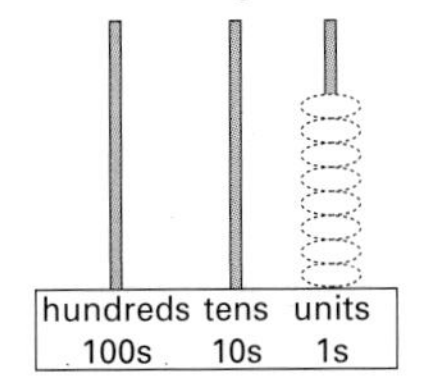

8 × 10 = ?

3

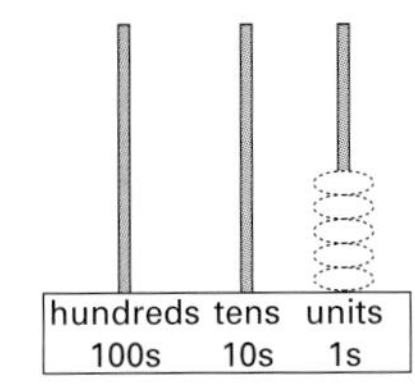

5 × 10 = ?

4

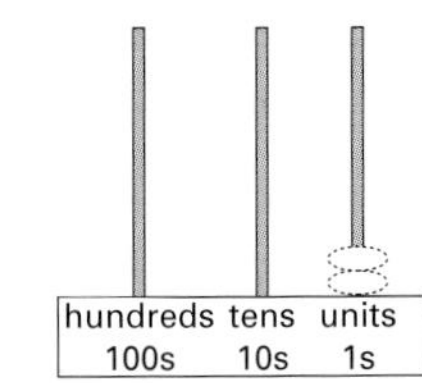

2 × 10 = ?

5

hundreds tens units
100s 10s 1s

7 × 10 = ?

6

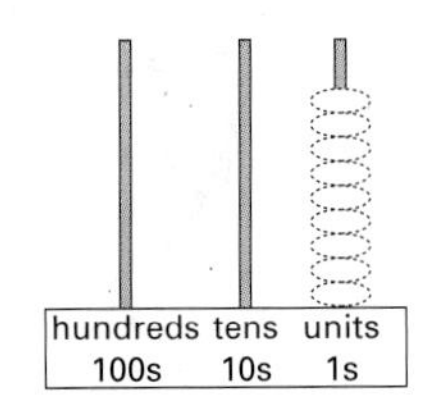

9 × 10 = ?

7

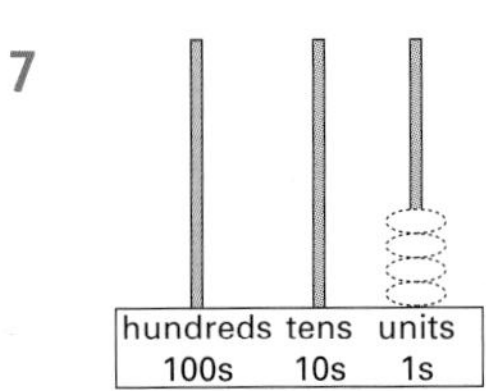

4 × 10 = ?

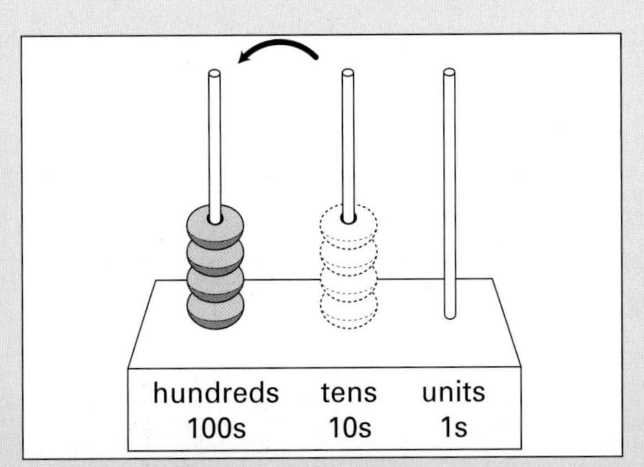

When we use the abacus to **multiply by 10**, we move the rings to the next spike on the left. **The next spike on the left is always 10 times larger.**

The 4 rings on the **tens** spike have been moved to the **hundreds** spike. It is one place to the left of the **tens** spike. It is worth 10 times more than the **tens** spike. **40 × 10 = 400**

Exercise 4

Show these '×**10**' multiplications by re-drawing the abacus in each question.
Write the answers below your drawings.

1
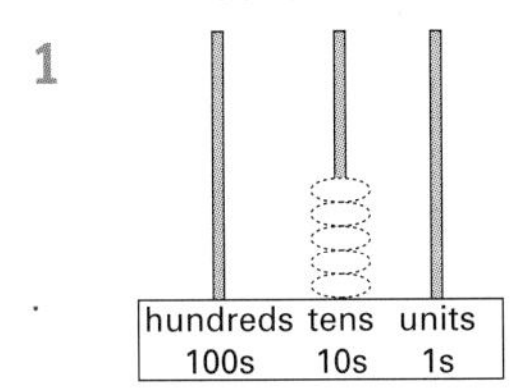

$50 \times 10 =$?

2
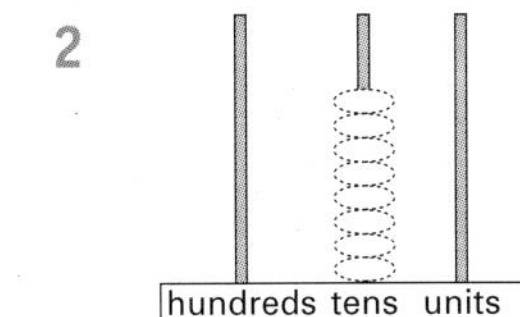

$80 \times 10 =$?

3
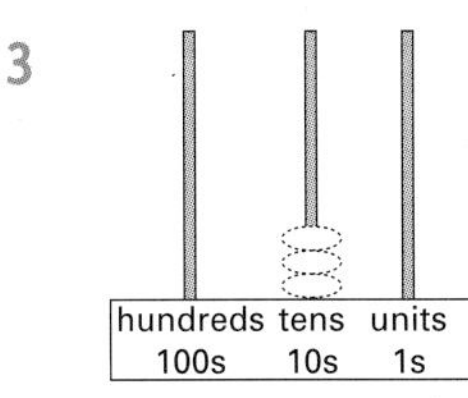

$30 \times 10 =$?

4
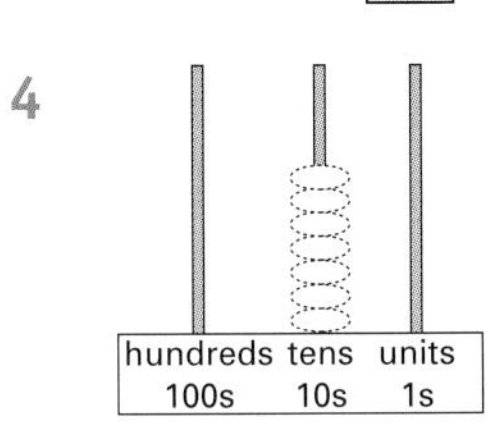

$60 \times 10 =$?

5
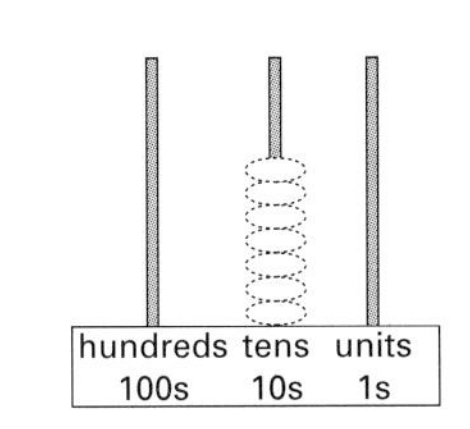

$70 \times 10 =$?

6
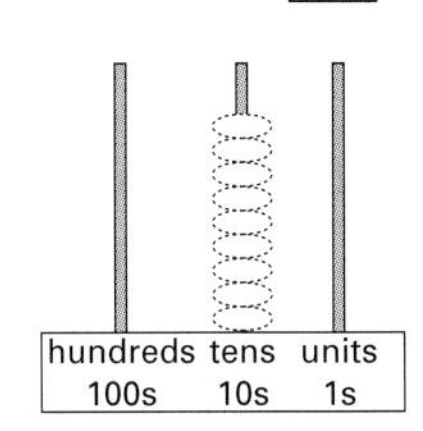

$90 \times 10 =$?

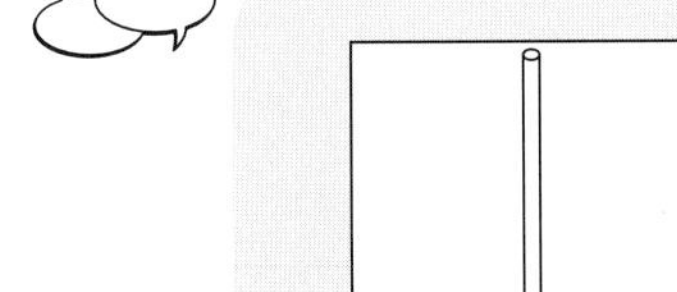

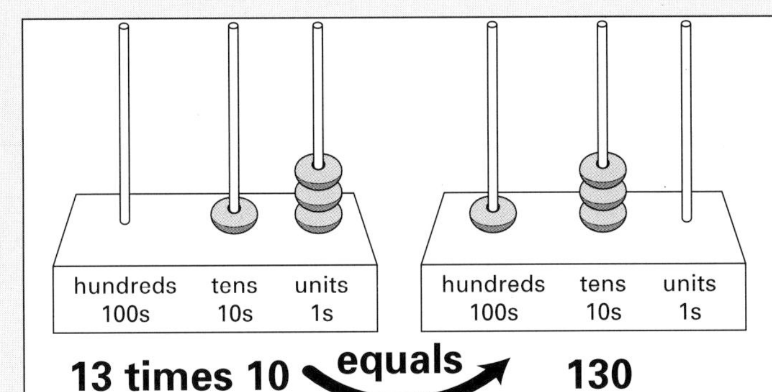

The **'one place to the left'** rule works for all numbers.
The rings on the **units** move **one place** to the **tens**.
The rings on the **tens** move to the **hundreds** spike.
13 × 10 = 130

Exercise 5

Re-draw these to show the numbers multiplied by ten.
Write the answers below your drawings.

1
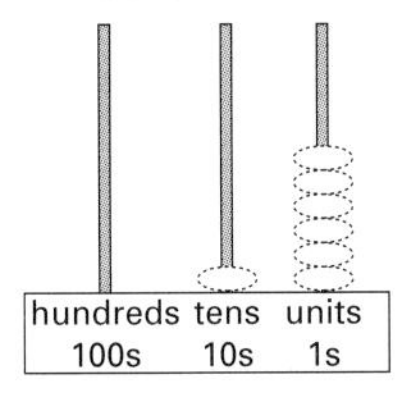

$16 \times 10 =$?

2
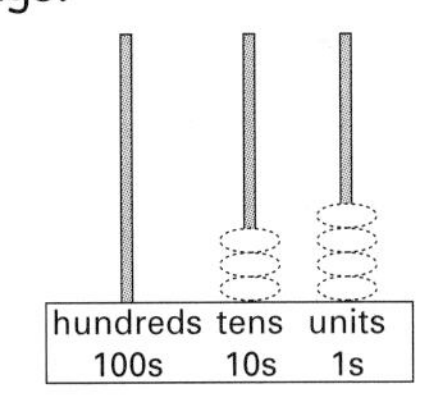

$34 \times 10 =$?

3
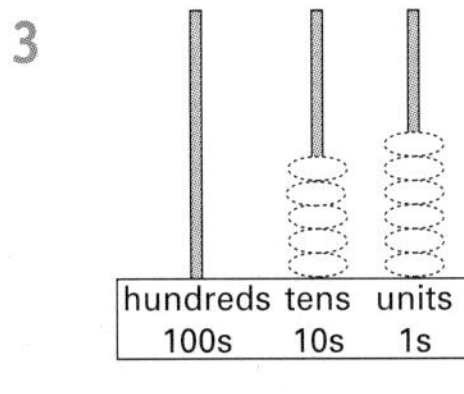

$56 \times 10 =$?

4
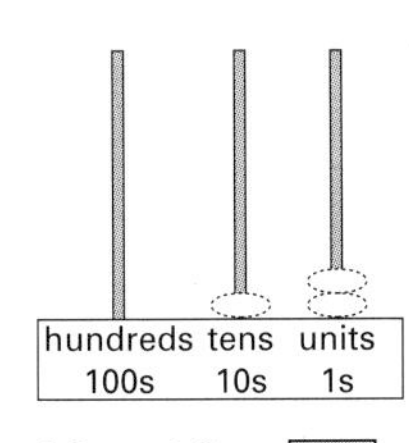

$12 \times 10 =$?

5
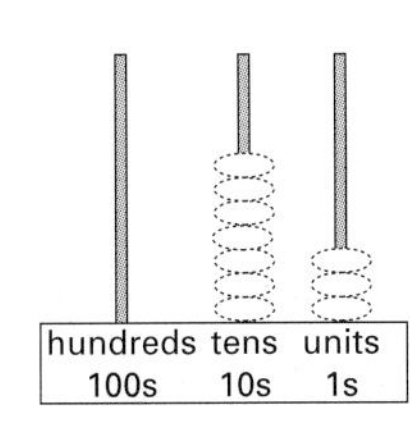

$73 \times 10 =$?

6
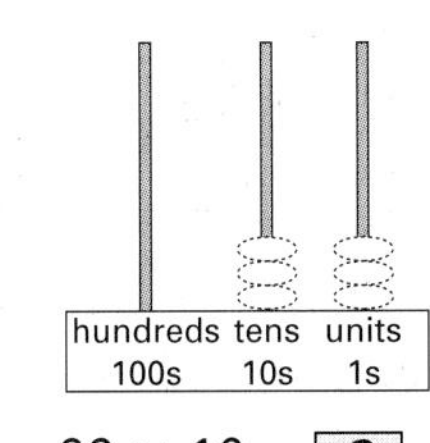

$33 \times 10 =$?

Multiplying by Ten

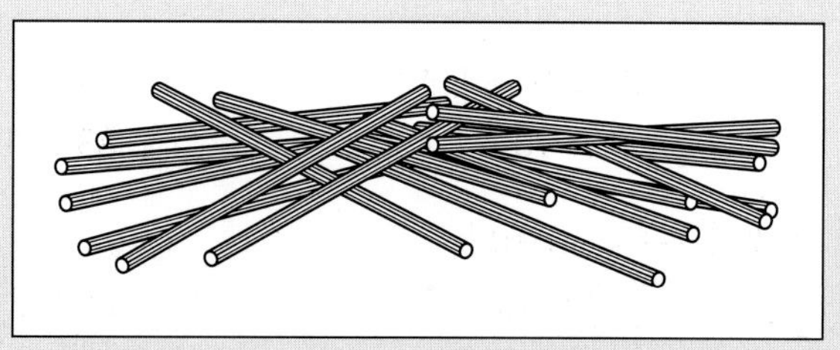

There are 16 straws in Mick's pile, each 10 cm long. He wants to work out how long they would be if they were put end-to-end in a straight line.

If he tries to add he will have a very long sum. 10 + 10 + 10 + 10 + 10 + 10 + ...
He will have to add 10, **16 times**. Mick can multiply **10 by 16** or **16 by 10.**

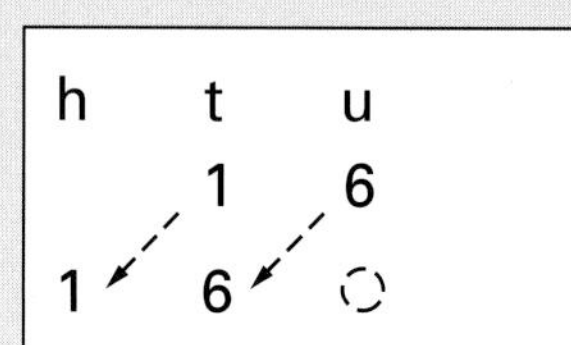

Each column is **10 times larger** than the column on its left.
To multiply a number by 10, move its position one place to the left.

The six **units** have been moved to the **tens** column so we have to put a **0** into the units place.

Exercise 6

Multiply these numbers by 10. Move the numbers one place to the left.
Do not forget the **0**. Write out the questions.

1 $10 \times 7 =$?
2 $10 \times 9 =$?
3 $10 \times 12 =$?
4 $10 \times 15 =$?
5 $10 \times 13 =$?
6 $10 \times 17 =$?
7 $10 \times 11 =$?
8 $10 \times 16 =$?
9 $10 \times 18 =$?
10 $10 \times 20 =$?
11 $10 \times 30 =$?
12 $10 \times 10 =$?

Exercise 7

This graph shows how many people visited the museum during one week.
This face stands for every **10 visitors** to the museum. ☺
So, ☺ ☺ ☺ stands for **30 visitors**.

Day	Number of visitors
Sunday	☺ ☺ ☺ ☺ ☺
Monday	☺ ☺ ☺
Tuesday	☺ ☺ ☺ ☺ ☺ ☺ ☺
Wednesday	☺ ☺ ☺ ☺ ☺ ☺ ☺ ☺ ☺ ☺
Thursday	
Friday	☺ ☺ ☺ ☺ ☺ ☺ ☺ ☺
Saturday	90 people

1 How many visitors were there on Tuesday?
2 How many people visited on the busiest day?
3 Which day could the museum have been closed?
4 In your book, draw the faces needed to show Saturday's attendance.
5 Think of a way that you could show that 45 people visited.

Exercise 8

1 Multiply these numbers by 10.

(a) $23 \times 10 =$? (b) $65 \times 10 =$? (c) $21 \times 10 =$? (d) $25 \times 10 =$?

(e) $19 \times 10 =$? (f) $79 \times 10 =$? (g) $50 \times 10 =$? (h) $83 \times 10 =$?

2 What numbers are being multiplied by 10 in order to get these answers?

(a) $10 \times$? $= 50$ (b) ? $\times 10 = 90$ (c) ? $\times 10 = 60$ (d) $10 \times$? $= 40$

(e) $10 \times$? $= 100$ (f) $10 \times$? $= 130$ (g) ? $\times 10 = 600$ (h) ? $\times 10 = 540$

3 Have you found any 'shortcuts' when you multiply by 10?
Explain it to your partner. Did they find a 'shortcut'?

4 Make up some questions about multiplying by 10 and answer them using your own 'shortcut'. Check your answers on a calculator.

Exercise 9

Multiply by 10 to answer these problems.

1 A pipeline is built from pipes 10 m long. How long is the pipeline if it uses 8 pipes?

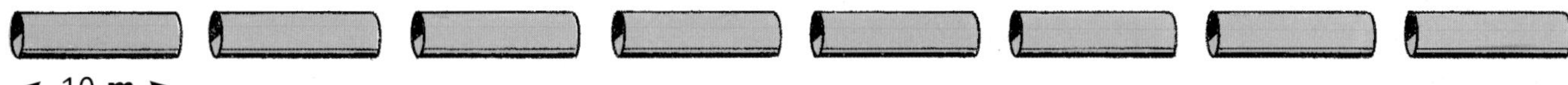

2

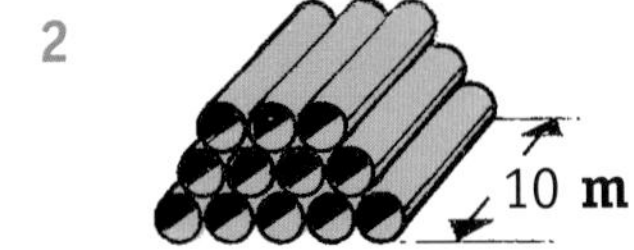

(a) How many pipes are there in the pile?
(b) If the pipes were laid end-to-end, how far would they reach?

3 A bottle of champagne costs £16.
How much will it cost for ten bottles?

4

The school minibus takes 10 students at a time. The hockey teams (34 players) and the rugby team (16 players) are travelling to their games on Saturday morning.
How many trips will the bus have to make to get everyone to the games?

Key ideas

A figure can stand for different numbers. It depends upon its place.

hundreds	**tens**	**units**
1	**7**	6

The **7** stands for 70 because it is in the **tens position** or 'place'.

To multiply a number by **ten**, move it **one place to the left** and put a zero into the units place.

Chapter 15 Decimals

Step-up 1

This shape has been divided into **four** equal parts.
One part out of **four** is shaded.
We say that one **quarter** ($\frac{1}{4}$) of the shape is shaded.

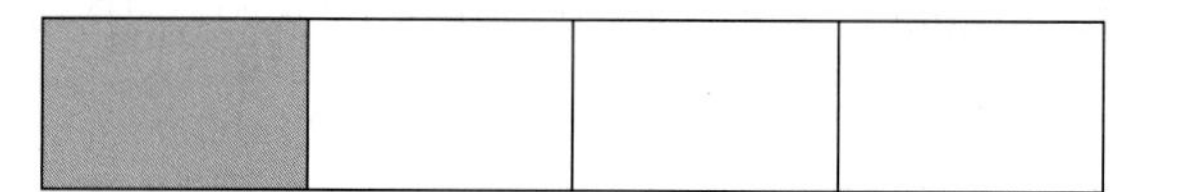

1 Decide what fraction of each shape is shaded.

(a)

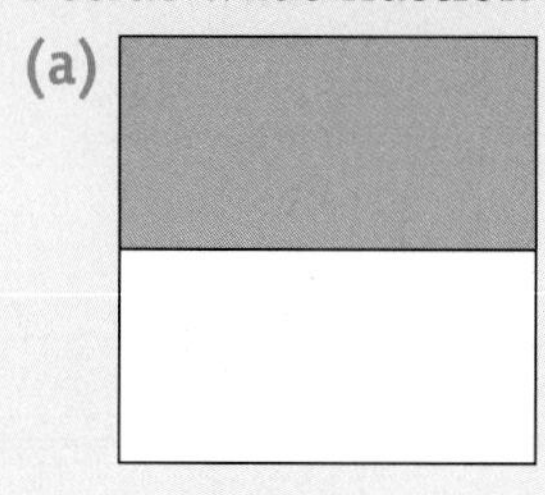

$\frac{1}{2}$ or $\frac{1}{3}$

(b)

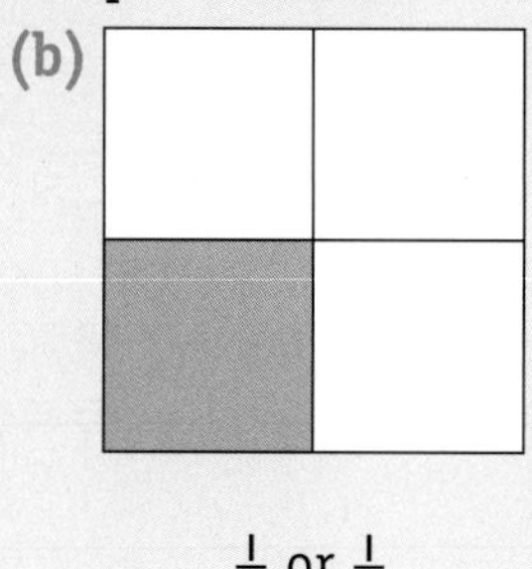

$\frac{1}{4}$ or $\frac{1}{2}$

(c)

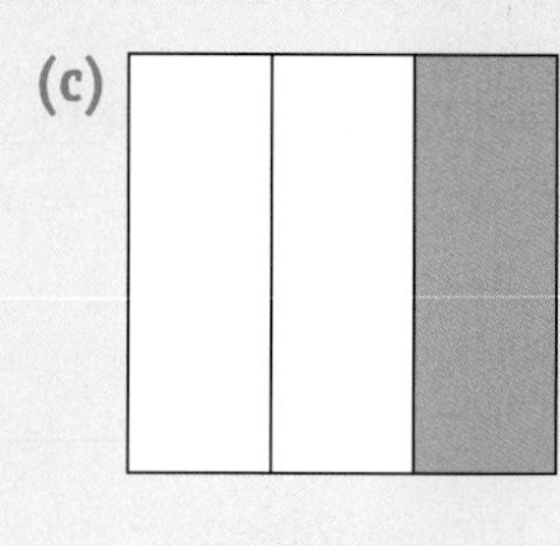

$\frac{1}{3}$ or $\frac{1}{4}$

(d)

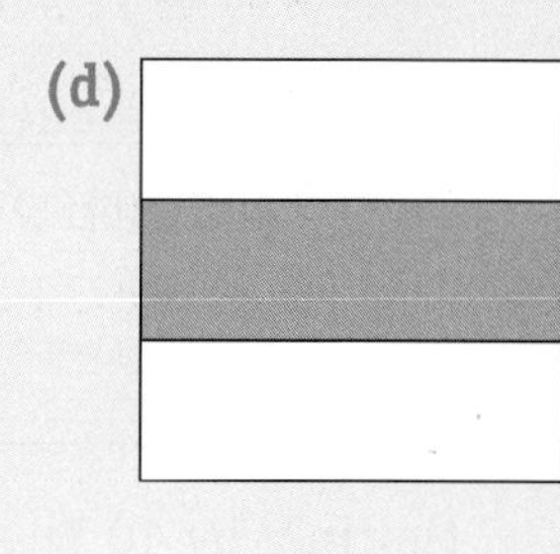

$\frac{1}{3}$ or $\frac{1}{2}$

This shaped is divided into **ten** equal parts.
One part out of **ten** is shaded.
How would you write this as a fraction?

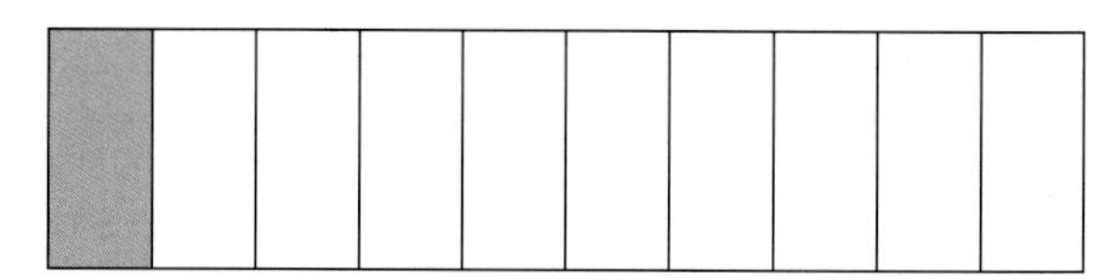

When you divide something into ten equal pieces, each piece is a **tenth** ($\frac{1}{10}$).

2 Each of these shapes has been divided into **ten** parts.
Match each shape with a fraction.

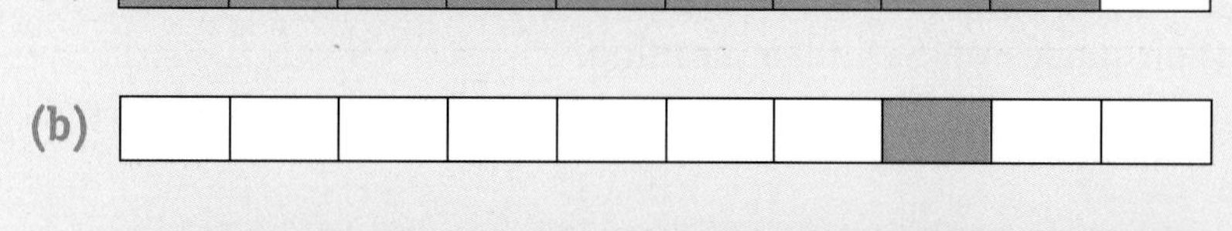

(a)

(b)

(c)

(d)

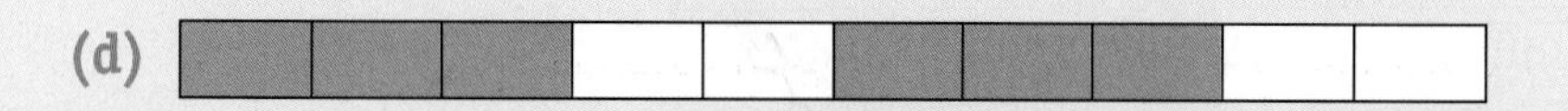

(e)

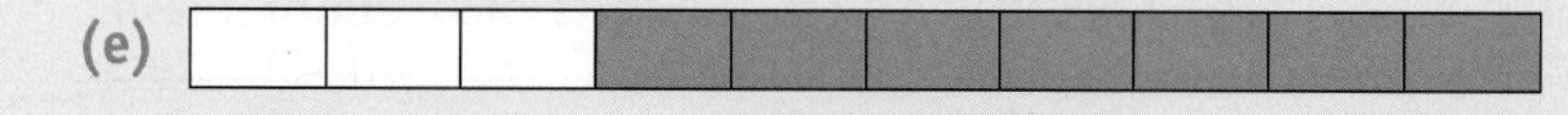

(f)

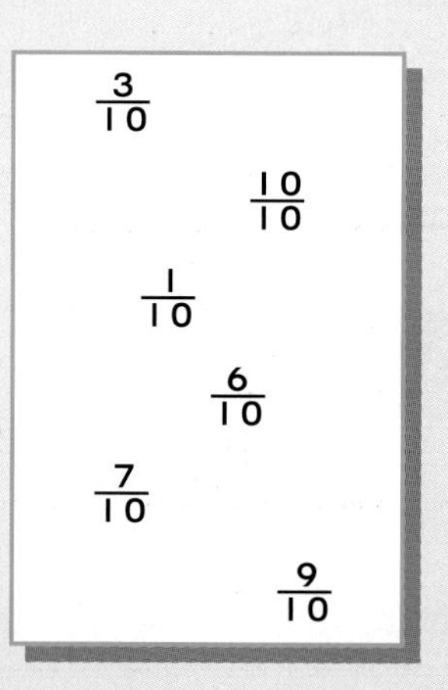

Step-up 2

This number line rises in units of 5 and 10. The 10s are shown by the red marks. The blue marks show the 5s.

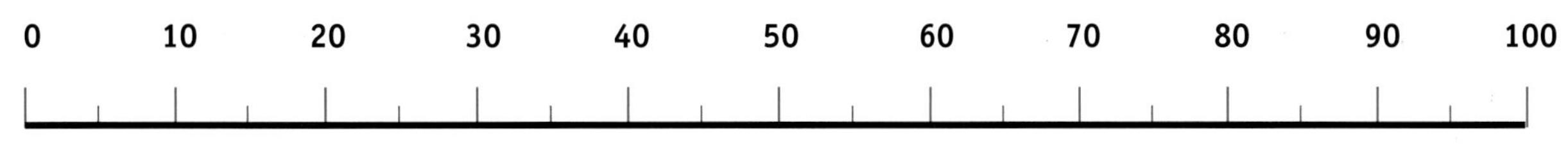

The green line ends between 60 and 70. It is closer to 70, so we say that the green line is 70 units (**to the nearest 10**).

The yellow line ends between 30 and 40. **To the nearest 10**, the yellow line is 30 units long. It is closer to 30 than 40.

3 Look at the coloured lines below. What are the lengths of the lines when they are written to the **nearest 10 units**?

(a)

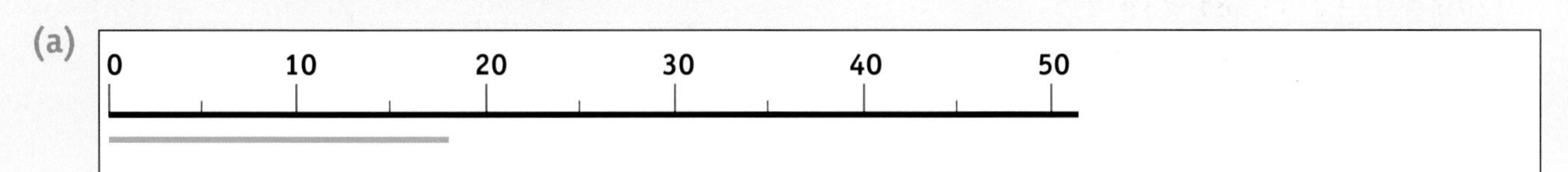

(b)

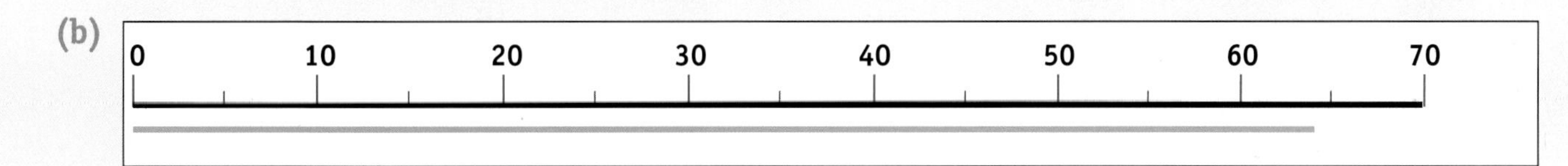

(c)

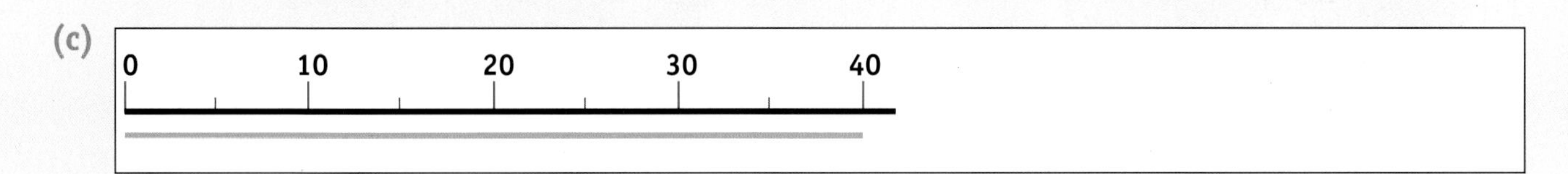

(d)

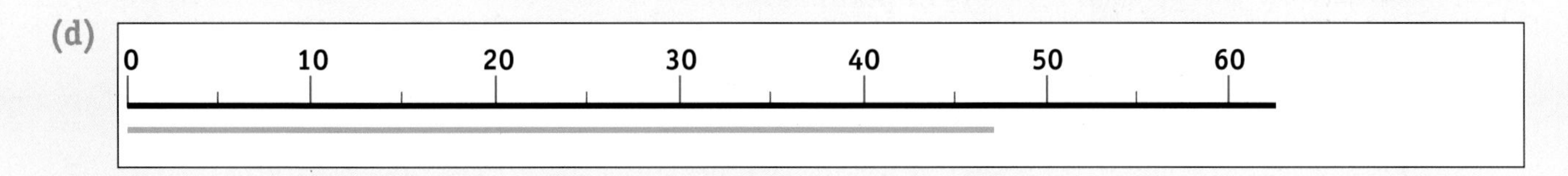

(e)

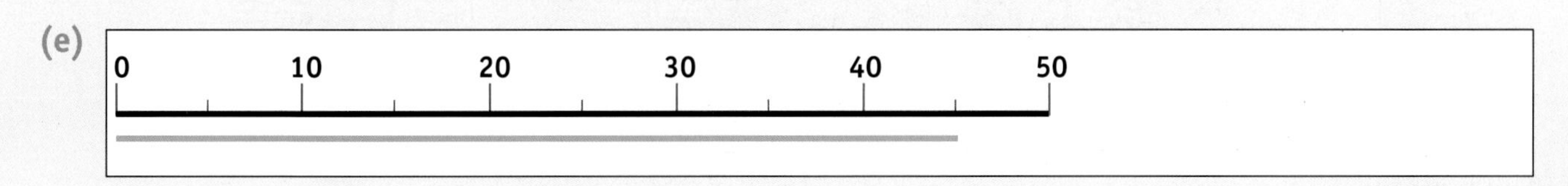

This strip of card has been divided into **ten** equal parts.
Each part is called **one tenth**.

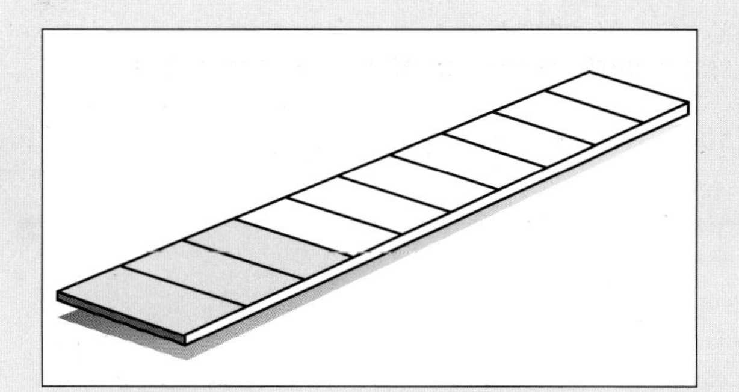

As a **fraction** it is written: $\frac{1}{10}$

As a **decimal** it is written: 0.1

$\frac{3}{10}$ of the strip has been coloured blue. As a **decimal** this is written **0.3**.

Exercise 1

Copy these strips into your book. Say how much of each strip has been coloured.
Write: '$\frac{3}{10}$ *is shaded, this is 0.3*'.

1

2

3

4

5

6

7

8

9

10

11 There are 10 players in one whole team.

(a) What decimal part of each team are in **striped** shirts?

(b) What decimal part of each team are in **plain** shirts?

Most of the rulers in your classroom will look like this.

It is numbered in **centimetres**.

Each centimetre is divided into 10 parts.

Each of these small parts is $\frac{1}{10}$, or **0.1** of a centimetre.

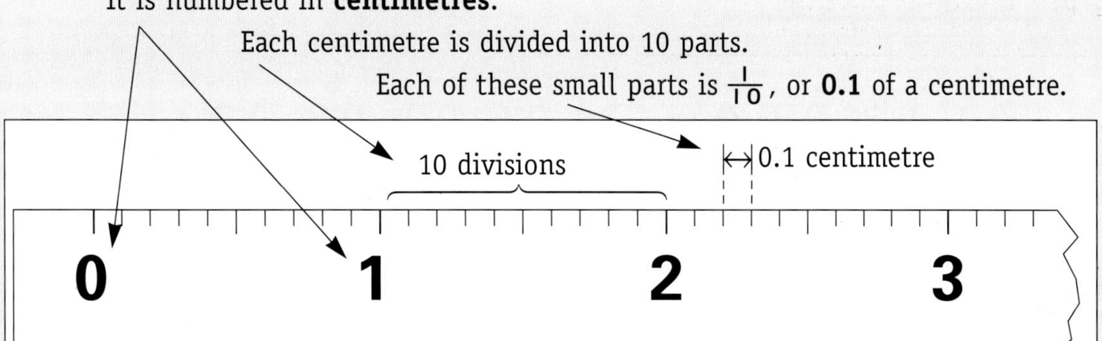

Exercise 2

This line is less than 1 centimetre long.
It is 0.4 centimetres long.

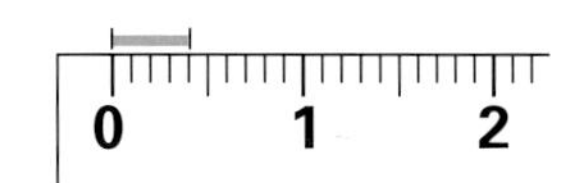

How long are these lines?

1 0 1 2

2 0 1 2

3 0 1 2

4 0 1 2

5 0 1 2

6 0 1 2

7 0 1 2

8 0 1 2

Exercise 3

Write the decimal that matches the shaded part of each strip.

1

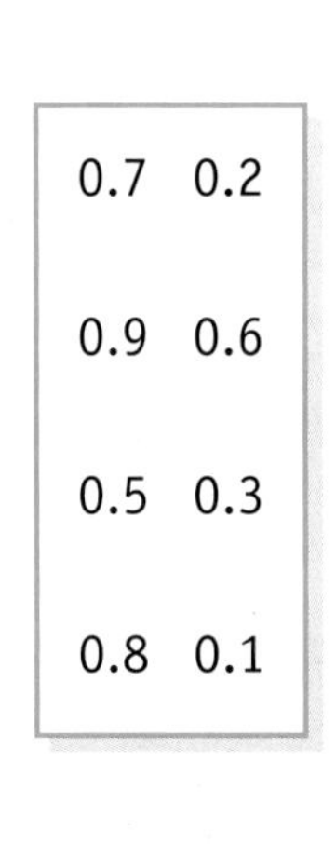

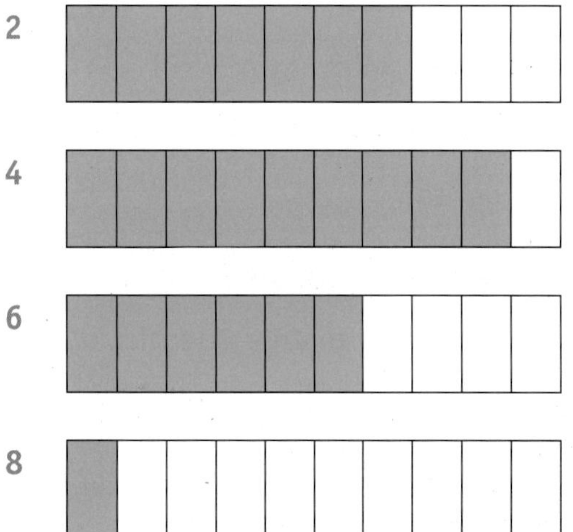

3

5

7

This is another decimal scale. It has been enlarged to make it easier to read.

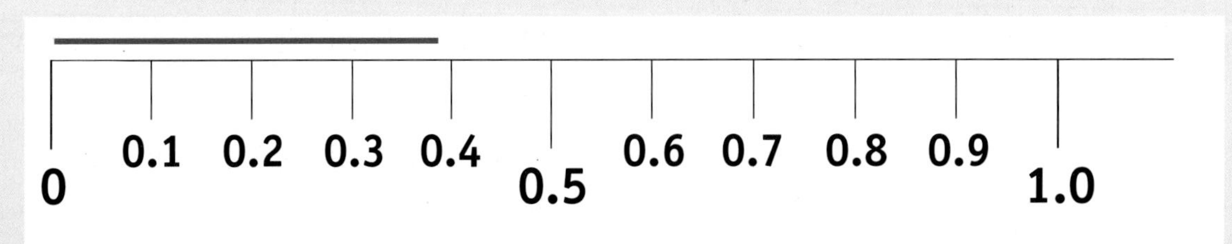

The scale starts at **0** and goes up to **1**, in steps of **0.1**.
We say that the red line is **0.4 cm** long because it is closest to **0.4 cm**.

Exercise 4

Estimate the length of these lines to the nearest decimal number.
Write: *The line is nearly 0.1 cm long.*

1

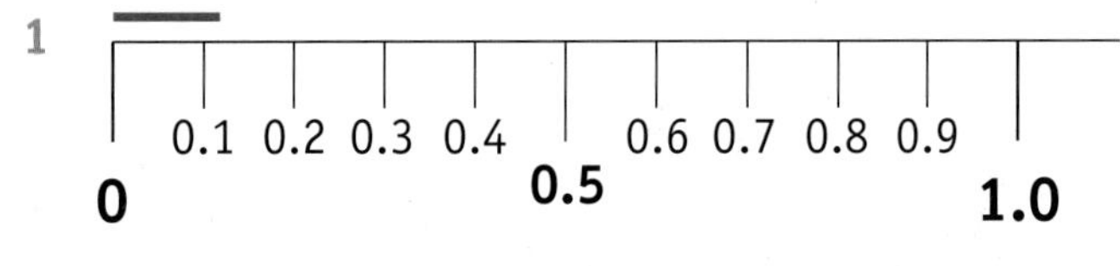

2

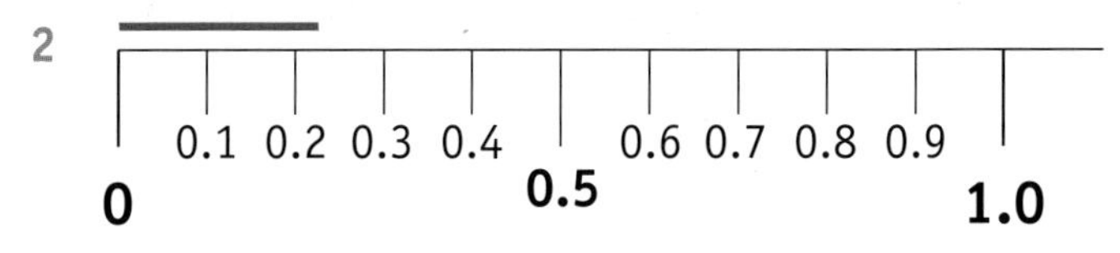

3

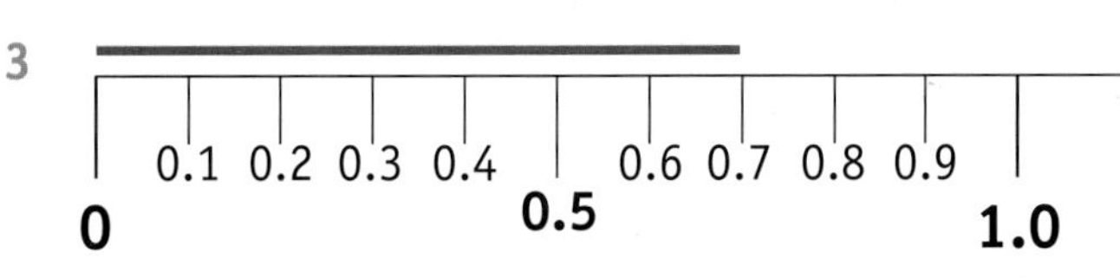

4

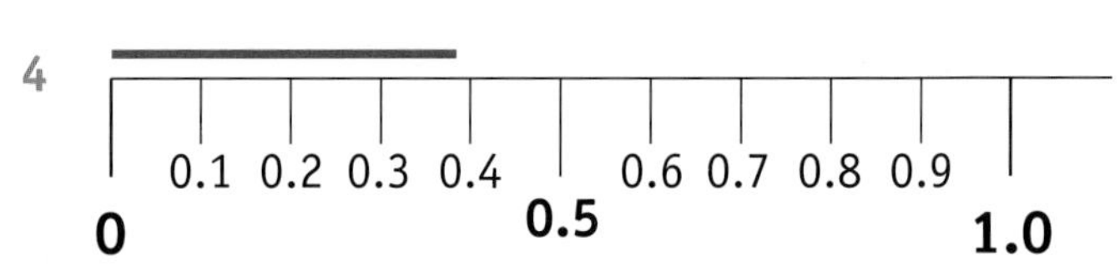

5

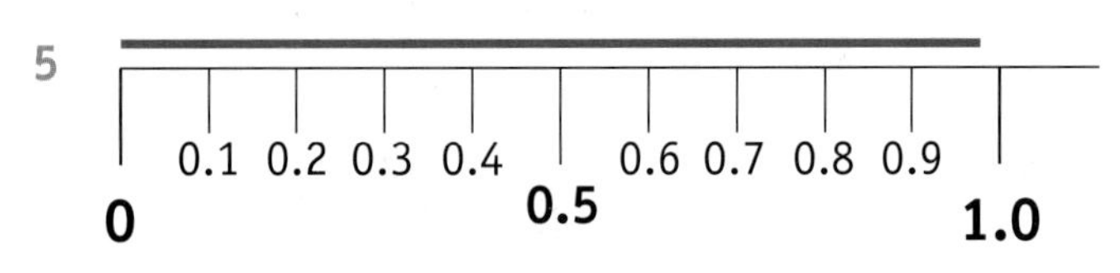

6

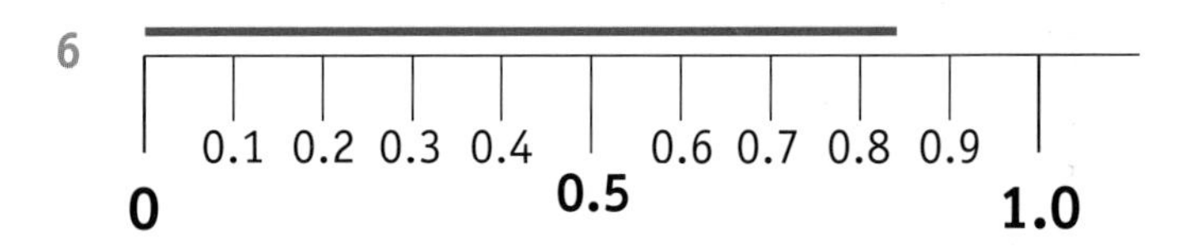

Use this decimal scale to help you with questions 7 to 12.

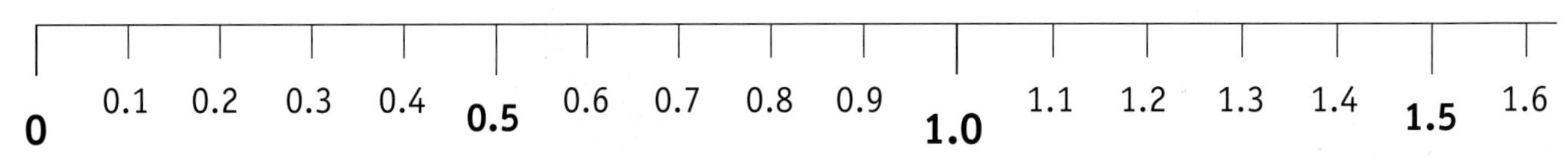

7 Starting at 0.4 count on another 5 tenths (0.5) like this, 0.5, 0.6, 0.7, ... and so on. Where do you get to?

8 Starting at 0.6 count on another 6 tenths. (Does this remind you of 6 + 6 = 12?)

9 Starting at 0.7 count on another 3 tenths. What sum does this remind you of?

10 By starting from 0.8 and moving 3 tenths, what **two** decimal numbers could you reach?

11 Count backwards from 1.3 to 0.7. How many tenths have you subtracted?

12 Write the problem above as a decimal subtraction 1.3 ...

This scale shows that the parcels weigh **2.4** kg.

This means **2 whole** kilograms and **0.4** kilograms.

Exercise 5

These are decimal scales. Write down the reading on each one.
Write: 'This scale shows …' (Be careful to write the proper units when needed.)

1
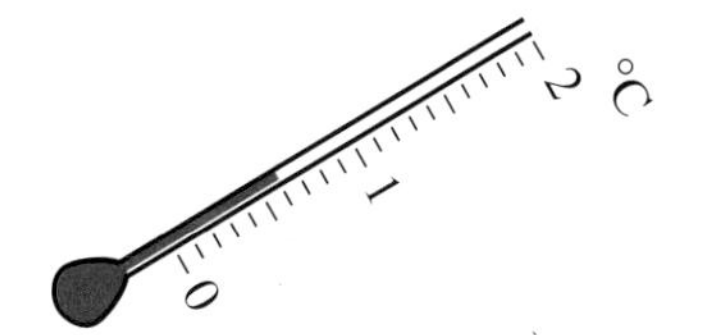

2
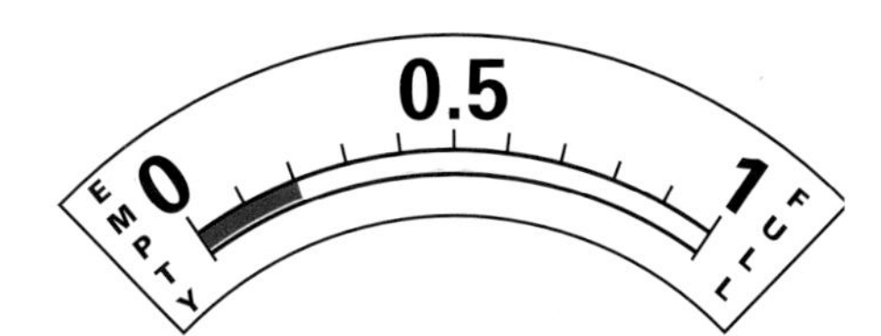

3
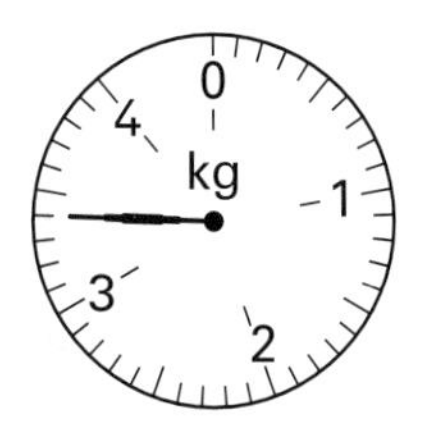

4
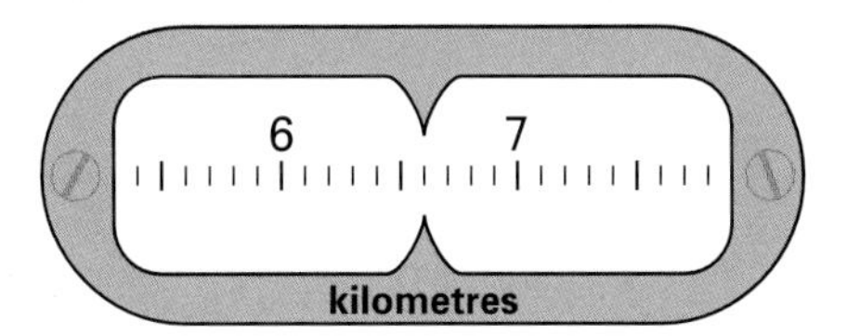

5
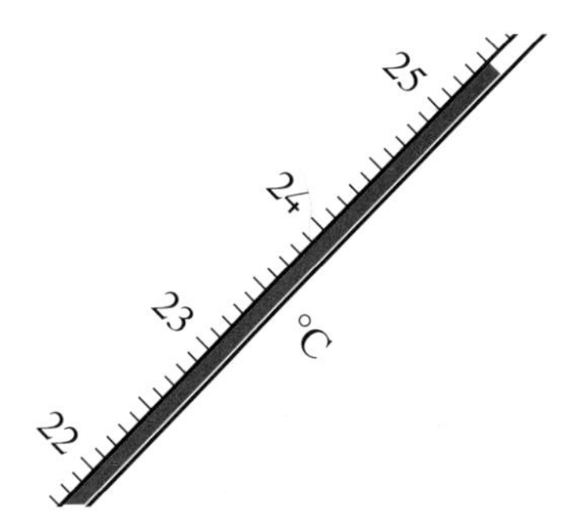

6
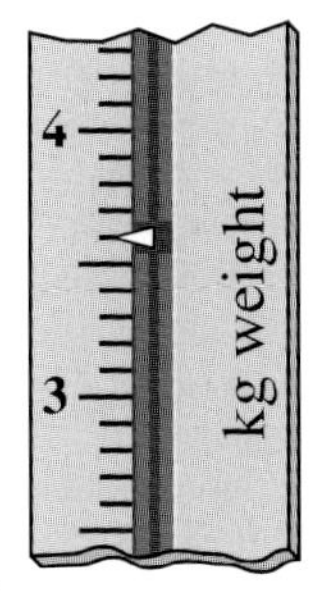

7
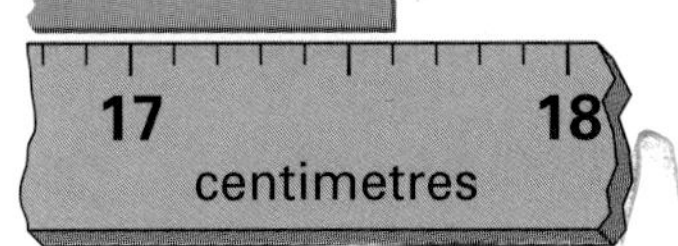

8
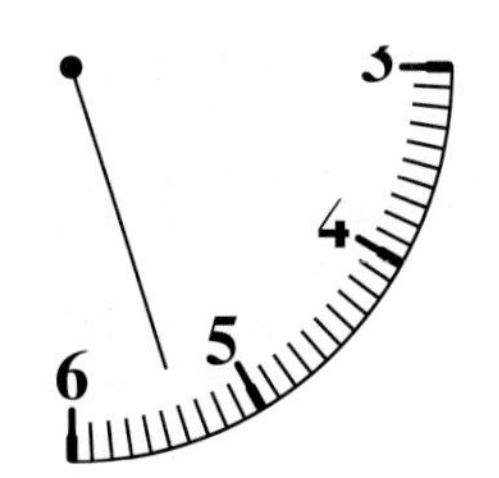

Here is a bar of chocolate.

There are 10 pieces.

Each piece is 0.1 of the whole bar.

0.1	0.1	0.1	0.1	0.1
0.1	0.1	0.1	0.1	0.1

1 Whole Bar

Exercise 6

Each of the bars below has pieces missing. Draw up a table and record what decimal part is missing, and what decimal part is left.

	Decimal part missing	Decimal part left
1	**0.7**	**0.3**
2		
3		
4		
5		
6		

7 What is the number that links all of these questions?

8 How many 0.1s are there in 1 whole?

Making Whole Ones

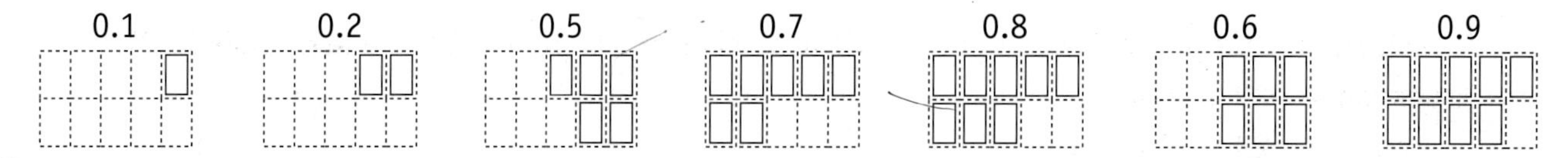

You can make **1 whole unit** by adding these decimal parts together: **0.6 + 0.2 + 0.2 = 1.0** (**not 0.10**).

9 Using the decimal numbers above, see how many different ways you can make **1 whole unit.** Start with pairs.

10 Add different pairs together so that the answers are more than **1 whole unit.** Like this: **0.6 + 0.7 = 1.3**

Here is 2.3 add 1.5. The total is 3.8.

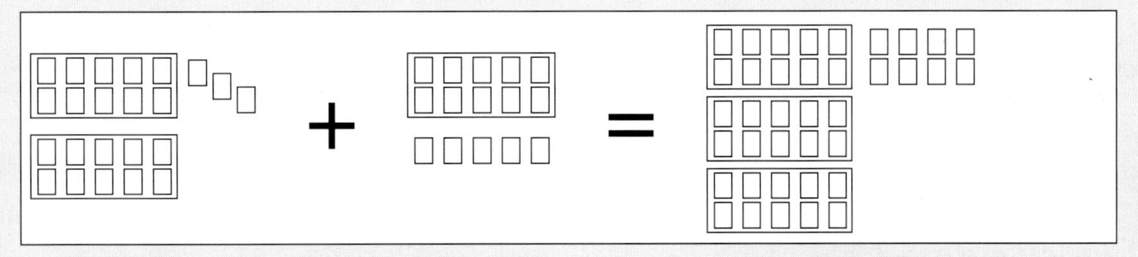

2.3 + 1.5 = 3.8

Exercise 7

Write out each drawing as a sum and add the total.

1

2

3

4

5

6

7 Write out some decimal additions which will add up to 3.5, like this: 2.1 + 1.4 = 3.5

Key ideas

A decimal is what you get when you divide a number by 10 (unless the number ends in 0).

For example 20 ÷ 10 = 2

but 23 ÷ 10 = 2.3

and 5 ÷ 10 = 0.5

Each decimal part is a tenth written as 0.1.

0.1 + 0.1 + 0.1 + 0.1 + 0.1 + 0.1 + 0.1 + 0.1 + 0.1 + 0.1 = 1.0 10 × 0.1 = 1 whole

Decimals are often used to mark scales: temperature, weight, rulers.

Chapter 16 Money

British notes and coins

Fifty pound note £50

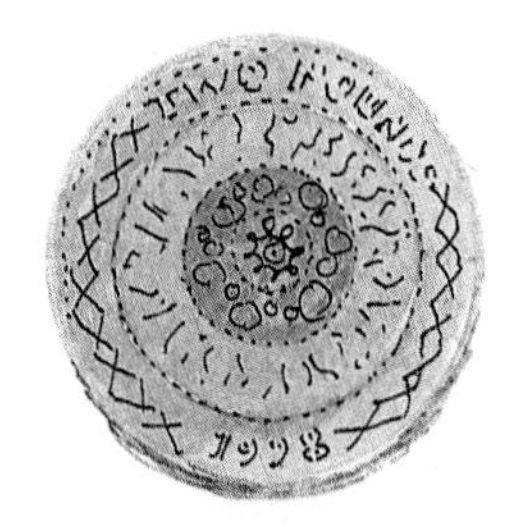

Two pound coin £2

One pound coin £1

Twenty pound note £20

Fifty pence coin 50p

Ten pound note £10

Twenty pence coin 20p

Ten pence coin 10p

Five pound note £5

Five pence coin 5p

Two pence coin 2p

One penny coin 1p

Exercise 1

How much money is shown in each group? Give your answers in pounds, e.g. £25.

1

2

3

4

5

6

Exercise 2

Calculate how much money is in each group? Some answers will be in pounds, for example £10. Others will be in pence, for example 37p.

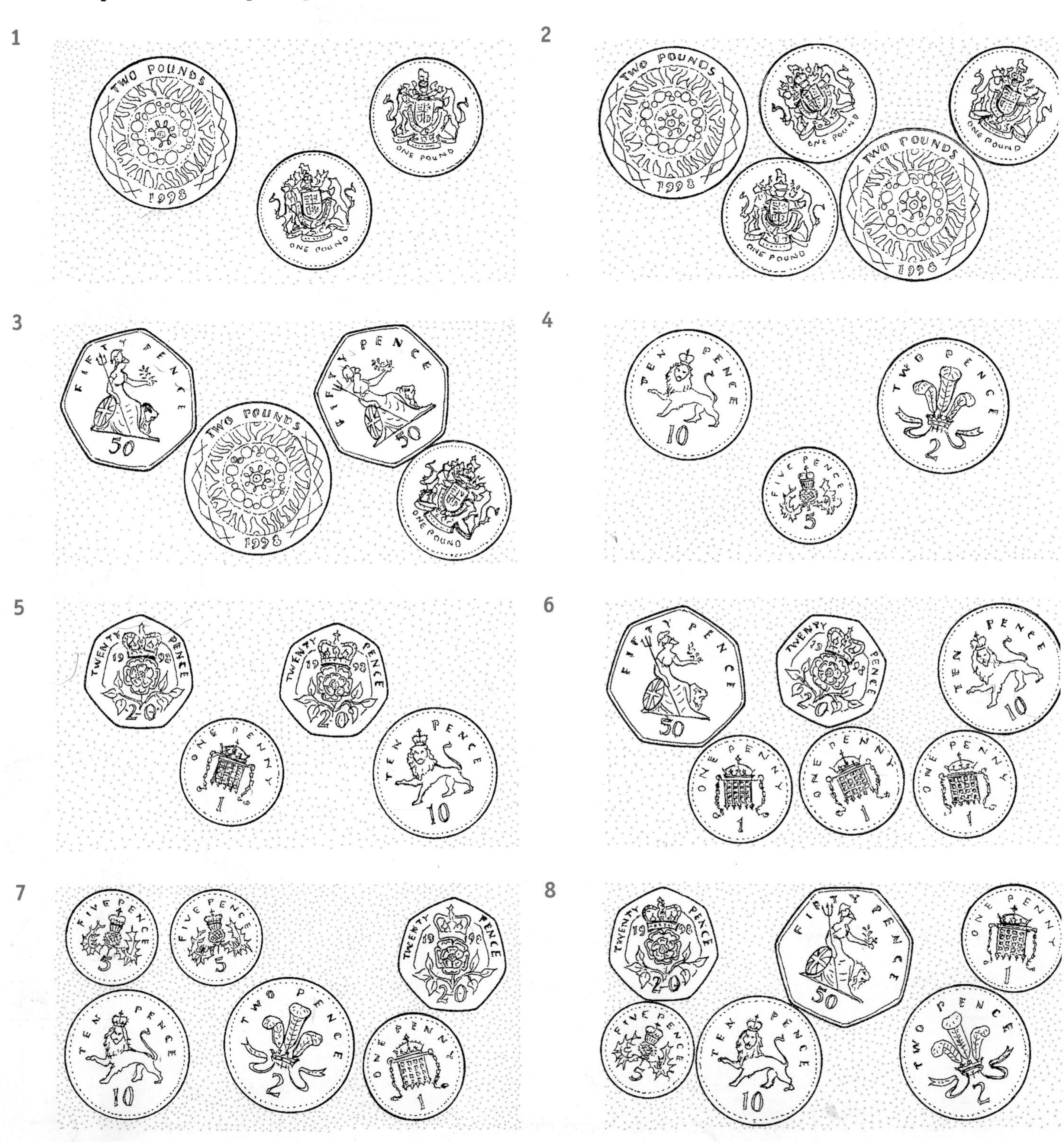

Exercise 3

How many pence are in each pile of coins?

1

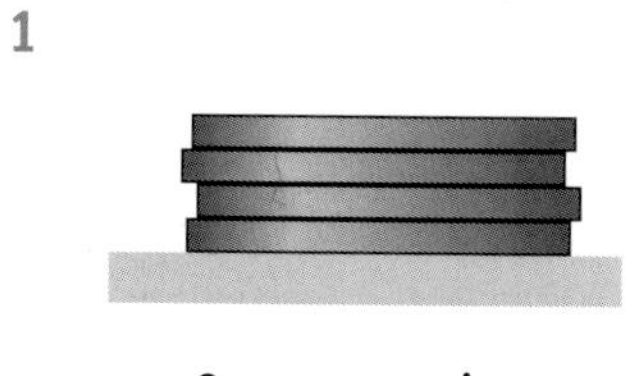

2 pence coins

2

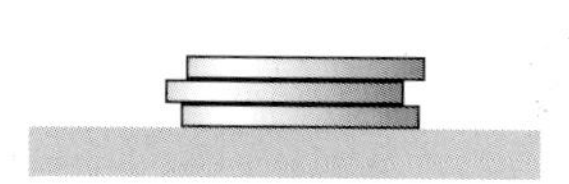

5 pence coins

3

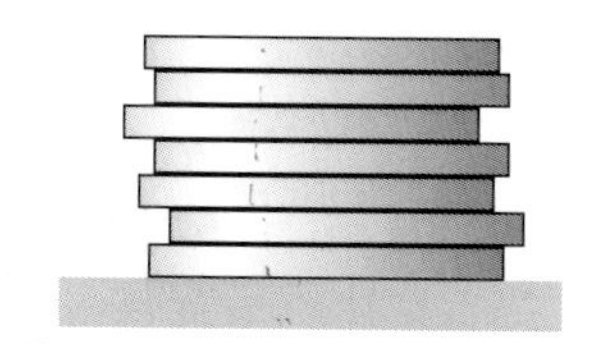

10 pence coins

4

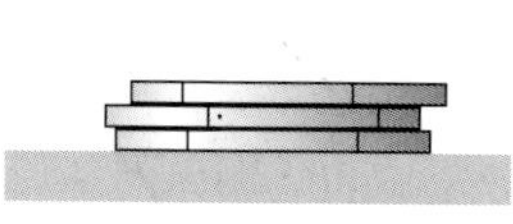

20 pence coins

5

5 pence coins

6

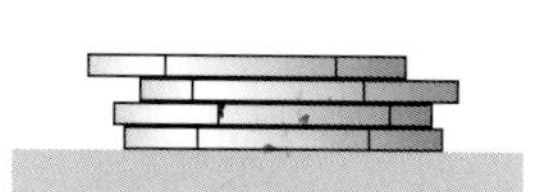

20 pence coins

7

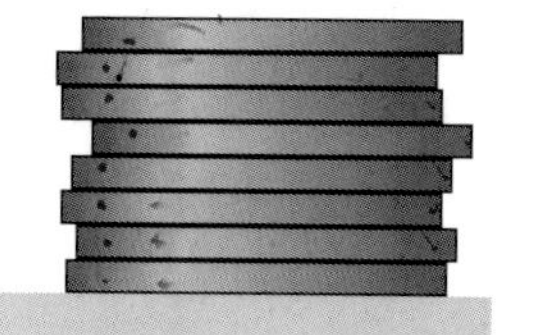

2 pence coins

8

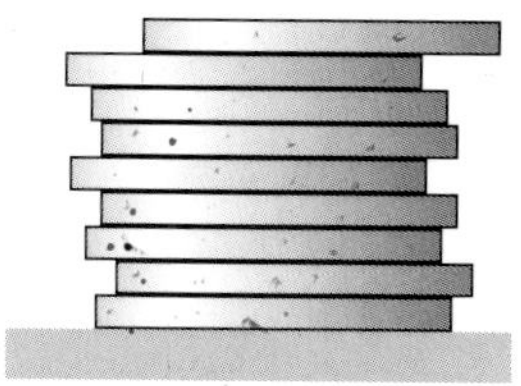

10 pence coins

Exercise 4

Answer these questions.

1 (a) Which is the dearest item?
  (b) Which is the cheapest item?

2 How much will 2 lollies cost?

3 How much will a lolly and a pack of toffees cost?

4 How much will 2 bags of crisps cost?

5 How much will a can of cola and a pack of toffees cost?

6 How much will a pack of mints and a bag of crisps cost?

7 How much will 2 packs of gum and a lolly cost?

8 How much will a bag of crisps, a pack of gum and a pack of toffees cost?

9 If you bought a bag of crisps, how much change would you get from 50p?

10 If you bought a can of cola, how much change would you get from £1?

11 If you bought a lolly and a pack of gum, how much change would you get from 50p?

12 If you bought a bag of crisps and a can of cola, how much change would you get from £1?

13 Semra has 90p. How many ways could she spend the money?
Your answers must be as near as possible, **but not more than**, 90p.

14 Chan wants to buy 2 packs of toffees, a pack of gum and a bag of crisps.
He has £1.20. How much more does he need?

Crisps 40p

CRUNCHY CRISPS SALT 'N' VINEGAR

Gum 25p

Lolly 10p

Toffees 30p

Toffee

Mints 45p

Cola 50p

Exercise 5

100 pence make one pound (100p = £1).

Which of these amounts come to exactly £1?

1	2	3	4	5	6
60p	35p	50p	90p	35p	82p
+ 40p	+ 50p	+ 50p	+ 30p	+ 65p	+ 18p

Exercise 6

How much money is in each wallet?

1

2

Exercise 7

Compact disc £12

jigsaw £3.50

Perfume £16

Headphones £19

1 How much would the headphones and the jigsaw puzzle cost in total?

2 How much would the CD and the perfume cost in total?

chocolates £4

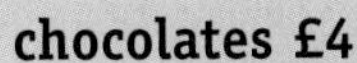

3 How much would the chocolates and the book token cost?

4 How much would the book token and the jigsaw puzzle cost?

5 How much would the perfume and the chocolates cost?

6 How much would the CD and the headphones cost?

7 How much change would you get from £10 if you bought the book token?

Book token £5.00

8 How much change would you get from £10 if you bought the jigsaw puzzle?

9 How much change would you get from £10 if you bought the chocolates?

10 How much change would you get from £20 if you bought the perfume?

Money Card One

Addition

1 £ . p	2 £ . p	3 £ . p
2.13	3.24	4.20
+ 1.21	+ 2.23	+ 3.46

4 £ . p	5 £ . p	6 £ . p
4.06	0.06	7.53
+ 1.51	+ 4.51	+ 2.16

Money Card Two

Take Away

1 £ . p	2 £ . p	3 £ . p
3.56	4.87	8.63
− 2.12	− 1.34	− 1.52

4 £ . p	5 £ . p	6 £ . p
5.62	6.85	7.84
− 4.42	− 4.05	− 7.34

Rounding off money to the nearest £ (pound)

When you are **estimating** a bill you do not need to be totally accurate.

Look at this bill: £1.80
+ £3.10

To estimate the bill you would round off the two amounts.
£1.80 rounded up is £2, £3.10 rounded down is £3.

So the estimate of the bill is £5.

Exercise 8

Round off these amounts, then estimate the bills. The first question is done for you. You can use it as an example.

1 £4.10 + £4.80
£4.10 ➔ **£4.** £4.80 ➔ **£5.** The estimate of the bill is **£9.**

2 £1.90 + £5.20 = ?

3 £2.60 + £4.10 = ?

4 £1.20 + £3.10 + £5.70 = ?

5 £1.69 + £ 2.25 = ?

6 £5.15 + £4.99 = ?

7 £2.85 + £7.09 = ?

Key ideas

The 'shorthand' for **penny** = **p**, and for **pound** = **£**
There are 100 pennies in a pound.

There is paper money – **notes** (£5, £10, £20 and £50)
and metal money – **coins** (1p, 2p, 5p, 10p, 20p, 50p, £1, £2)

Chapter 17 Algebra – Fun with Numbers

Step-up

1 With your partner, talk about the patterns below so that you can find the missing animals in each sequence.

(a)

(a)

(c)

(d)

2

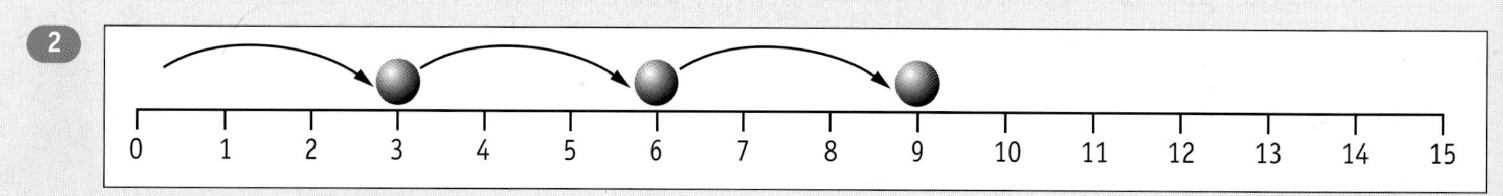

(a) How long is each bounce?

(b) The ball bounces three more times. Onto which three numbers will it bounce?

3 Do these calculations in your head. Write the answers in your book.

(a) 4 + 2 + 2 + 2 = ?

(b) 12 – 2 – 2 = ?

(c) 25 – 5 – 5 = ?

(d) 9 – 3 – 3 = ?

(e) 6 + 4 + 4 + 4 = ?

(f) 3 + 3 + 3 + 3 = ?

4 John is given a number and he adds on 6. Marie takes his answer and multiplies it by 2. What are Marie's answers when John starts with:

(a) 3? (b) 5? (c) 0? (d) 1? (e) 4?

5 Will they get the same results if they swap the order so that John goes last? Give two of your calculations to show that you are correct.

6 Make a repeating pattern of shapes.
Use four or five shapes.
Ask your partner to continue the pattern at least once.

Exercise 1

Copy and complete these patterns.

1 M □ X △ ◓ M □ X ? ? ? ?

2 △ ○ □ X △ ? □ X ? ○ □ ? ? ○ □

Exercise 2

In which order would you use these tiles to continue the pattern below?

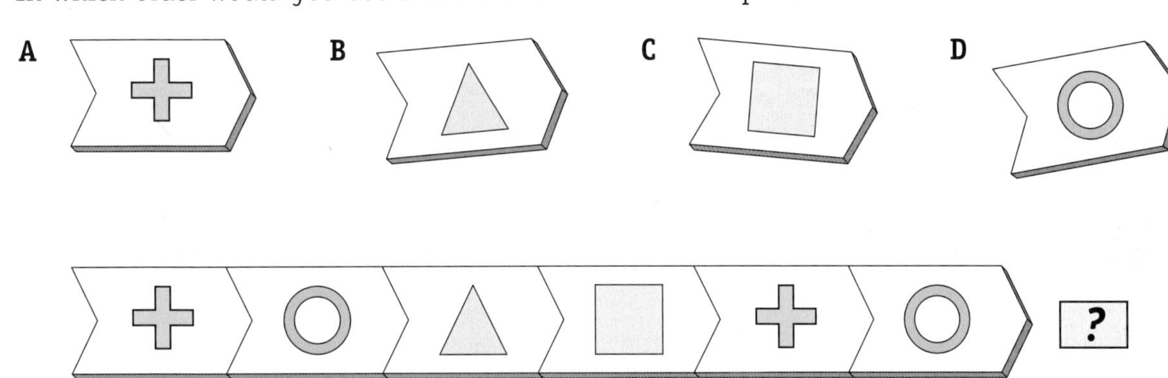

Exercise 3

Here is a repeating pattern made with tiles.
Some of the tiles are the wrong way round.
Give the grid squares for those tiles you think are wrong.

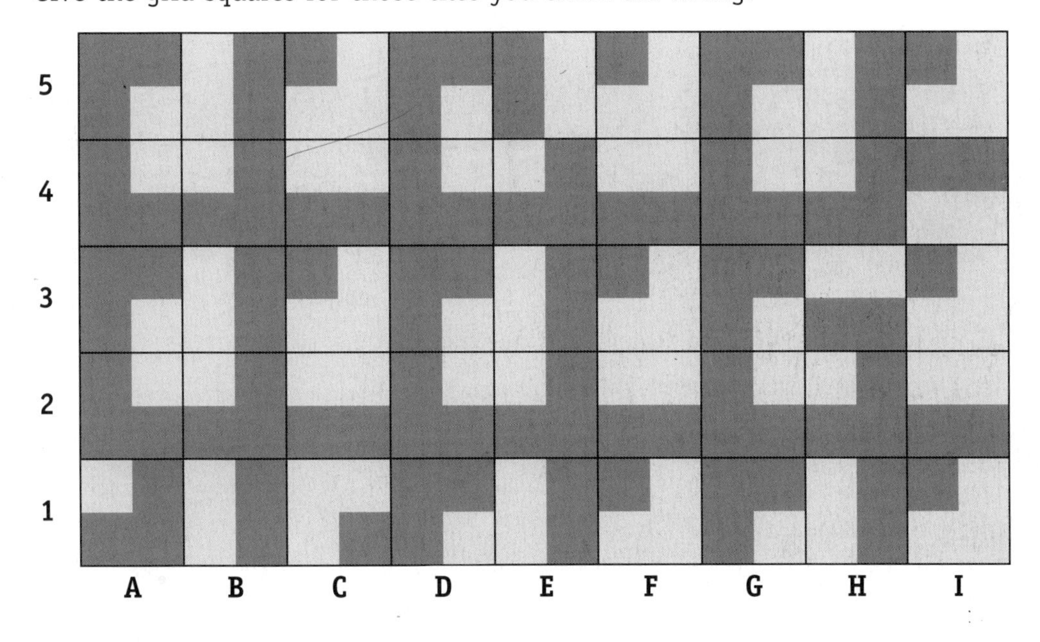

A **pattern** is a group of shapes or numbers that repeat.

This string of beads has a pattern that repeats one green bead and two orange beads.

Exercise 4

1 Which group of beads (**A**, **B**, **C**, or **D**) will complete the pattern below?

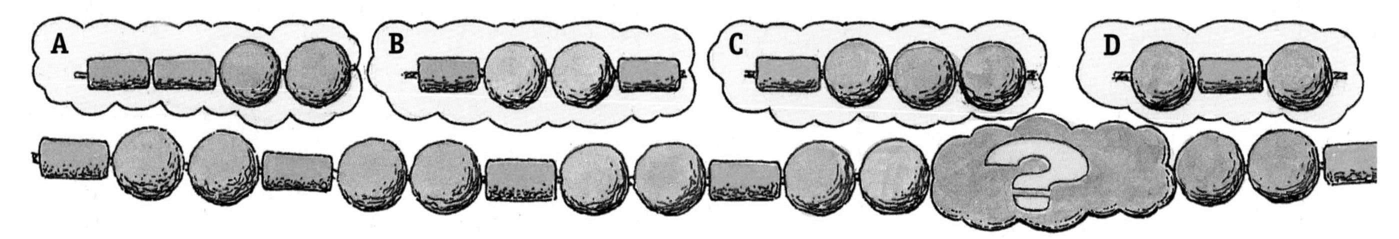

2 Which group of beads (**A**, **B**, **C**, or **D**) will complete the pattern below?

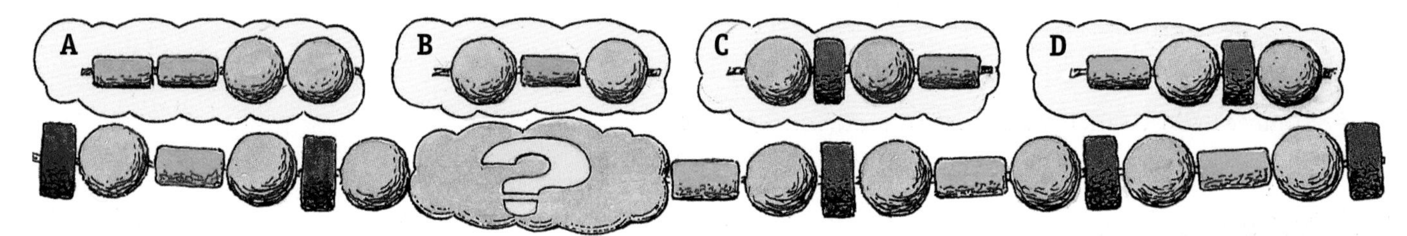

3 Which group of beads (**A**, **B**, **C**, or **D**) will complete the pattern below?

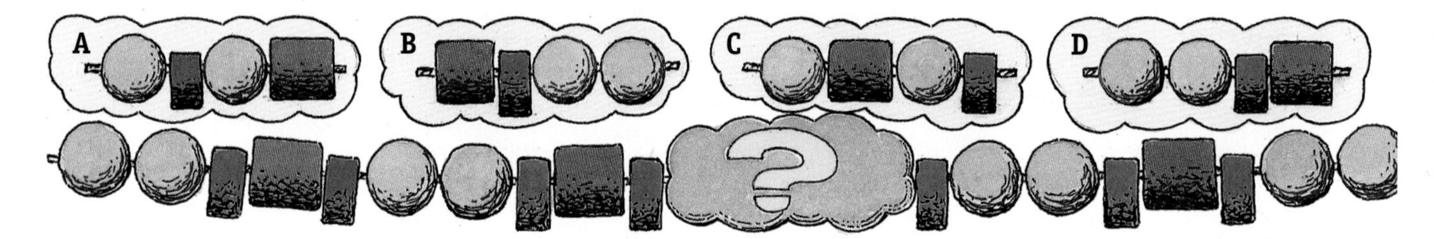

4 Which group of beads (**A**, **B**, **C**, or **D**) will complete the pattern below?

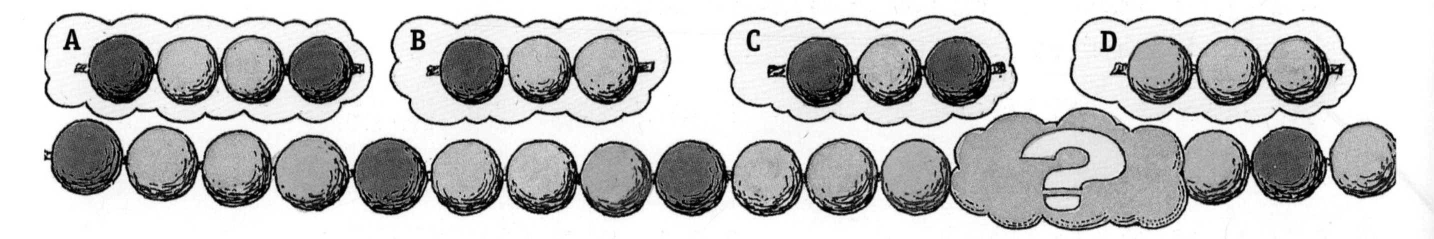

Some **patterns** change according to a rule.

In this pattern a circle is added each time.

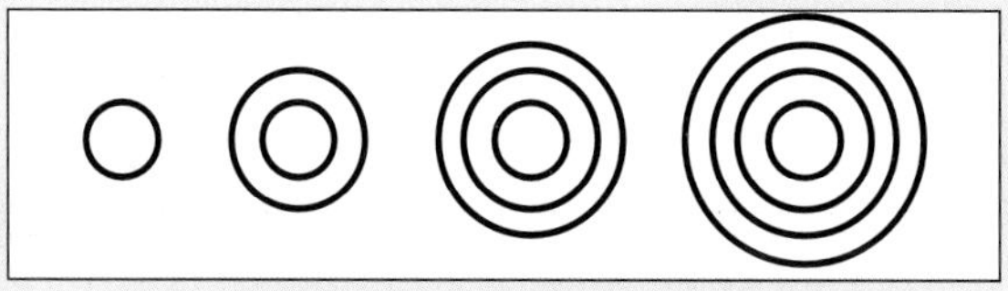

Exercise 5

Draw the next picture in each pattern.

1

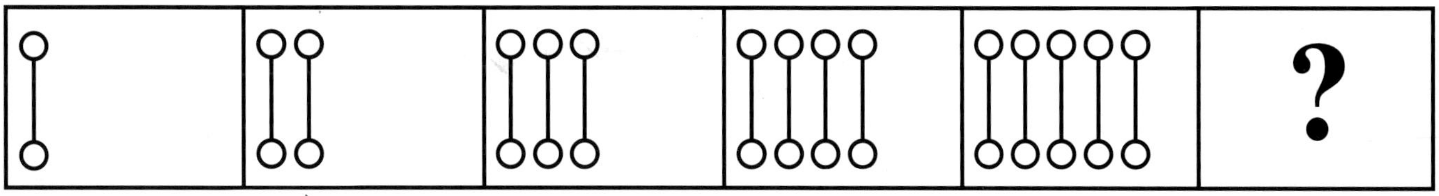

2

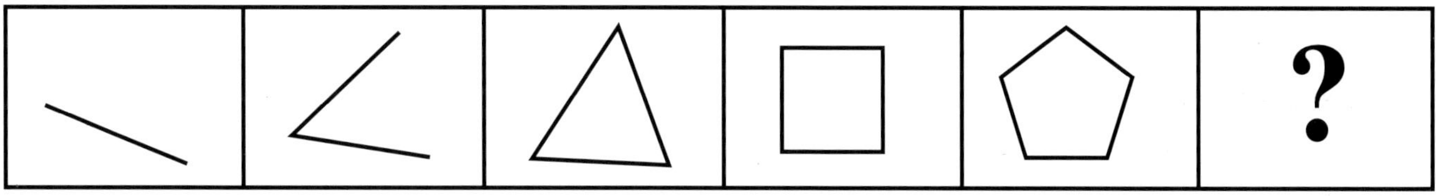

Exercise 6

Numbers can change according to a pattern or rule.
What are the missing numbers from these number patterns?

1 Add one each time — 1, 2, 3, 4, 5, ?, ?, ?

2 Add two each time/even numbers — 2, 4, 6, 8, ?, ?, ?

3 Add three each time — 4, 7, 10, 13, 16, ?, ?, ?

4 Take away four each time — 23, 19, 15, 11, ?, ?

5 Take away three each time — 43, 40, 37, 34, ?, ?

Exercise 7

What are the missing numbers from these number patterns?
What rule or pattern do you find for each one?

1 6, 8, 10, 12, ?, ?, ?

2 5, 10, 15, 20, 25, ?, ?, ?

3 16, 14, 12, 10, 8, ?, ?, ?

4 80, 70, 60, 50, ?, ?, ?

5 8, 11, 14, 17, 20, ?, ?, ?

6 3, 7, 11, 15, 19, ?, ?, ?

7 0.1, 0.2, 0.3, 0.4, ?, ?, ?

8 3.6, 3.5, 3.4, 3.3, ?, ?, ?

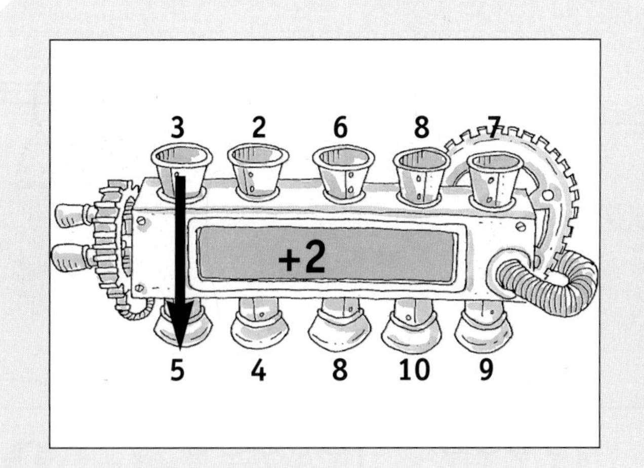

This machine **processes** numbers.

It changes them.

The blue panel shows how the number is changed.

When a number is put into the top of this machine, 2 is added.

The new number comes out at the bottom of the machine.

Exercise 8

Check the blue panel on the machine to see how it will change the numbers that are put in. Write the numbers that come out of each number machine.

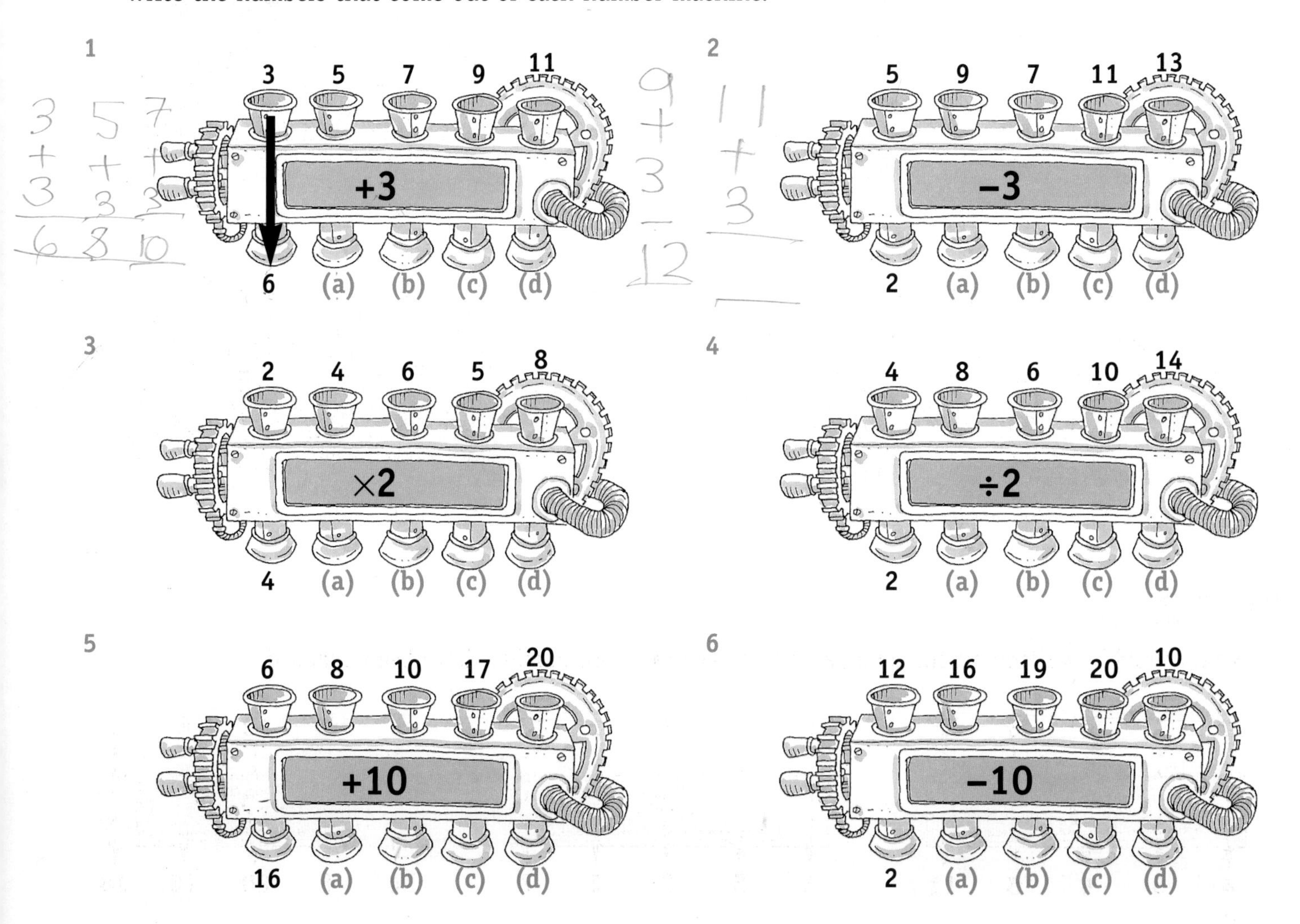

This number machine is more complicated.

The blue panel shows that the number is changed in **two steps**.

In this machine the number is multiplied by 3, then 1 is added to give the total.

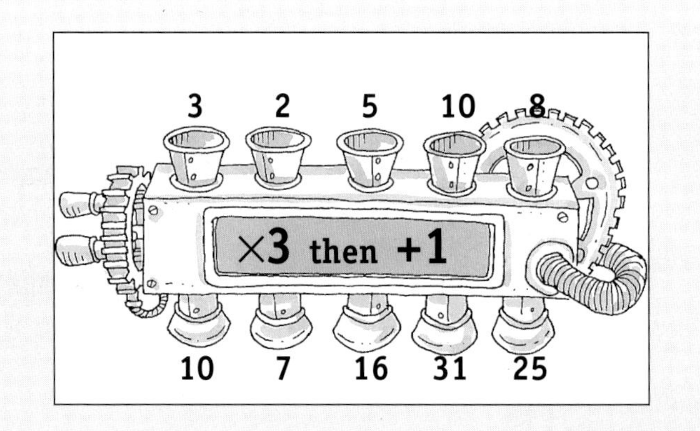

Exercise 9

Check the blue panel on the machine to see how it will change the numbers that are put in.
Write the numbers that come out of each number machine.

1

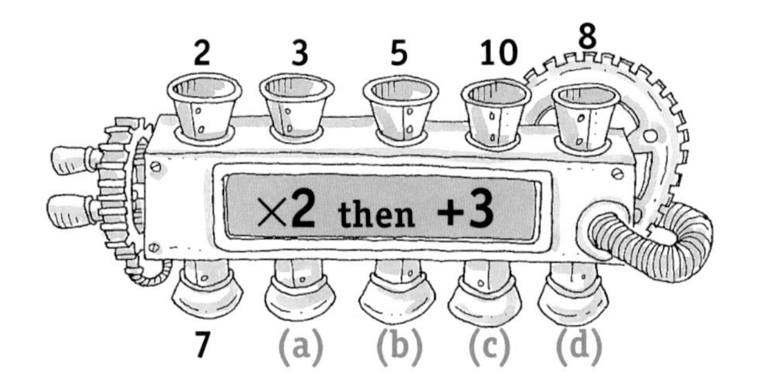

2

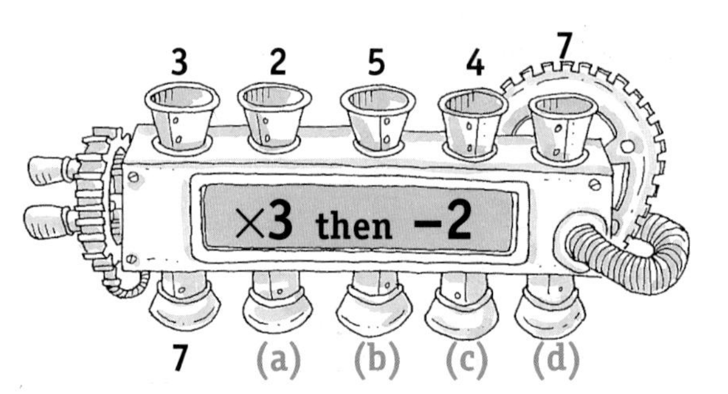

3

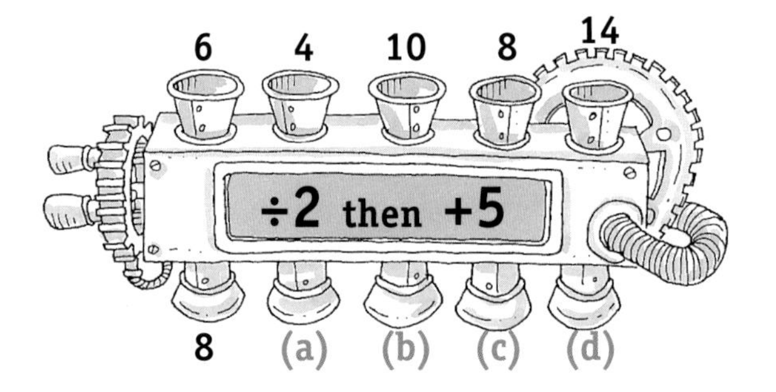

4

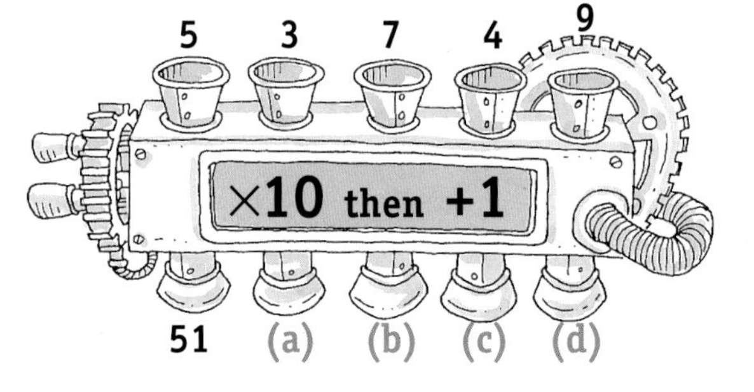

Exercise 10

What should be written on the blue panel to show how these numbers have been changed?

1

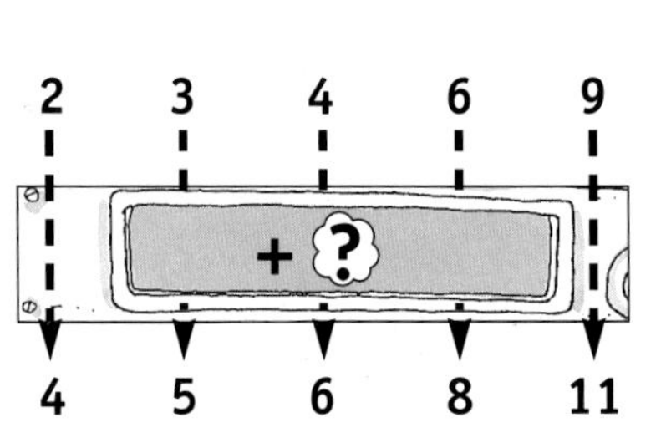

2

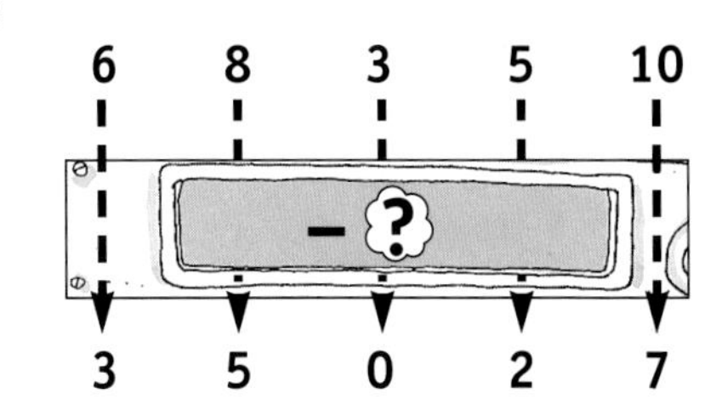

3

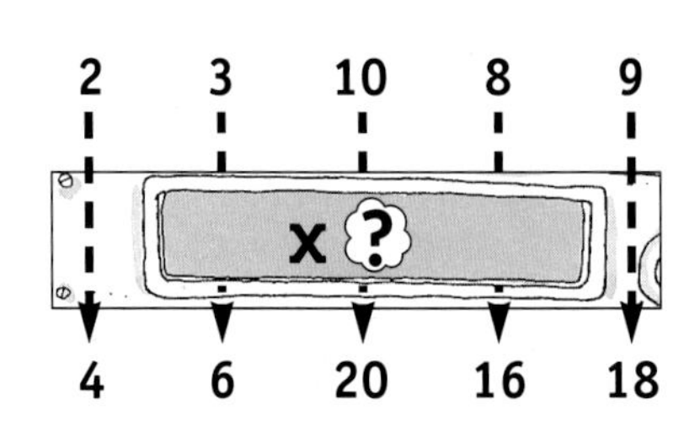

This **number machine** changes numbers. You put a number into the machine and it **adds 3**.

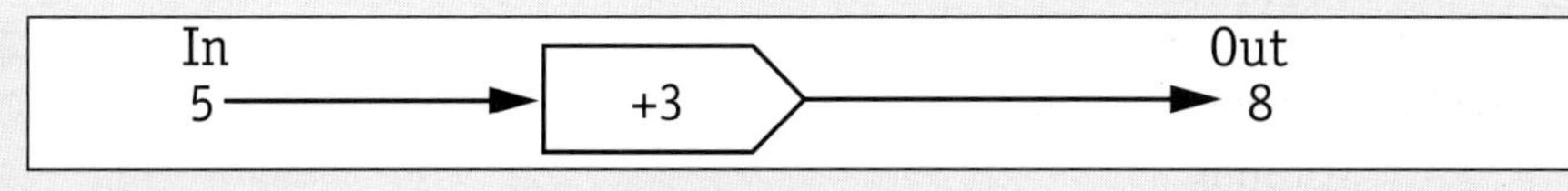

Put 5 in. The machine adds 3. 8 comes out.

If you put 2 into the machine, what number do you think will come out?

Exercise 11

Copy these number machines and fill in the numbers which come **out**.

1 4 → +5 → ?
2 6 → +7 → ?
3 11 → +4 → ?
4 9 → −6 → ?
5 10 → −5 → ?
6 14 → −6 → ?
7 4 → ×3 → ?
8 7 → ×2 → ?
9 10 → ×3 → ?
10 8 → ÷3 → ?
11 9 → ÷3 → ?
12 15 → ÷5 → ?

Exercise 12

Copy these number machines and fill in the numbers which went **in**.

1 ? → +3 → 7
2 ? → −5 → 2
3 ? → ×2 → 8
4 ? → ÷3 → 3
5 ? → +10 → 17
6 ? → −8 → 4

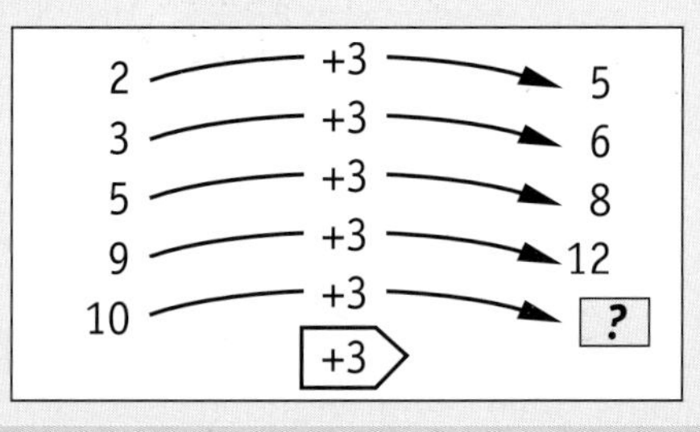

Mappings help us to find rules between pairs of numbers.

Here, the rule is **add 3**.

What number do you think you will find at ?

Exercise 13

Copy and complete these mappings.

1
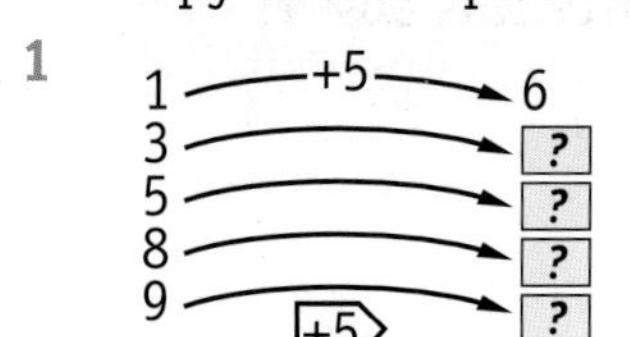

2
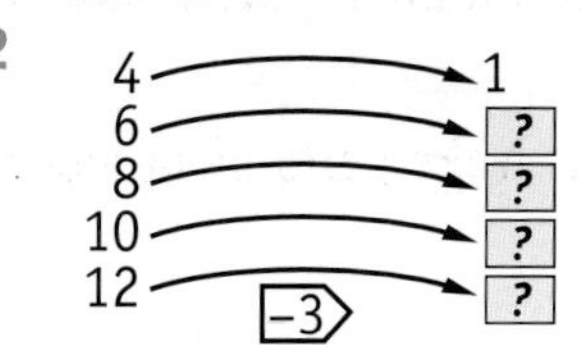

3
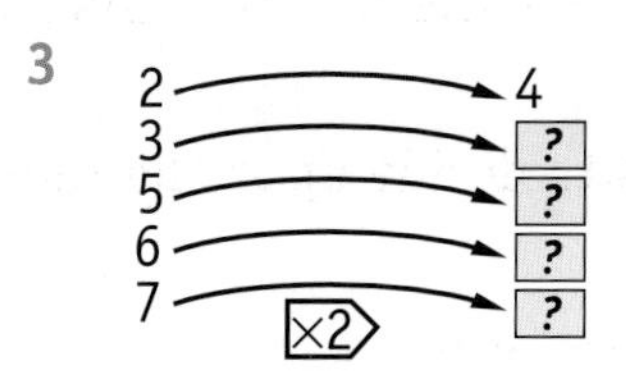

4
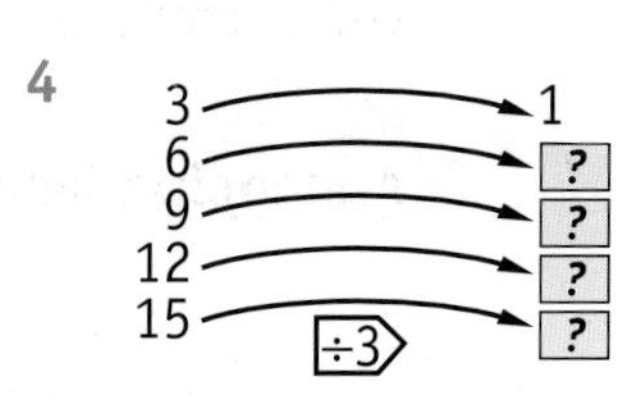

Exercise 14

These mappings are more difficult.
Each rule has **two steps** in the calculation.
Copy and complete the mappings.

1

2 → ×2 +3 → 7
3 → ?
5 → ?
8 → ?
10 → ?
×2 +3

2

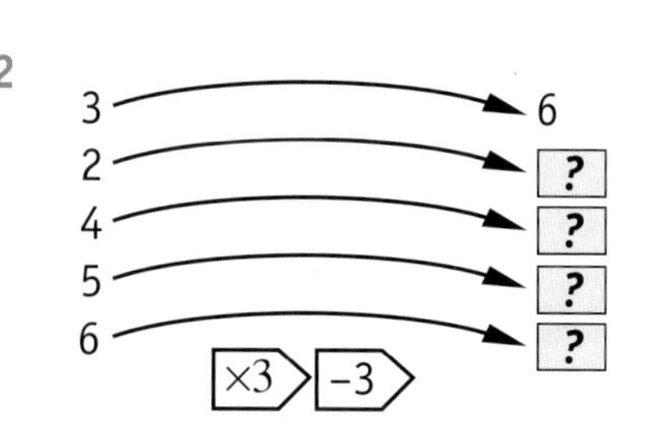

3

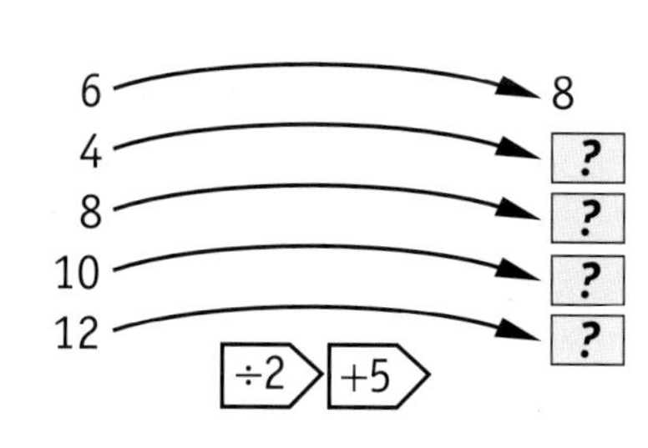

Exercise 15

The rule is not shown in these mappings.
Work out the rule for each mapping.

1

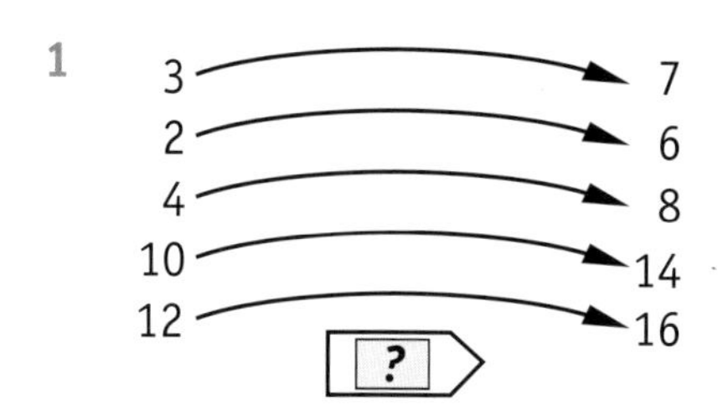

2

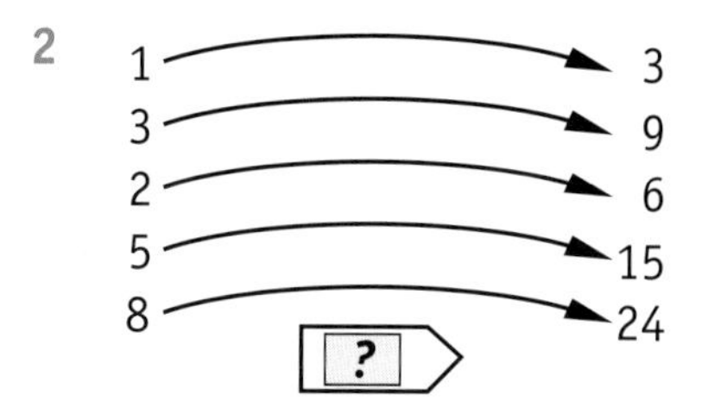

3

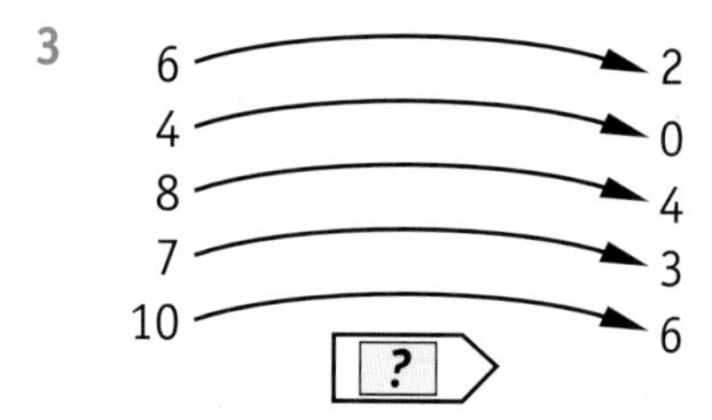

4

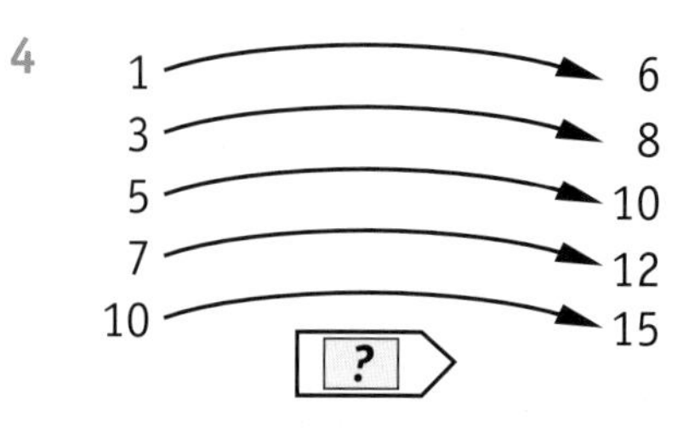

5

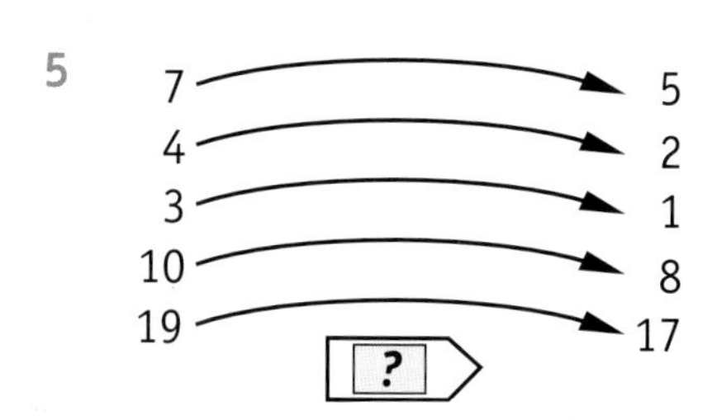

6

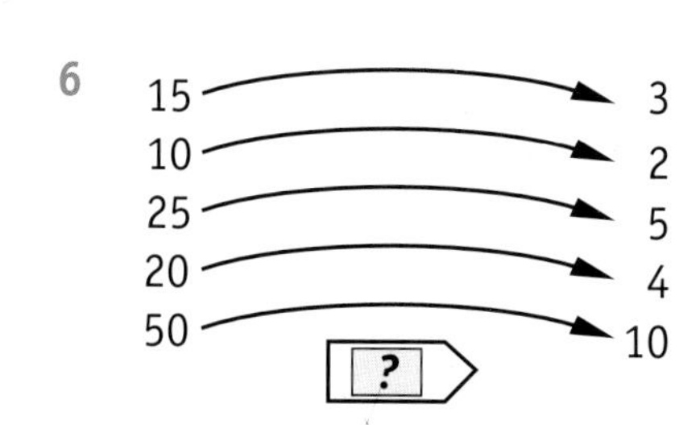

Key ideas

Patterns are drawings or mathematical ideas that keep repeating themselves.

A **rule** is the mathematical step that links numbers in a pattern.
For example: 2, 4, 6, 8 – the rule that links these numbers and makes the pattern is **add 2.**

A **mapping** helps us to decide upon the rule that links pairs of numbers.

The Day Out

The Brown family are going to Action World for the day.
There are five of them: Mr and Mrs Brown, Emma, Roy and Grandma.

A

This is how the dials on the car's dashboard look at the start of the journey.

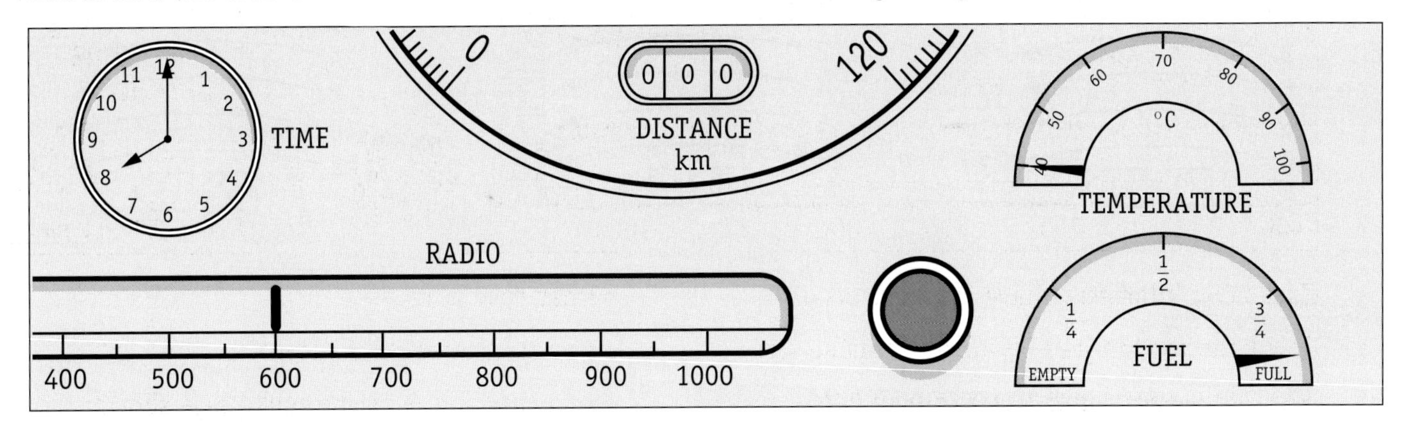

1 Is the fuel tank full or empty?
2 What time is it?
3 What temperature is shown?
4 What wavelength is the radio tuned to?
5 Is the distance measurer set at zero?

B

As the family begin their journey they pass a number of road signs.
Which sign will they see at each point along the road?
Write: **1** *Bend to the right* .

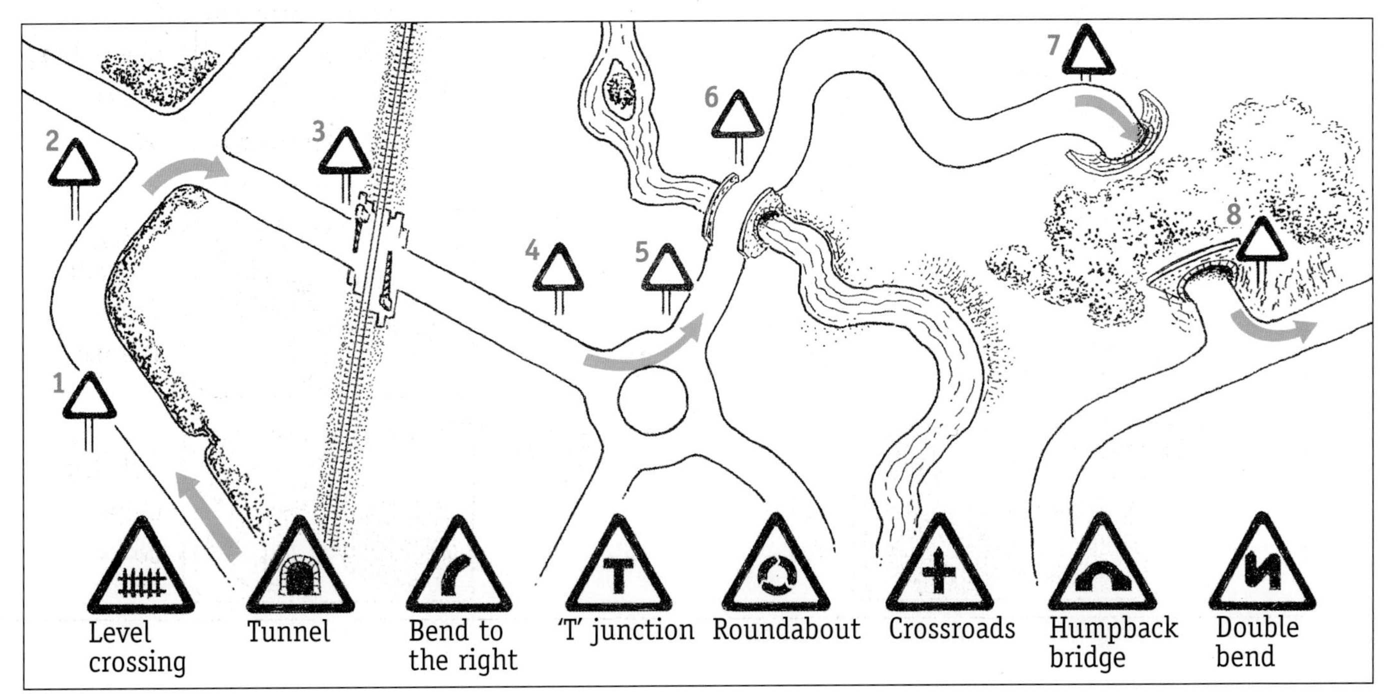

C

The family stop for a break. Answer these questions about the dials on the dashboard.

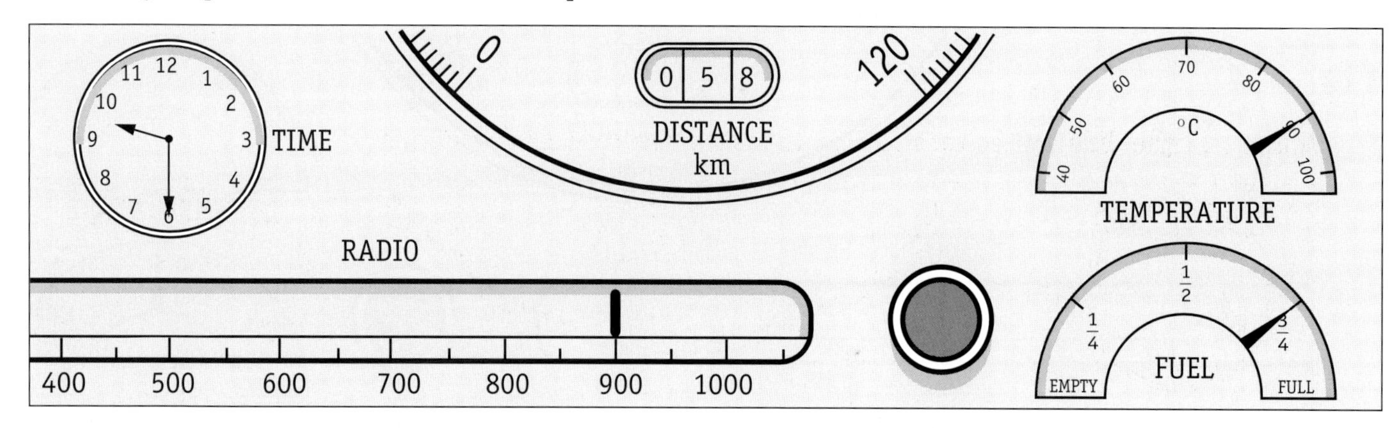

1 How many kilometres have they travelled?

2 What time is it?

3 How long has the journey taken them so far?

4 What temperature is shown?

5 What wavelength is the radio tuned to?

6 What fraction does the fuel gauge show?

D

They decide to eat. Use the menu to work out how much each meal costs. 

Menu

Burger	£1.50
Cheeseburger	£2.00
Chicken nuggets	£2.50
Hot dog	£1.80
Fish burger	£1.50
Chips	£0.80
Sweet corn	£1.00
Orange	£0.80
Cola	£0.50
Coffee	£0.60
Tea	£0.50

Mum's tray 1 Sweet corn, Fish burger, Coffee

Gran's tray 2 Cheeseburger, Chips, Cola

Emma's tray 3 Chicken nuggets, Chips, Orange

Dad's tray 4 Burger, Chips, Tea

Roy's tray 5 Hot dog, Chips, Cola

The family arrive at Action World.

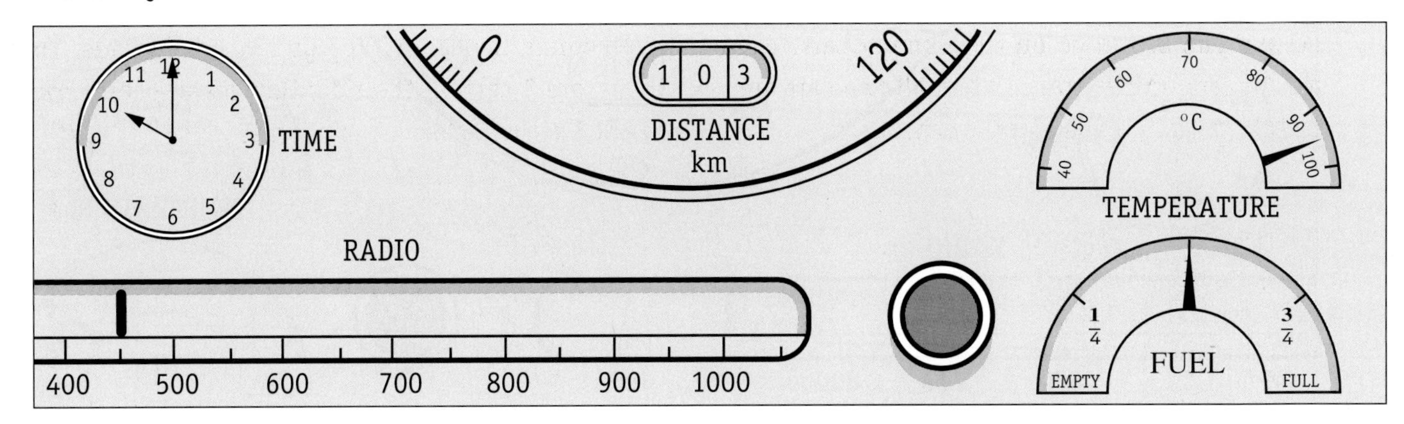

1 How many kilometres have they travelled?

2 How long has the journey taken them?

3 What fraction of fuel has been used?

4 What is the temperature?

5 What wavelength is the radio tuned to?

6 How much will Mrs Brown have to pay to get the family into Action World?

7 Emma and Roy decide to buy some souvenirs.

(a) What is the total cost of Emma's souvenirs?

(b) What is the total cost of Roy's souvenirs?

F

The family go on the rides. Answer the questions.

1 Mr and Mrs Brown go on the Bumper Cars. There are 10 cars on the track. When all the cars are full, how many people are on the track?

2 Gran, Emma and Roy go on the Sky Ride. There are 3 cars on the ride. How many people can the Sky Ride carry at one time?

3 Gran and Roy go on the Star Ship. There are 4 rockets on the Star Ship. How many people are on it when it is full?

4 There are 8 cabins on the Big Wheel. How many people can it carry in total?

5 There are 8 cars on the Octopus. How many people can it carry in total?

1 Which of the monster faces (A to F) are symmetrical?
A
B
C
D
E
F
2 What decimal part of each roof (G to I) is shaded blue?
G
H
I
HORROR COTTAGE
3 How many square tiles are there on each patio (J to L)?
J
K
L
WOODLAND CAFÉ
M
4 How many squares of glass are in the café window (M)?
TERROR CAR
N
5 How many circles can you see on the Terror Car (N)? How many rectangles? How many triangles?

H

1 A record is kept of how many people travel on each ride during the day. The graph displays these figures.

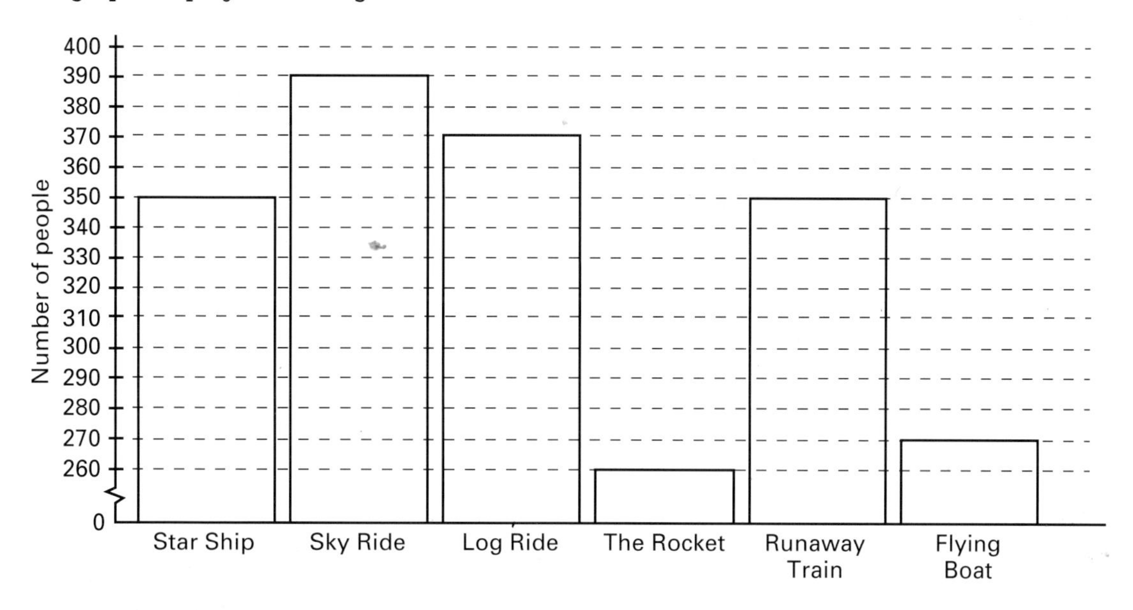

(a) Which was the **most** popular ride?
(b) What was the **least** popular ride?
(c) How many people went on the Sky Ride?
(d) How many people went on the Runaway Train?
(e) On which ride did 270 people travel?
(f) On which two rides did the same number of people travel?

2 Mrs Brown started the day with this much money:

She ended the day with this much money:

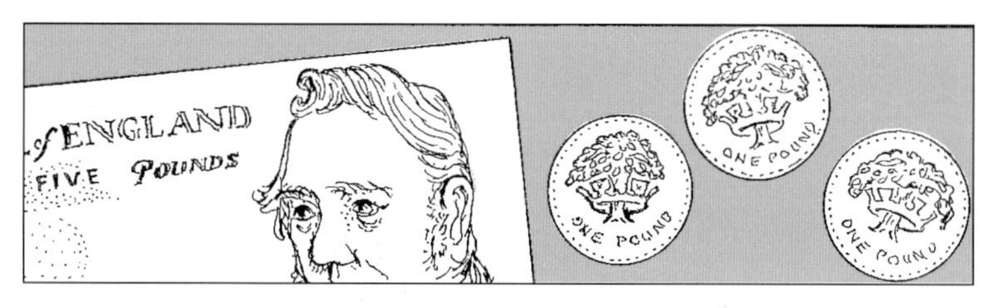

How much money did she spend?